Donald D. Snyder

MAR 2 2 1966

D1398334

PHYSICAL SCIENCE

FOR LIBERAL ARTS STUDENTS

John Wiley & Sons, Inc., New York · London

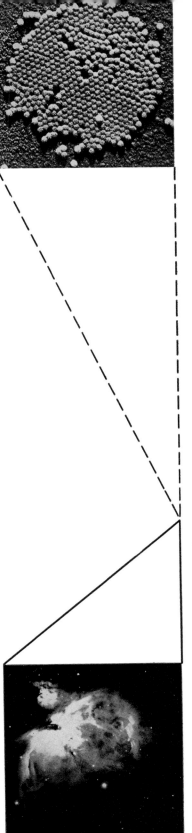

PHYSICAL SCIENCE
FOR LIBERAL ARTS STUDENTS

Hugo N. Swenson, Ph.D.
Professor of Physics, Queens College

J. Edmund Woods, Ph.D.
Late Professor of Physics, Queens College

Preface

THIRD PRINTING, AUGUST, 1962

Copyright © 1957 by John Wiley & Sons, Inc.

All Rights Reserved

*This book or any part thereof must not
be reproduced in any form without
the written permission of the publisher.*

. . . .

Library of Congress Catalog Card Number: 57–8899
Printed in the United States of America

The required courses in the liberal arts curriculum are frequent targets for the criticism of students who are forced to take them. Among the natural science students the criticism usually is directed at the humanities and the social sciences, whereas those whose interests lie in the languages, arts, or social sciences rail against the required courses in mathematics and the natural sciences. The objections are numerous.

Many students believe that the best educational plan is that which permits them to take as many courses as possible in the field of chief interest and, consequently, as few courses as possible in fields which they consider irrelevant to their interests. Sometimes this desire for education à la carte rather than table d'hôte merely displays a youthful resentment against coercion, but perhaps more frequently it shows a lack of understanding of the liberal point of view in education or a lack of sympathy for its principles.

Indeed, some educators also believe that the best education is that which prepares most rapidly for a career. This is the theme of the specialist. Fundamentally, it reflects a belief that society functions best if it is largely composed of individuals whose knowledge is concentrated and intense, though in a field which is necessarily restricted. Moreover, it is believed by some that this specialization should begin very early in the education of the individual. The shortest educational path, like the Euclidean straight line between two points, is also supposed to be the best.

The opponents of this school of thinking need not deny the value of the specialist to society. Rather, such educators believe that there is a real danger in too much specialization too soon in the life of the student. The specialist, whose entire stock of knowledge lies within narrow limits, is notoriously shortsighted and unsympathetic with points of view other than his own or outside his profession. This is manifestly unhealthy in a democratic society where individual expression on large issues and general problems is necessary. Such educators distinguish between the person who is merely trained and the person who is also educated. This is not meant to be an apology for the dilettante who knows a little something about almost everything but whose knowledge is so scattered as to be useless to society. Those who defend the liberal education believe that it is possible for the average student to get, in four years of college, a good start in the direction of a profession and at the same time to gain a significant insight into the content and special methods (logical, experimental, aesthetic) of the social sciences, the natural sciences, mathematics, languages, literature, art, and music. To the scholar in any of these fields the insight gained in such a short time will probably seem superficial, but it is not a profound understanding that is necessary; that is a lifetime assignment. Rather, the believer in liberal education hopes to develop in students a sympathy for these various fields and for the people who labor in them; he hopes to make it clear that our society derives its energy from numerous and vastly different sources. The strength of a democratic society lies in its ability to capitalize on the contributions of a large number of versatile minds, and it is the business of the liberal arts college to educate such minds.

There is much talk these days about cultural and non-cultural courses. Frequently, the natural sciences are classified as non-cultural because, it is asserted, they are preprofessional and therefore meant for the specialist, or because they are not concerned with the finer things in life. This is a misuse of the word "culture." If the word is taken to mean the sum total of the important aspects of a civilization, then it would be nonsense to say that the vast field of the natural sciences is not cultural. If "culture" is taken to mean the refined and subtle aspects of our civilization, then it must be remembered that the methods and conclusions of the natural sciences form a very important part of philosophy, and what is more refined and subtle than philosophy? The only defensible criticism concerns the manner in which the natural sciences are taught to liberal arts students. To put non-science majors into courses designed for science majors is usually a mistake and frequently a fatal one. The emphasis in such courses must of necessity be on the factual content and technical skills as a preparation for future courses, with little or no time left for the historical or philosophical aspects or for the meaning of that branch of science to society. Some few students will find their way through the maze of facts and formulas to the underlying fundamentals, but most of them will come away with a distaste for science—with a memory of bad odors if the subject was chemistry, and a permanent dislike for frogs and snakes if the subject was biology.

In this volume we shall concern ourselves with descriptions and illustrations of the special methods and disciplines, experimental and logical, that have been found useful in the physical sciences. We do not propose to probe into the scientist's mind with the hope of revealing such details of its mechanism that in the end we can contrast the scientist's mind with that of the non-scientist. Nor is it the purpose of this course to describe a recipe for creative scientific thinking so detailed that the expert, or even the layman, can follow the steps in this prescription and thus make substantial scientific contributions. If the mind is free (we hope it is), it is paradoxical to say that its workings can be understood.

Finally, it is not the purpose of this course to summarize or survey the spectacular or practical achievements of modern science. This would be both impracticable and useless for the non-science student. Rather, we shall watch the scientist as he goes about his business and we shall attempt to describe his activity in such a way that the most important features of his procedures will be evident. This does not mean that there will be no facts or data—quite the contrary. It would be impossible to describe the scientific activity without data. The natural sciences begin and end in experimental facts. But these data have been carefully chosen to illustrate some point or principle, and they are not presented here as they would be to a scientist who needs to make practical use of them. To make sure that this point does not escape the student, each unit of work will be introduced with a statement explaining the purpose of that section.

A NOTE TO TEACHERS

Since the material of this text has been selected and arranged so as to form a logical continuity, it is recommended that there be no serious changes in the order of presentation of subject matter. However, since a good deal of illustrative material has been included to round out the discussions, a teacher, pressed for time, will find sections which may be omitted or passed over lightly without serious damage to the logical development. For many reasons this selection is best left to the instructor, after careful reading of the text and after preparation of a schedule based on the total time available and on the level of achievement expected in such a course. In general, practical applications such as the battery, motors, generators, electric power transmission, etc., fall into the class of topics which may be omitted without serious sacrifice.

Acknowledgments

The authors are deeply indebted to many of their colleagues who have participated in the teaching of the science course required of liberal arts students at Queens College. It is from the cooperative effort and the rich suggestions of this group that the text has grown. Those most steadily associated with the course have been Dr. Morris Abramson, Dr. Erna Herrey, and Dr. Aaron Spector. In the early days of Queens College, President Paul Klapper gave the authors complete freedom to design a course for which there was, at that time, relatively little precedent, and which was therefore an especially stimulating challenge. For this privilege we are deeply grateful. We are indebted to Dr. Simon Share for a critical reading of the manuscript, and to Mrs. Ethel Marion for the typing of several mimeographed editions of this book.

H. N. S.
J. E. W.

New York
February, 1957

Contents

1

The Evolution of Natural Science

INTRODUCTION

The intellectual life concerns itself with what is hopefully called "truth," but the methods of obtaining this truth and the tests for its soundness are as varied as the intellectual fields themselves.

Many have believed that truth could be deduced by purely logical methods. This was the conviction of the Greek schools begun by Socrates, Plato, and Aristotle. It was Aristotle, in fact, who invented the logical device called the *syllogism*. This consists of three statements in the following order: a general premise, assumed to be true, a statement of a specific case to which the general premise can be applied, and finally a conclusion. As an example, consider the following:

1. The law of conservation of energy holds for all machines.

2. An inclined plane is a machine.

3. Therefore, no energy is lost or gained in the use of the inclined plane.

The foregoing looks like a reliable recipe for arriving at truth, and indeed it is, provided the first statement is true and the second and third statements follow certain logical rules. This is the essence of the *deductive method:* a specific problem is solved by the application of a general principle. But what was the source of the general truths needed to start the logical machinery going? They were the kind of statement which we usually preface by "it is self-evident that . . .", "it is a matter of common knowledge that . . .", "common sense tells us that . . ." Consider the following examples designed in imitation of the style of Aristotle:

1. All celestial bodies must move in paths which are geometrically perfect.

2. Only circular paths are geometrically perfect.

3. Therefore, the planets must move in paths which are circles, or combinations of circles.

Or this:

1. All bodies move in the most natural motions.

2. On earth, a downward motion is most natural for heavy bodies.

3. Therefore, heavy bodies on earth fall down and not up.

Now it is clear that this whole logical structure may yield nothing more reliable than superstition and gossip, because any weakness in the first statement is transmitted to the conclusion. Not only that, but the statements may contain terms which are ill-defined or even undefined. The first of the three examples is valid; all the terms used are defined in physics, and the first statement has been substantiated by another process which is called induction. In the *inductive method* we reverse the procedure used in deduction: a general truth is established by the use of many specific facts. The first illustration of the inductive procedure will be presented at the end of this chapter.

Socrates and Plato were so fascinated by logic that they felt it unnecessary to perform any experiments; they even distrusted experimentation, believing it absurd to suppose that truth could be discovered by the mere manipulation of material objects. Plato, in *The Republic*, states his point of view thus:

> When a person starts on the discovery of the absolute by the light of reason only, and without any assistance of sense, and perseveres until by pure intelligence he arrives at the perception of the absolute good, he at last finds himself at the end of the intellectual world, as in the case of sight at the end of the visible.

Some, like Rousseau, have not even trusted logic and reason but have believed that our significant problems are solved by intuition, as though profound knowledge were hidden away in our subconscious minds, to be discovered only by probing deeply into our sentiments and by placing our faith in instinct and feeling rather than in reason. "I venture to declare," Rousseau wrote, "that a state of reflection is contrary to nature; and that a thinking man is a depraved animal."

Kant, in his *Critique of Pure Reason*, states the case for *"a priori"* knowledge. His argument is that, although reasoning is initiated by experience, the mind is aware of, and makes use of, many instinctive truths which are independent of experience. This belief that there is a sort of intellectual conscience that guides us instinctively in our thinking, and which is quite apart from the sensory reality, is called *transcendentalism*.

Philosophically, all these points of view are both interesting and important, particularly since the flavors of them remain to this day. They must be carefully examined before it is possible to appreciate the special strength and, indeed, the limitations of the methods which the natural sciences employ.

Finally, a few individuals in all ages have believed, as did Galileo, that a factual knowledge of nature is profoundly significant and that such knowledge does not emerge from some hidden recess of the soul but is discovered only by direct observation and experimentation. We shall call this the *experimental point of view*, avoiding the ill-defined and much-abused word, "scientific."

In the natural sciences, then, experiment and observation are recognized as the ultimate sources of knowledge—the very essence of natural science is experimentation. The results of experiments are accepted even though they conflict with intuition, established opinion, or personal prejudice; they are accepted even though they seem at the moment to contradict reason and logic. An experimental observation can be challenged only by another experimental observation.

THE ORIGIN OF NATURAL SCIENCE

Man has always regarded nature with a mixture of fear, reverence, and curiosity. To us in this modern age nature seems generous and beneficent, but in primitive times the chief ingredient in this mixture was surely fear—and no wonder! In those days man pitted his skill and strength against the beasts of field and forest, against the storming seas and the capricious elements, and he survived only if he was clever and strong and lucky. Primitive life must have been a succession of narrow escapes from a treacherous animal kingdom, from starvation and diseases, from storms and floods. The most formidable of these were the intangible agencies of nature which could not be fought hand to hand or controlled by the simple tools and methods then known. The world which primitive man knew seemed full of these mysterious forces threatening to extinguish him if he did not watch his step, and the earth outside his tribal range was a fearsome and monstrous mystery. In those days natural phenomena were miracles, and miracles are terrifying.

But nature was not always malicious. In contrast with the harshness of the hurricane, man experienced the gentleness of refreshing rain and cooling breezes; he knew the kindly shelter of trees and the generosity of the good earth which bore him fruit. Then, too, confidence was inspired by the regularities which he observed in such phenomena as sunrise and sunset, the orderly procession of the stars during the night, the predictable changes in season. Man began to suspect that there were friendly agencies in nature as well as hostile ones, so that his fear became tinged with reverence.

Out of this primitive fear and reverence came a multitude of superstitions, spirits, gods, and theologies. There were demons in the winds, thunder was due to the clamorous wrath of the gods, comets and falling stars portended evil. In helplessness and desperation, human attributes were conferred on material objects and natural forces in the hope that they would be susceptible to the same kind of control that was successful in dealing with members of the tribe. In those days the world was truly haunted— haunted by a host of supernatural powers, some kindly disposed and some malicious. They directed the weather and the changes in season. They inhabited plants as well as animals. All natural phenomena were like the events in a puppet show, with hidden demons pulling the strings behind the scenes. This was *animism,* man's first attempt to rationalize nature, and the factors which inspired it were certainly not trivial; man felt that his very life was at stake. At first glance it might seem as though nothing but confusion could result from such a bewildering collection of spirits and an equally bewildering number of mystic ceremonies and incantations for dealing with them, but this was in reality a simplifying step. Man felt himself powerless to deal with miracles without apparent causes, but he thought he could control spirits and demons by the familiar methods of entreaty, injunction, or diplomacy. With such a magical trap he tried to catch the wild unknown so that he might domesticate it.

But even while man was busy trying to control the demons he had created, he began to use, perhaps accidentally at first, another method to make his position more secure against nature. It took more than strength to subdue the animal kingdom and more than courage to battle the forces of nature; it required a kind of mechanical ingenuity or inventiveness without which he never could have risen above the primitive stage and without which he might not even have survived. He protected himself from the elements by shelter of his own construction; he invented weapons which he could use offensively and defensively at a distance without hand-to-hand combat; bodies of water were no longer barriers after he learned to use boats; he fashioned tools to ease his labor. At the same time he was gathering systematic and detailed information about natural processes and common objects; he was learning the physical properties of materials such as woods, rocks, and metals; he used simple geometry in his constructions and measurements, and he guided himself at night by the stars.

No one can say just how or when these things happened, but it is interesting to speculate, for example, on the circumstances which led to the discovery of the principle of the lever. Perhaps it was discovered by imitation of the many lever systems found in nature, but how did man hit upon the idea of using a wheel? There are no wheels in nature. When did man first learn how to kindle a fire and begin to use it to his advantage? What genius first thought of using a bow to project an arrow or first used a sail to drive a boat? These were great events in the history of mankind, though they happened too long ago to be recorded.

To be sure, this activity was mostly practical engineering but it was the beginning of science. It involved experimentation (trial and error) of a kind, and, to some extent, it involved coordination of the facts observed. Curiosity played a very small part in this first accumulation of factual knowledge. It was inspired by immediate needs, frequently by matters of life and death. Man was, again by necessity, inventive.

It is highly significant that the scattered bits of knowledge thus acquired and the experiences so gained were inherited by succeeding generations, who made further additions of new facts and who not only improved the old tools and weapons and mechanical devices but invented new ones. These, in turn, became the heritage of their successors, so that each generation was able to profit from the experiences of those preceding. This conscious hoarding of accumulated knowledge accounts for the rapid advance of science once its methods were respected and its exponents free from persecution. It is just this possibility, characteristic of the natural sciences, that enables one generation of scientists to proceed steadily beyond the point reached by the previous generation. Newton, near the end of a lifetime of great achievements, expressed his scientific indebtedness to the past with modesty and elegance: "If I have seen farther than others, it is because I have stood on the shoulders of giants."

As data and experience accumulated, tools and machines became more and more efficient, with the consequence that man began to feel relatively secure from dangers which in earlier days had threatened his existence. There was less to fear from his immediate environment. Then, too, he began to see regularities in many natural phenomena which in the past had seemed utterly miraculous. When a miracle happens with predictable regularity, it loses its fearful aspect. Imagine, for example, how terrifying a sunrise or a sunset would be if experienced for the first time as an isolated event.

But as man feared less he became more curious about natural objects and natural processes, and his increased safety began to provide the leisure in which to gratify that curiosity. Such curiosity is an innate characteristic of human beings and manifests itself in the desire to take things apart just to see how they are made; it makes us want to probe into the unknown, to know the causes of all events and the hidden mechanisms in every process. It leads, therefore, to philosophy, and it leads to what is known as pure research, that is, research which is not inspired by immediate practical needs. Thus, the urge to experiment began with fear and ended with curiosity.

Of course, practical problems have continued to demand solutions through research so that scientists are now motivated both by necessity and curiosity, although curiosity is still very important in modern times. To be sure, in the end it turns out that the data yielded by pure research eventually become of practical value even though the original motive may not have been a practical one. It is just the peculiar power of science that none of its data, however pure, can be said to be impractical; some day a bit of "impractical" knowledge may solve a practical problem if society allows it.

THE EMERGENCE OF THE EXPERIMENTAL POINT OF VIEW

Actually, then, the experimental method began so long ago that the details of its origin are hidden in historical obscurity, but thousands of years passed before society became fully aware of the method which some of its members had used to such advantage. Furthermore, even after the uniqueness of the method became apparent, society was a long time in approving it.

The slowness with which the experimental method emerged was due, in part, to the fact that it was rather intimately mixed in varying proportions with many other methods which mankind had come to use in the solution of its vexing problems. In the constant battle with the unknown, man sought for weapons in magic, witchcraft, astrology, and alchemy; he relied variously on intuition, revelation, and established authority. So scrambled were these methods that it was not easy to tell from just which elements a seemingly sound conclusion derived its validity. Was the successful prediction of an eclipse due to a rigorous application of geometry to the observed facts, or was it the result of faith in astrological concepts? When a patient recovered from a disease, was it a genuine physiological reaction to a drug or a treatment, or was it the result of magic and ritual, or was it simply because of the tenacity of the patient?

It has never been easy to tell which is cause and which is effect, nor is it easy (or perhaps even possible) to separate the objective from the subjective. Many of the greatest minds of antiquity could not distinguish between logical and intuitional methods, between that which was experimental fact and that which was superstition or hearsay. The same Ptolemy who wrote the *Almagest* also wrote the *Tetrabiblos*. The former was a rigorous geometrical description of the motions of the heavenly bodies and was based on observation; the *Tetrabiblos* has served as a textbook of astrology for almost two thousand years. The epicycles which Ptolemy described in the *Almagest* are discussed in Part Two. In contrast, here is a sample taken at random from the *Tetrabiblos* (Book III, Chapter 13):

> If Saturn alone is ruler of the soul and dominates Mercury and the moon, if he has a dignified position with reference to the universe and the angles, he makes his subjects lovers of the body, strong-minded, deep thinkers, austere, of a single purpose, laborious, dictatorial, ready to punish, lovers of property, avaricious, violent, amassing treasure, and jealous; but if his position is the opposite and without dignity, he makes them sordid, petty, mean-spirited, indifferent, mean-minded, malignant, cowardly, diffident, evil-speakers, solitary, tearful, shameless, superstitious, fond of toil, unfeeling, devisers of plots against their friends, gloomy, taking no care of the body.

It is difficult to believe now that the author of the preceding passage was also a great mathematician and a sound and reliable geographer. Kepler, who resolved the seemingly complex planetary motions into three compact and rigorous mathematical laws, also devoted himself seriously to the casting of horoscopes. Pliny the

Elder, the Roman historian of the first century, wrote the *Natural History*, which is a fascinating mixture of truth, rumor, and fantasy. For example, he describes (Book II, Chapter 7) eclipses of the sun and the moon with the clarity and precision of a modern astronomer, but there are many accounts in his history which are fantastic in the light of modern knowledge. Pliny was not a fraud, nor could he be accused of carelessness by the standards of that day. He was one of the most reliable of the Roman historians to concern himself with science. He did what most researchers in the field of history do. He searched the available literature; he read the private correspondence of eminent scholars and travelers, and he himself carried on an extensive correspondence with anyone who might possess some scientific knowledge; he obtained information by word of mouth. He tried to evaluate this hodgepodge of material critically, but in the end he was forced to rely largely on hearsay. He had no other choice. The world of Pliny was not our modern world with a network of direct communication connecting its peoples or with rapid and comfortable transportation. To travel in those days, even modestly by modern standards, was a major undertaking involving risks and hardships which few people were willing or able to endure. These early accounts, like the science of that day, have to be judged in terms of the physical environment and the intellectual atmosphere that prevailed. The result makes fascinating reading but it is not always to be relied upon as a source of scientific facts. As an example of reliable explanation, here is Pliny's lucid account of solar and lunar eclipses (*Natural History*, Book II, Chapter 7):

> For it is evident that the sun is hid by the intervention of the moon, and the moon by the opposition of the earth, and that these changes are mutual, the moon, by her interposition, taking the rays of the sun from the earth, and the earth from the moon. As she advances darkness is suddenly produced, and again the sun is obscured by her shade; for night is nothing more than the shade of the earth. The figure of this shade is like that of a pyramid or an inverted top; and the moon enters it only near its point, and it does not exceed the height of the moon, for there is no other star which is obscured in the same manner, while a figure of this kind always terminates in a point. The flight of birds, when very loftly, shows that shadows do not extend beyond a certain distance. . . . It is from these causes that the moon is eclipsed during the night. The two kinds of eclipses are not, however, at the stated monthly periods, on account of the obliquity of the zodiac, and the irregular wandering course of the moon.

On the other hand, he also wrote this fantastic account of the strange properties of water (Book XXXI, Chapters 17, 18):

> At Crannon [in Thessaly] there are certain hot springs, though not at boiling heat, the water of which, mixed with wine, preserves it warm in the vessels for a period of three days. The same is the case, too, with the springs of Mattiacum [the modern Wiesbaden] in Germany, the water of which retains its boiling heat three days. . . .
>
> Ctesias informs us that, in India, there is a lake of standing water, upon which nothing will float, every object instantly sinking to the bottom. Caelius says that in the waters of Lake Avernus, in our own part of the world, the very leaves of the trees even will sink; and, according to Varro, these waters are fatal to such birds as fly towards them. On the other hand, in the waters of Lake Apuscidamus, in Africa, nothing will sink.

And how did he establish the truth of these accounts? In Book VII, Chapter 1, he stated the test by which this material was judged:

> In most points I shall not be content to pledge my own credit only, but shall confirm it in preference by referring to my authorities, which shall be given on all subjects of a nature to inspire doubt. My readers, however, must make no objection to following the Greeks, who have proved themselves the most careful observers, as well as of the longest standing.

This quotation is selected as one out of many from numerous authors who have relied on the voice of authority. Passages like the following are the result (Book VII, Chapter 2):

> In the vicinity of those who dwell in the northern regions, and not far from the spot from which the north wind arises, and the place which is called its cave, the Arimaspi are said to exist, a nation remarkable for having but one eye, and that placed in the middle of the forehead. This race is said to carry on a perpetual warfare with the Griffins, a kind of monster with wings, as they are commonly represented, for the gold which they dig out of the mines, and which these wild beasts retain and keep watch over with a singular degree of cupidity, while the Arimaspi are equally desirous to get possession of it. Many authors have stated to this effect, among the most illustrious of whom are Herodotus and Aristeas of Proconnesus.

Elsewhere he described races of people who had two pupils in each eye and who could kill those on whom they fixed their gaze, races who "have only one leg but are able to leap with surprising agility," "tribes of men who have the heads of dogs and instead of speaking they bark," "tribes who are without necks and have eyes in their shoulders."

Much of the scientific literature through the middle ages was no more reliable than this. It contained more superstition than fact, and the medical literature contained more magic than medicine. The monumental work of Lynn Thorndike is rightly called *A History of Magic and Experimental Science*.

Studied in retrospect, these ancient accounts, aside from making fascinating reading, can teach us a great deal. It has never been easy, either in ancient or modern times, to obtain reliable information. Our own age, in which books and periodicals on astrology are so widely read, is certainly not free of the weakness which is now so obvious to us in the records of antiquity. In the natural sciences the problem has been largely solved through widespread and repeated appeal to experiment and direct observation and by insistence on high standards of honesty in reporting and communicating information.

The danger in relying on superstition or hearsay lies not only in the possible falseness of the immediate conclusion; given a little time, it crystallizes into dogmatic authority and thenceforth is not even open to question. People have always been reluctant to change their minds. It is as uncomfortable to give up an idea as it is to relinquish a custom or a tradition—another example of the inertia of the human mind. The insidious aspect of hearsay really lies in the fact that some of it is true. The writings of Herodotus, Pliny, Celsus, and Vitruvius contain much information which is substantiated by modern knowledge. When Marco Polo, at the end of the thirteenth century, returned from that remarkable journey to the court of Kublai Khan, he told, among other things, of a kind of cloth which could be thrown into fire without burning. This must have seemed like a very tall story to the natives, but it was true; the cloth was woven out of asbestos fiber. How is one to separate the true from the false? In the natural sciences it is experiment and direct observation that provide the controls.

But there was another reason why the experimental point of view came into its own so late. When the various methods of arriving at truth began to be more clearly differentiated, it was inevitable that they should clash. Conclusions drawn solely from experiment and direct observation sharply contradicted many of the popular beliefs which had crystallized into dogma and which had originated in superstition, or in the application of Greek logic, or in transcendentalism. Those who believed in these methods did not see eye to eye with those who relied on experiment; they could not even understand the nature of one another's arguments. There are abundant examples of clashes, such as those concerning the spherical nature of the earth, or the existence of the antipodes, or the validity of the Copernican theory. Lactantius, about the beginning of the fourth century, stated his case against a round earth; "Is there anyone so senseless as to believe that there are men whose footsteps are higher than their heads? . . . that the crops and trees grow downward? . . . that the rains and snow and hail fall upward toward the earth?" Through the whole middle ages, a great deal of what then passed for natural science was dominated by methods other than the experimental. Only after the time of Galileo (1564–1642) did experimentation emerge into relative safety and respectability.

This experimental method which began to take hold about the time of Galileo attaches great significance to sensory experience, for the senses constitute the mechanism of communication between our subjective selves and the external reality. The sum total of that which we see, hear, touch, smell, and taste—that is the stuff out of which the whole scientific structure is built. Occasionally, it is admitted, one or more of our senses may deceive us. It is not difficult to set up an optical experiment in which our eyes will be completely deceived (all optical images are really illusions), but such an arrangement would not deceive the sense of touch. A natural phenomenon is usually studied through so many related phenomena that one sense is continually being checked by others. Also, it is significant that many experimenters progressively check their sensory impressions against those of many other experimenters so that the chances of deception are very small. It need only be assumed that all of our senses do not unitedly and consistently deceive us.

The exponents of the experimental method believe, then, that sensory experiences reveal to us important aspects of an exterior objective reality which is independent of ourselves. This belief really involves two fundamental assumptions:

1. There exists a physical reality outside the mind.

2. Significant information about the physical reality is revealed through sensory experience.

These assumptions can, of course, neither be proved nor disproved; they are matters of faith; but it is a faith which has been confessed by many of the great philosophers of all ages, and it is a faith which results in the greatest meaning and significance for the natural sciences.

The experimental method is best described by example, as in Chapter 12, but a few important features are worth setting down here. Once the experimenter has set himself a problem, specific or general, he organizes a fact-finding campaign and it is especially at this point that the unique features of the method are apparent. The experimenter tries to eliminate, insofar as it is humanly possible, subjective likes and dislikes; wishful thinking is avoided. He does not try to deduce the facts by logical reasoning from general premises; he shares the belief of Lord Bacon that the syllogism is no match for the subtlety of nature. He does not hope for facts to be revealed to him transcendentally or by intuition. He sets aside hearsay, folktales, popular beliefs, and superstitions and goes directly to nature for answers to his questions.

But an experiment is more than mere observation of undisturbed nature; it is a deliberate and carefully planned intrusion into natural phenomena and an interference with natural processes so as to produce new and unusual situations which might otherwise never be observed. It is sometimes said that an experiment is a trap designed to trick nature into revealing itself. Unfortunately, this gives the impression that nature resists investigation and is perverse in a human sort of way. Nature is not like a child who behaves unnaturally or puts on an act when it knows that it is being watched; nature reveals itself consistently and dispassionately no matter how much it is disturbed or needled by the experimenter. It is the extreme subtlety of nature which gives the impression of perverseness.

Once a fund of experimental data has been accumulated, it is found that some of these data may be logically united into general laws and theories by what we have called the inductive method—the method of reasoning from specific cases toward general conclusions. The fact that this is possible, that data do seem to make logical sense, seems sufficient justification for the faith which the scientist places in the order and consistency of nature.

It must not be supposed that the theories so obtained are permanent. Every theorist can testify to the high mortality of theories which have not survived the test of accounting for new experimental data. Neither must it be supposed that these theories offer us a true picture of the ultimate physical reality. That is too much to expect of any branch of human knowledge. The value of a theory or a model lies, rather, in its ability to correlate and to organize data and to aid in predicting new phenomena. Later on, there will be numerous illustrations selected to display the success of this procedure.

As an example of the use of induction in physics, consider this illustration taken from Faraday's *Experimental Researches in Electricity*. By 1833 many discoveries had been made in the field of electricity. Volta had made the first battery out of two different metals immersed in a salt or acid solution and by that means had caused a current to flow. Much earlier, electrostatic charges had been produced by rubbing amber with fur, or glass with silk. Faraday himself had produced electrical effects by changing the magnetic field around a coil of wire. Seebeck had been able to produce an electric current by heating the junction between two different metals. Finally, Cavendish and others had discovered that some animals like the electric eel

TABLE 1

Electricity	Physiological Effects	Magnetic Deflection	Magnets Made	Spark	Heating Power	True Chemical Action	Attraction and Repulsion	Discharge by Hot Air
Voltaic	X	X	X	X	X	X	X	X
Common (friction)	X	X	X	X	X	X	X	X
Magneto	X	X	X	X	X	X	X	
Thermo	X	X	+	+	+	+		
Animal	X	X	X	+	+	X		

(called the torpedo) produced effects like that of Volta's battery. It was now time to inquire, "Do all these varied mechanisms generate the same kind of electricity?" To answer this question, Faraday tried each of these sources in turn to see if similar effects were produced by all of them. Would these electric currents heat a wire, produce a spark, set up a magnetic field, cause a shock, etc.? Table 1 (p. 7) shows how systematic this investigation was. The X's indicate that Faraday was able to produce the effect on first attempt. The plus signs indicate success attained after his first attempts. Some spaces were left vacant but it was reasonable to suppose that these effects were too small to observe. The evidence was thus overwhelmingly for the affirmative; there is only one kind of electricity, no matter what the source may be.

PROBLEMS

1. Make up two syllogisms, one of which is true and one of which is false. In the valid syllogism, how do you know that the first general premise is true? In the false syllogism, just where does the error lie?

2. Francis Bacon (1561–1626) once wrote: "The syllogism is no match for the subtlety of nature." What is your interpretation of this statement?

3. Select an example of inductive reasoning in the field of the natural sciences and one example in some other field. Repeat this for deductive reasoning.

4. Reasoning is said to be *a posteriori,* as opposed to *a priori,* when it is based on sensory experience, on observation or experiment. Give examples of both kinds of reasoning.

5. Look up the words *objective* and *subjective* in a good dictionary. Give examples of both objective and subjective reasoning. Which type of reasoning do you think you use most?

6. What would be your response to the question: "How do you know that all sensory experience is not an illusion?"

7. How would you determine whether or not the accounts of flying saucers are in the same class as Pliny's story about the race of people with only one eye?

.   .   .   .

REFERENCES

1. *Science and Common Sense,* James B. Conant, Yale University Press, 1951.
2. *A History of Science,* Part One, George Sarton, Harvard University Press, 1952.
3. *A History of Western Philosophy,* Bertrand Russell, Simon and Schuster, 1945, Chapters I–VIII.
4. *The Autobiography of Science,* Forest R. Moulton and Justus J. Schifferes, Doubleday & Co., 1950, Chapters I, II, and III.

Historical Perspective

The first great contributions to science came from the Greek culture, but long before the age of Pericles the Babylonians and Egyptians had laid foundations for the scientific structure. More than 2000 years before the Christian era they had begun to make careful observations of the positions of the sun and the moon, the stars and the planets. How fruitful these data turned out to be will be shown in the discussion of astronomy.

Greek science began in Ionia, in what is now the west coast of Turkey, facing the Aegean Sea. Then it spread to southern Italy and Sicily and to Athens. The Athenian school was centered around the famous teacher-pupil sequence Socrates, Plato, and Aristotle. The interests of Socrates (470–399 B.C.) and Plato (427–347 B.C.) lay chiefly outside the field of natural science, and they discouraged experimentation and observation of nature. Aristotle (384–322 B.C.), however, took great interest in the natural sciences, and his writings include discussions on astronomy, biology, botany, and physics. In biology and botany he showed his greatest genius. In these fields he was an extremely keen observer and a competent classifier, but his astronomy was of little value because he did not believe that terrestrial laws were valid for the perfect heavens. In physics, Aristotle's mistakes were most unfortunate since many of them could have been corrected by rather simple experimentation. The most famous of these mistakes was his conclusion that the velocity of a falling body is proportional to its weight and also to the distance fallen. In general, scientists have taken a very unsympathetic attitude toward these mistakes, although philosophers and historians of science have been more generous. It must be remembered that at the time of the Athenian school there was no tradition of experimentation as we know it now; systematic investigation of nature was unknown, and, besides, there was a general feeling among the Greeks that labor of that kind was undignified and degrading.

When Alexander the Great invaded Egypt and established the city of Alexandria in 332 B.C., a group of philosophers gathered around what came to be called the Museum. The mathematics that came out of that school was magnificent. Here Euclid (about 300 B.C.) wrote the plane geometry which has since been taught without significant modification for over 2000 years. Here Apollonius worked out the beautiful theory of conic sections and defined the geometrical figures for which he invented the names ellipse, parabola, and hyperbola. Eratosthenes, who, like Apollonius, was a librarian at the Alexandrian Library, calculated the circumference of the earth by a method to be described later (pp. 19–20). Diophantus began the branch of mathematics which we call algebra and Pappus collected odds and ends of the geometrical knowledge of his day.

In astronomy the contributions were almost as impressive. Aristarchus first described a solar system with a stationary sun which had planets, including the earth, rotating around it—the first heliocentric theory. Ptolemy, fitting a theory to the observed facts, expanded the notion, originated by Apollonius, of epicyclic motion for the planets.

In the Alexandrian school the experimental method was much more strongly represented than in the Greek school at Athens. Archimedes (287–212 B.C.), who spent some time in the Museum, stands out both as an experimenter and as a mathematician. It was he who solved the problem of the crown which King Hieron of Syracuse decided to present to his gods. After the crown was finished, according to Vitruvius, the king suspected that the contractor who had made the crown had substituted some silver for the more valuable gold. Archimedes settled the matter by a simple experiment; he determined the volume of water displaced by the crown when immersed, and then repeated the experiment for an equal weight of pure gold. Since the crown displaced more water than an equal weight of pure gold, the fraud was detected. The idea for the experiment, says Vitruvius, came to Archimedes while he himself was displacing the water of his bath. He performed many other experiments and built numerous mechanical devices.

Ptolemy, the geographer and astronomer, performed experiments on the bending of light beams by transparent substances, and Euclid, the geometer, must have performed many experiments on the reflection and refraction of light in order to write his books on optics.

In addition to Archimedes, there were a number of people whom we might classify as inventors or engineers. Chief among these were Hero of Alexandria, who invented the very first steam engine, and Ctesibius, who made water clocks and water pumps and even a hydraulic pipe organ.

This was an auspicious beginning, but the rapid progress which it seemed to promise did not materialize. The Greeks yielded to the Roman power and the Romans, who inherited the Greek contributions, did little to further the cause of experimental science. Pliny the Elder, Vitruvius, Lucretius, and Celsus were essentially scientific historians, who collected and preserved the knowledge of Athens and Alexandria but added little to it.

During the first few centuries of the Christian era the civilized world was harassed by wars, by social and political instability, and by religious and theological conflict. Parts of the philosophies, first of Plato and then of Aristotle, were incorporated into the Christian theology. Aristotle's notion that terrestrial laws were not valid for the celestial regions and his belief in a geocentric universe fitted in rather well with the theological views of that time. As theology developed, fierce quarrels broke out concerning the interpretation of the Greek philosophy and the manner in which it could be reconciled with the Christian theology. The emphasis was on ethical and moral problems and on fine points of theological differences, rather than on nature study. In fact, natural science came to be considered pagan. In 391 Theophilus, Bishop of Alexandria, destroyed its remaining library (the Serapeion) and in 529 Justinian closed the Academy of Athens. It was not an atmosphere favorable to progress in the natural sciences.

When the Arabs came into power in the eighth century they, too, like the Romans, began to seek out the Greek classics and to translate many writings from both Greek and Latin into the Arabic language. Although the experimental method certainly did not flourish among the Arabs, we do note among them, in addition to continued interest in astronomy, a revived interest in alchemy and medicine. Unfortunately, one of the principal problems of alchemy was that of transmuting base metals into gold, and the hope of success in such a venture naturally attracted many charlatans to this field. Many who were interested in medicine also dabbled in alchemy. There is an enormous literature of mystic formulary which has survived from the middle ages and which is written, for the most part, in incomprehensible jargon. But not all the alchemists were frauds; here and there the writings reveal an honest attempt at chemical experimentation and an honest effort to record what was actually observed.

A few of the Arabic scientists made substantial contributions to what we now call physics. Notable among them was Alhazen (Ibn-al-Haytham, 965–1038), who wrote on many topics in the field of optics and performed experiments to substantiate or refute previous theories and conclusions. Thus, Alhazen found that Ptolemy had stated the law of refraction of light wrongly.

When Aristotle's writings were rediscovered in the thirteenth century and his complete works translated (first from the Arabic), great scholars like Albertus Magnus and Saint Thomas Aquinas completed the reconciliation of Aristotle's philosophy with theology, a reconciliation which had begun earlier in the Christian era. That is how Aristotelian science came to be accepted as authoritative by the established church and why people like Galileo, who disagreed with Aristotle, ran the risk of being accused of heresy. It must be added that this was no fault of Aristotle's; he could not have foreseen how his writings would be used fifteen centuries after they were written. (See Charles Singer, *A Short History of Science*, Oxford University Press, 1943, p. 49).

The damage which such reliance on authority can do is illustrated by the fact that it kept the natural sciences at an almost complete standstill for centuries. Then in the fifteenth and sixteenth centuries the spirit of adventure and of independent thinking broke loose again. In 1453 Constantinople had been captured by the Turks and many Greek scholars had fled to Italy and eventually contributed to the movement which we call the Renaissance. It was a renaissance not only concerned with art and literature but with science and geographical exploration as well.

But victory over the scholasticism of the middle ages was not easily won. A scientist in Galileo's days could not investigate natural phenomena and report his conclusions objectively without running the risk of being accused of heresy, and heresy was no trivial matter. Nevertheless, the urge to experiment and the desire for free inquiry into nature and its fascinating mechanisms were far too strong to be suppressed even by threat to personal safety; during the lifetime of Galileo contributions of new thought began to appear in astronomy, physics, and physiology. By the time of Newton (1642–1727) the experimental attack on natural problems was firmly founded, and since that time it has steadily gained in power and prestige.

PROBLEMS

1. On the assumption that practical needs inspire scientific activity, can you by inference explain why the Egyptians learned so much about astronomy, geometry, and anatomy?

2. Figure 1 is a reproduction of a problem from an Egyptian arithmetic book copied on papyrus about 1650 B.C. (*Rhind Mathematical Papyrus*, translated by A. B. Chace and H. P. Manning, published by Mathematical Association of Amer-

FIG. 1. A problem from the Rhind Papyrus. Calculation of the area of a circle.

ica, Oberlin, Ohio, 1927.) The hieratic text is shown above and the hieroglyphic transcription below. Freely translated it means:

> Given a round field of diameter 9 khet [a unit of length], find its area. Take away ⅑ of the diameter, namely 1; the remainder is 8. Multiply 8 times 8; it makes 64. Therefore it contains 64 setat [unit of area equal to one square khet] of land.

Restate this solution as a general formula, using D as any diameter and A as the area. Compare the formula with that which we now use and calculate the percent difference.
Ans. 0.59%.

3. In Fig. 1, the part inclosed in solid lines is the solution, freely translated above. Compare this in compactness with the modern formula for the area of a circle.

4. The Egyptians obtained the product of two numbers in the following way: Suppose 19 to be multiplied by 35. Then set down two columns

19	35
9	70
4	140x
2	280x
1	560
Sum	665	is the required product

The numbers in the left column represent successive divisions by 2 to the nearest whole number down to 1. The numbers in the right column represent successive multiplications by 2. The numbers in the right column are then added, excluding those which occur alongside any even numbers in the left column (in this case, 4 and 2). This sum is the required product. Study this procedure carefully and explain *why* it works. *Hint:* Try the procedure first on smaller numbers.

. . . .

REFERENCES

1. *A History of Science,* William Dampier, The Macmillan Co., 1930, Chapters I and II.
2. *The Growth of Physical Science,* Sir James Jeans, Cambridge University Press, 1948.
3. *A Short History of Science,* Charles Singer, Oxford, Clarendon Press, 1943.
4. *Augustine to Galileo,* A. C. Crombie, Falcon Educational Books, 1952.   A summary of scientific activity during the middle ages.
5. *The Exact Sciences in Antiquity,* O. Neugebauer, Princeton University Press, 1952.

Geometry as a Tool of Measurement

INTRODUCTION

As previously stated, the natural scientist believes that a physical reality exists outside of his own mind, or consciousness, and he believes, further, that significant information about this reality comes through sensory experience. These beliefs cannot be proved in any absolute sense. Neither can those of the *solipsist,* for example, who believes that the only reality is that of the mind itself and that anything that seems real outside of the mind is an illusion. Every philosophy or school of thinking or intellectual field must begin by such statements of basic beliefs which, in the final analysis, cannot be proved. They are declarations of faith like that which occurs in one of our most cherished documents: "We hold these truths to be self-evident. . . ."

Since we cannot judge the truth or validity of the postulates or basic assumptions by any absolute standards, the test must be of another nature. Does anything worth while result from the basic beliefs? Do the practical consequences justify the assumptions? Is the logical structure which emerges from our beliefs impressive? With such tests in mind we shall set ourselves the problem of describing the physical universe and determining its dimensions. We shall begin with our present position on earth and work our way outward into space to the distant stars. If the result is impressive, have we not been justified in our basic beliefs?

ANCIENT ASTRONOMY

The ancients had good reason to be interested in the stars. To them the heavens not only declared the glory of their gods, but also foretold in celestial symbols every event in their lives from birth to death, if they only had the subtlety to interpret them. Again, man's genius for practical application was evident; no one knows how long ago it was that man first began to guide himself on land and sea by using the stars as a reference frame. This practical use of the stars in navigation still remains as an important reason for modern interest in astronomy, but there are many other reasons, too.

Philosophically, astronomy is of importance because it was one of the very first of the natural sciences to emerge and the first to display clearly the conflict between the objective scientific manner of thinking and other approaches. Astronomy, in its early days, was heavily astrological. Among the Babylonians and the Chaldeans the astrologers and soothsayers represented an important and highly respected profession, and it took centuries for astronomy to shake itself free from astrological nonsense. It took a long time, too, for astronomy to free itself from the constraint imposed by the scholasticism of the middle ages. But the important point is that it did triumph; no intelligent person now doubts that the earth is round or that the Copernican theory is valid. It may even seem strange to us now that the mere dimensions or geometrical aspects of the physical universe could have had such a profound influence on men's minds. Actually, it was not the dimensions as such that mattered but, rather, the method by which they were obtained. A new and powerful system of thinking had established itself, and it was as if men's minds and insights expanded with the physical dimensions of the universe which they began to comprehend. Even to Pliny, in the first century of the Christian era, it was evident that the study of astronomy had produced a new intellectual liberation. Referring to Thales, who had predicted an eclipse, and Hipparchus who had predicted the 600-year cycle of eclipses, he wrote (*Natural History,* Book II, Chapter 9):

> All this has been confirmed by experience, and could only be acquired by partaking, as it were, in the councils of nature. These were indeed great men, superior to ordinary mortals, who, having discovered the laws of these divine bodies, relieved the miserable mind of man from the fear which he had of eclipses, as foretelling some dreadful events or the destruction of the stars. . . . Hail to your genius, ye interpreters of heaven! Ye who comprehend the nature of things and who have discovered a mode of reasoning by which ye have conquered both gods and men!"

As stated previously, many substantial contributions to astronomy were made before the Christian era. The Babylonian star data have already been mentioned. These were so accurate that as early as 343 B.C. a Babylonian astronomer, Cidenas, had noted from them that the positions of the constellations changed slightly from year to year as the seasons repeated themselves. This change is called the "precession of the equinoxes" and was described more fully by Hipparchus later on. Aristarchus of Samos (310–230 B.C.) had also made some interesting astronomical calculations (see p. 23). He had measured the angular separation of the sun and the moon when the moon appeared half-illuminated by the sun and, by rigorous application of geometry, had calculated the relative distances of the sun and moon from the earth. He had also calculated the relative sizes of the sun and moon. It was Aristarchus, too, who concluded that the sun was stationary and that the earth revolved around it. Eratosthenes (273–192 B.C.) had made an ingenious calculation of the circumference of the earth (see pp. 19–20). He had recognized that the change in elevation of the sun above the horizon at noon due to a change in latitude must mean that the earth was round. At noon the sun in Alexandria was lower in the sky than it was at Syene, which was south of Alexandria and at the same longitude. From the difference between the two angular positions of the sun and from the distance between Alexandria and Syene, it was simple geometry to calculate the circumference of the earth. His result compares favorably with the modern value.

THE EARTH

An investigation of the physical world with the purpose of learning, so far as possible, of what it is made and how it operates is a vast undertaking indeed. The attempt might soon be abandoned were it not for an innate conviction that we live in an orderly universe in which nature is describable by law and does not act whimsically. If that is so, a given set of conditions may always be expected to yield the same consequences, and our problem becomes the still formidable but at least reasonable one of discovering these natural laws.

With what shall we begin our investigation? Common sense suggests starting with the earth itself and endeavoring to learn its shape and dimensions. It is easy to propose that this be done by observation but, as residents of the very earth which we wish to study as a whole, we must be aware that our observational opportunities are limited as compared with those we might have if we could ascend a few hundred miles above the earth. Accordingly, in this and in other inquiries we shall often have to supplement our direct sensory experience with various logical techniques. Especially must we utilize the logical discipline known as geometry.

At an early age children are told that the earth is spherical. Usually this information is imparted to them as an assertion without evidence to confirm it, and, although they may challenge such statements at the time, older children and young adults are likely to accept them obediently enough. This is, too frequently, because they find it less troublesome to agree with the pronouncements of authority than to exercise logical doubts. Yet, a casual view of an extensive plain or a large body of water seems to contradict any assertion that the earth is round. On what evidence, then, is this seemingly fallacious declaration based?

One could reply that circumnavigation proves the earth to be a globe and numerous round the world voyages by air, sea, and land have established the point beyond question. But 2500 years ago the Greek geometer, Pythagoras, argued that the earth was a sphere, and he certainly had no opportunity to circumnavigate it. How can we *infer* the earth's sphericity without extensive traveling?

First of all, there is the horizon. A flat world could hardly show a sharp line between earth and sky unless this boundary were actually the edge of the earth. If it were, the same edge would remain visible, even though we rose to considerable elevation. What the elevated observer sees, however, is a new horizon, more remote than the one he saw at sea level. Moreover, the horizon recedes in all directions as he ascends, and this would be possible only for a globular figure. The familiar observation that when a ship disappears over the horizon, the hull vanishes first and the superstructure last, is merely a variant of the same argument.

When the full moon is partially eclipsed by the earth, it is sometimes possible to detect the boundary of the earth's shadow on the moon. When this occurs, the boundary is the arc of a *circle*. This was the evidence cited by Aristotle, who also believed the earth to be round.

Most people know how to locate the North Star (Polaris) at night, and it is a simple exercise to estimate its angular elevation (or "altitude") above the ground. If this is done at various latitudes [1] between the North Pole and the equator, the most northerly observer finds Polaris to be practically overhead, whereas the most southerly one sees the star practically on the horizon. In between, the altitude of Polaris becomes larger as the latitude of the observer becomes larger; —indeed, the altitude of Polaris *equals* the lati-

. . . .

[1] For definitions of latitude and longitude, see Appendix C.

tude, as can be shown by simple geometry (see Fig. 2). These changes in angular elevation are easily explained if the earth is assumed to be spherical. They cannot be explained at all if the earth is regarded as flat and if we assume the stars to be very distant.

Within recent years aviation has given us convincing pictorial evidence of the earth's sphericity. Photographs taken from high-flying planes

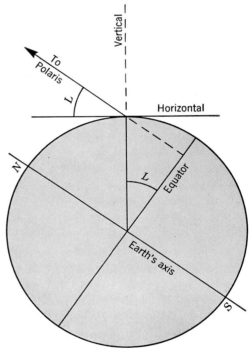

FIG. 2. Angle of elevation of Polaris equals the latitude angle *L*.

and rockets actually show the horizon to be an *arc* (Plate I). Inasmuch as the earth is a large sphere by ordinary standards of distance, it is not surprising that its roundness is unapparent unless the horizon is viewed from a great height.

THE RADIUS OF THE EARTH

The disappearance of objects over the horizon furnishes a means of determining the earth's radius with the aid of simple geometry.

Figure 3 represents a ship sailing away from New York with an observer at the stern looking at the Empire State Building tower through a telescope. Just as the top of the tower vanishes below the horizon, he notes by the ship's log how far he has sailed from New York. This distance

Official Photograph, U.S. Navy

PLATE I. Photograph taken from Navy's rocket No. 12 which climbed to a height of 144 miles above the earth on Feb. 4, 1955. Looking toward the west, it shows the Gulf of California, lower California, and the Pacific Ocean. The horizon is nearly 1100 miles from the camera and is obviously curved.

will be practically the same as the distance S in the diagram. The observer's line of sight will be tangent to the earth and hence perpendicular to

FIG. 3. We watch the Empire State Building disappear over the horizon and calculate the size of the earth.

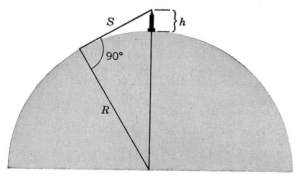

the radius R. According to a familiar geometrical theorem (the square of the hypotenuse of a right triangle = the sum of the squares of the legs),

$$S^2 + R^2 = (R + h)^2$$
$$= R^2 + 2Rh + h^2$$

Now, h is a very small height in comparison with the radius R, so that h^2 is negligible in comparison with $2Rh$. We are justified, therefore, in disregarding h^2 in the above equation. Then,

$$S^2 = 2Rh \qquad \text{whence } R = S^2/2h$$

The Empire State Building has a height of about $\frac{1}{5}$ mi, and the distance S is about 40 mi. Substituting, the radius of the earth is found to be

$$R = \frac{(40)^2}{(2)(\frac{1}{5})} = 4000 \text{ mi}$$

This value is in good agreement with others obtained by more precise methods.

Since we have made some approximations in order to get this result, it is now desirable to show why h had to be retained in the term $2Rh$ even though h^2 alone was considered negligible.

Substituting numerical values in

$$S^2 = 2Rh + h^2$$
$$1600 = (8000)(\tfrac{1}{5}) + \tfrac{1}{25}$$

and it is evident that h affects the term $2Rh$ to an important degree, whereas h^2 by itself makes practically no contribution to the equation.

THE CIRCUMFERENCE OF THE EARTH

If the earth is a sphere and its radius is known, we can easily compute its circumference, and this we are now able to do. Nevertheless, it will be interesting to consider another ancient geometrical method of determining the earth's circumference. This method was devised during the third century B.C. by the Greek astronomer Eratosthenes, and his result was substantially the same as the value which is accepted today as correct.

The principle of Eratosthenes' method, represented in Fig. 4, was as follows: Assuming the earth to be spherical, if a distance along its circumference is known, as well as the central angle

FIG. 4. Method of Eratosthenes for calculating the circumference of the earth.

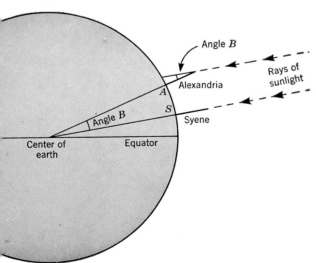

subtended by that distance, the whole circumference can be calculated by proportion.

Eratosthenes chose for his observation points two cities in upper Egypt, Syene and Alexandria, the first of which was 5000 stades or about 490 mi due south of the second. On a certain day of the year the sun at noon was known to be directly above Syene, so that the solar rays came down vertically upon this place. The sun was not directly over Alexandria, however; hence its rays fell upon that city somewhat obliquely at noon. A pole was set vertically into the ground at Alexandria and a careful measurement of the length of its shadow was made at noon of the day when Syene was vertically below the sun.

From the length of the shadow and the height of the pole, it was possible to compute the angle B shown in the diagram, for

$$\frac{\text{Length of shadow}}{\text{Height of pole}} = \text{Tangent of angle } B \ ^2$$

and this angle proved to be $\frac{1}{50}$ of a complete circle.

The lengths and angles in Fig. 4 are greatly exaggerated in order to exhibit the geometrical fact that this angle is also the central angle subtended by the arc SA.

Inasmuch as the entire circumference of a spherical earth would subtend a central angle of $360°$, we may set up the proportion:

$$\frac{\text{Circumference}}{490} = \frac{360°}{\frac{1}{50} \times 360°}$$

Therefore the length of the circumference is 24,500 mi.

It is to be remembered that this method involves two assumptions: (1) that the earth is a sphere and (2) that the sun's rays are parallel. Neither assumption is strictly true. The earth is a spher*oid,* and the sun, radiating light in all directions, cannot possibly have all its rays parallel to one another. Nevertheless, two places relatively close to each other, as these were, yet a very great distance from the sun, receive their radiation along *practically* parallel paths, so that little error is introduced on this account.

The errors become even smaller if the observations are made using a convenient star in place of the sun, and if the distance between stations is made smaller. The geometrical argument is the same, using data obtained with good tele-

· ·

[2] See Appendix B for definition of tangent.

scopes and circular scales. This has, in fact, been done from a large number of positions on the earth with the result that we now know the shape of the earth to a high degree of accuracy; it is an oblate spheroid—like a plastic sphere which has been somewhat distorted by pressing the north and south poles together. The difference between the polar and equatorial diameters is about 27 mi.

DISTANCE AND SIZE

The most conspicuous bodies in the sky are the sun and the moon. They appear to the eye to be the largest of all celestial bodies. It would be foolish to believe the evidence of eyesight alone, however, on a question of size, inasmuch as we are well aware that a seemingly small object may actually be rather large and its apparent smallness due merely to its remoteness. Evidently we cannot tell whether the sun and the moon are really large bodies until we have determined their distances from the earth.

DISTANCE BY TRIANGULATION

The distance separating the moon from the earth can be found by a method called triangulation, which is extensively used by surveyors in making land measurements. This method utilizes a simple property of triangles known as the *Law of Sines,* which may be stated as follows:

In a plane triangle the lengths of any two sides have the same ratio to each other as do the sines[3] of the angles opposite those sides.

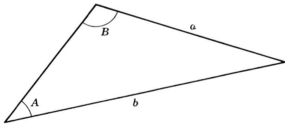

FIG. 5

Consulting Fig. 5,

$$\frac{a}{b} = \frac{\text{sine of angle } A}{\text{sine of angle } B}$$

Suppose, for example, it is required to find the distance between two points S and T on the op-

. . . .

[3] See Appendix B for definition of sine.

posite shores of a river (Fig. 6). The surveyor stretches a tape of known length from the point S to some other point R along the same shore. Mounting his transit (an instrument for measuring angles) at S, he sights along ST and then along SR to get the angle A between these two directions. A similar pair of observations from R give him the angle B. From the familiar geometric knowledge that the three angles of a triangle total 180°, he now obtains angle C by subtraction. Finally, he looks up the sines of angles

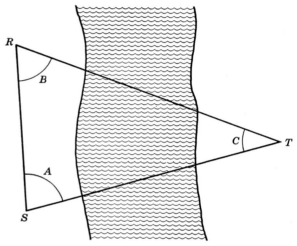

FIG. 6

C and B in a trigonometric table and substitutes them, as well as the distance SR, into the equation

$$ST = SR \times \frac{\text{sine of angle } B}{\text{sine of angle } C}$$

DISTANCE OF THE MOON FROM THE EARTH

When the triangulation method is employed for determining the distance to the moon, a complication enters because of the earth's curvature. A point on the moon is sighted from two places on earth, just as in the previous example, but the *straight-line distance* between the two places has to be calculated in this case.

Referring to Fig. 7, let one observer be stationed at Halifax and another at Port of Spain, Trinidad, which is approximately 2400 mi due south of Halifax. The *straight* line connecting these two places must pass within the earth, however, and it is consequently less than 2400 mi long. From the respective latitudes of the two places in question the straight-line distance HT

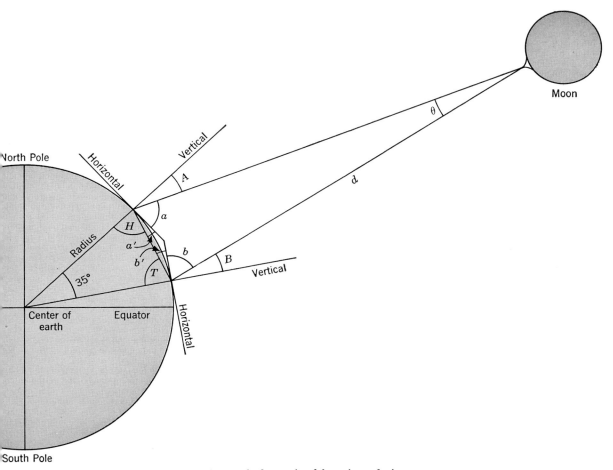

FIG. 7. Distance of the moon from the earth determined by triangulation.

can be found with the aid of the sine law. Thus, the latitude of Halifax is 45° and that of Trinidad is 10°; hence, the triangle formed by the two radii of the earth and the base HT has an apex angle of 35°. The base angles H and T are accordingly

$$\frac{180 - 35}{2} = 72.5°$$

each. Moreover, by the sine law,

$$\frac{HT}{\text{Radius of the earth}} = \frac{\sin 35°}{\sin 72.5°}$$

or

$$HT = \frac{3950 \times 0.574}{0.954} = 2380 \text{ mi}$$

The distance of the moon from the earth may be determined thus:

Each of two observers, one at Halifax and the other at Trinidad, sets his telescope in the plane of the meridian (the plane which cuts vertically through the earth along a line extending north and south). Since Trinidad and Halifax have very nearly the same longitude, both of them can be considered to lie on this line. Just as the moon is crossing the meridian, each observer measures with his telescope the elevation of the moon above the horizon. Assume that they have previously agreed on some specific marking, say a lunar peak, on which to set the cross hairs of their telescopes. These elevations are angles a and b.

Since

$$H + a + a' + A = 180°$$

and since H and A are known, $a + a'$ can be calculated. Similarly, $b + b'$ can be calculated

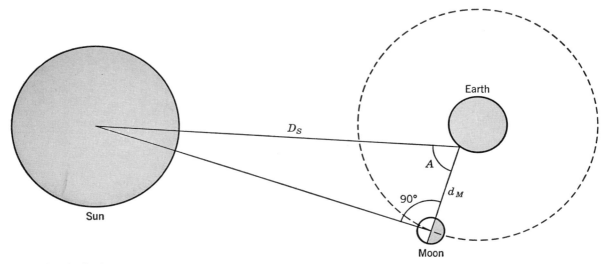

FIG. 8. Method of Aristarchus for determining the relative distances of the sun and moon from the earth.

Suppose it is found that $a = 72° 13'$ and $b = 72° 14'$. Then,

$$a + a' = 89° 43'$$

and

$$b + b' = 89° 44'$$

In the triangle formed by HT and the lines of sight to the moon,

$$\theta = 180° - (a + a') - (b + b') = 33'$$

Therefore, by the law of sines,

$$d = \frac{2380 \times \sin 89° 43'}{\sin 33'} = \frac{2380 \times 0.99999}{0.0096}$$

or

$$d = 248{,}000 \text{ mi for this particular observation}$$

The average distance of the moon is known to be about 237,000 mi from the surface of the earth.

DISTANCE OF THE SUN FROM THE EARTH

Inasmuch as the distance from the earth to the moon is far greater than any possible base line through the earth, the angle θ in the previous example is bound to be very small. But when we try the same method to determine the sun's distance, the angle θ is only a few seconds. Hence, we conclude that the sun is much farther away from us than the moon is.

The determination of such a small angle is not sufficiently accurate to recommend the triangulation method as a feasible one for estimating the sun's distance. On the other hand, ge-

ometry provides a ready means of determining the *relative* distances of the sun and the moon from the earth. This value may then be used in connection with the absolute distance of the moon to obtain the absolute distance of the sun.

The method is a modification of one which was first used in the third century B.C. by the Greek astronomer Aristarchus and is easily understood from Fig. 8. Here the sun, moon, and earth are represented as standing at the three vertices of a right triangle. This triangle is exaggerated in the drawing for clearer understanding. As the moon revolves continually around the earth, its path, as seen from the earth, is approximately circular. When it is passing between the sun and the earth, the moon is said to be "new," or in the *new phase*. About a week later, it reaches the position shown in the diagram, where the line bounding the moon's shadow and the line from the moon to the center of the sun form a right angle, and that part of the moon which is visible from the earth appears as a semicircle. Knowledge of any other angle in the right triangle so formed would enable us to calculate the ratio of distance d_M to distance D_S.

In making the actual determination, the observer directs his telescope toward the boundary line which separates the illuminated semicircle of the half-moon from the darkened half and then turns his instrument until it points toward the sun's center. The angle of turning is angle A, and the desired ratio is given by

$$d_M/D_S = \text{cosine } [4] \text{ of angle } A$$

We find the angle A to be 89° 50'. Trigonometric tables give the cosine of 89° 50' as 0.0029. Hence the relative distances $d_M/D_S = 0.0029$ and

$$D_S = d_M/0.0029 \qquad \text{or about 345 times } d_M$$

Since we have already found the moon to be about 248,000 mi from the surface of the earth, this result puts the sun at a distance 345 times as great or about 86,000,000 mi from the earth. It is interesting to note that, when Aristarchus used this method, he estimated the angle A to be 87°, thereby making the sun about 19 times farther away than the moon.

The sun's distance is actually determined by better methods than the one described but, inasmuch as they depend upon principles still to be explained, we shall defer their consideration until later.

Most readers will recall that the distance of the sun from the earth is usually quoted as 93,000,000 mi. One should bear in mind that this figure approximates the average distance. The sun's distance from the earth varies somewhat throughout the year.

THE ASTRONOMICAL UNIT

The distances involved in astronomical measurements are so great that it becomes inconvenient to express them in miles, and certain much larger units are commonly employed. One of these larger standards is called the *astronomical unit* (abbreviated A.U.) and is merely the average distance of the earth from the sun. Thus,

$$1 \text{ A.U.} = 93,000,000 \text{ mi}$$

DIAMETER OF THE MOON AND THE SUN

Once the distance of the moon from the earth has been determined, it becomes a simple matter to find the moon's diameter, and the same statement holds for the sun. Suppose that a telescope is directed toward a point on the circumference of the full moon and then rotated until it is trained on a point of the circumference diametrically opposite the first point. The angle through which the telescope turns is evidently the angle subtended by the moon's diameter. Although this diameter is a straight line, we can, without serious error, regard it as a small arc. The ratio of this arc to the measured angle of rotation will then be the same as the ratio of

the circumference of a circle ($2\pi R$), having the moon's distance as its radius, to 360°.[5]

It has been found that the angle of rotation is about 0.50° (30 min), and, if the distance of the moon for this particular observation is taken as 248,000 mi, the diameter of the moon comes out to be

$$\text{Diameter of moon} = \frac{0.50 \times 2\pi \times 248,000}{360}$$
$$= 2160 \text{ mi}$$

or about ¼ the diameter of the earth.

By similar measurements the sun, whose disk also subtends about ½° of arc, is found to have a diameter of 864,000 mi, or 109 times the diameter of the earth!

By geometrical reasoning and angular measurement we are thus led to the conclusion that, although the sun is indeed a large body many times larger than the earth, the apparently equally large moon is really far smaller than the earth.

UNCERTAINTIES IN MEASUREMENT

In connection with the last illustration it was mentioned that triangulation is unsatisfactory as a method for determining the distance of the sun. This raises an important question regard-

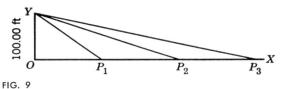

FIG. 9

ing limitations on measurement. How can we decide whether a particular measuring device or method is sensitive enough for its purpose?

Let us imagine that we have a transit capable of measuring angles to the nearest tenth of a degree, so that a reading of 14.3°, for example, means that the angle in question may have any value between 14.25° and 14.35°. How accurately can distances be estimated by triangulation with the aid of this instrument?

For an answer to this question we shall consider two lines, OY and OX at right angles to each other in the same plane (Fig. 9). Let one line OY have a known length of 100.00 ft. We wish to determine, by sighting from Y, the distances OP_1, OP_2, and OP_3 along the line OX. This will require measuring the angles OYP_1,

----

[4] See Appendix B for definition of cosine.

[5] See Appendix A for discussion of angular measure.

OYP_2, and OYP_3 and in each case applying the formula

$$OP = 100 \times \text{tangent of angle } OYP$$

Suppose that the angle OYP_1 measures 75.0°. This means that the true value of OYP_1 lies between 74.95° and 75.05°. A table of tangents reveals that

$$\tan 74.95° = 3.719$$

$$\tan 75.05° = 3.745$$

Accordingly, the true length of OP_1 is more than 371.9 ft but less than 374.5 ft and either figure differs by only about ⅓ of 1% from the average value of 373.2 ft. This is a rather small error.

Next, suppose that the angle OYP_2 measures 89.0°, meaning that the true value of OYP_2 lies between 88.95° and 89.05°. From a table of tangents

$$\tan 88.95° = 54.56$$

$$\tan 89.05° = 60.31$$

Hence the correct length of OP_2 is somewhere between 5456 ft and 6031 ft. The disparity of 575 ft between them represents a rather large uncertainty in the required distance. The difference between either one of these figures and their average of 5744 ft amounts to 5%, and we have no choice but to acknowledge that in this example the transit is responsible for a rather serious error of 5%. This error is not the fault of the observer, who is presumed to have been just as careful in the last observation as he was in the first. It is, rather, an instrumental error, attributable solely to the limitations of the transit.

The error is greatly aggravated when we come to measure an angle of nearly 90°, such as OYP_3, which we shall suppose to be given by the transit as 89.9°. Again we interpret the reading to mean that OYP_3 is truly between 89.85° and 89.95°. From the tables

$$\tan 89.85° = 381.97$$

$$\tan 89.95° = 1145.90$$

Therefore, OP_3 is any length between 38,197 ft and 114,590 ft. These lengths differ, however, by 76,393 ft, and this discrepancy is actually equal to the average of the two extreme lengths. In other words, we have no assurance that the average length, 76,393 ft, is anywhere near correct, for a value 50% smaller as well as one 50% larger could equally well result from the same measurement. It is obvious that the instrument used is utterly unsuited for the last determination.

UNITS AND MEASUREMENT

A great variety of familiar transactions involve expressions of quantity. A certain order of meat weighs *four pounds;* a certain garment requires *five yards* of cloth; a certain article costs *six dollars*—in each instance the figure is a multiple of some appropriate unit. Without the unit the quotation becomes meaningless. Now, it should be obvious that each repetition of the same unit must be identical if a statement of quantity is to be meaningful. It would not do to have four unequal pounds in the four-pound cut of meat. But in order that pounds or feet or seconds may be the same under all conditions, it is necessary that their magnitudes be rigorously defined and that copies of the standard units be reproducible with great fidelity. Exact copies of standard units are by no means easy to make. In the strictest sense they are impossible to make. Moreover, in the use of such copies or even of the original, there is an inevitable error, for measurement consists of comparing the thing to be measured with the standard, and such comparisons simply cannot be made with absolute certainty. The limitation on accuracy can be stated definitely, however, and to know the extent of uncertainty is the next best thing to knowing the exact value. The practical question which is implied in any measurement is: how precise must the measurement be for the purpose intended?

Suppose for example we set out to measure 100 yd along level ground. If this distance were to span the boundaries of a playing field, we might pace it off and get a satisfactory approximation to within 1 or 2 yd. The distance would then be described as 100 ± 2 yd with an uncertainty of 2%. Alternatively, the measurement might be made for the purpose of bounding a football gridiron, and, since altercations might arise during a game over the location of the ball, it would be important to measure the distance more finely, say, to the nearest inch. This might be done with a steel tape and the distance described as

$$100.00 \pm 0.03 \text{ yd}$$

(since 1 in. is approximately 0.03 yd). The ambiguous symbol ± means that the distance is uncertain by not more than 0.03. It may be as much as 1 in. greater than 100 yd or 1 in. less. It might even be 100 yd exactly, but that will never be known. Nor will it matter. The slightly uncertain value is just as serviceable for the purpose of the game as an exact one would be. To be sure, we could probably make a more refined measurement with the same tape, say, to the nearest quarter inch but it would be useless. The ball itself could not be located within a quarter of an inch.

In real estate claims a fraction of an inch sometimes provides ground for a legal dispute. If a piece of property with a frontage of 100 yd is to be transferred, the surveyor will measure the distance with the aid of a transit and a tape which shows still finer subdivisions,—say, as small as one-tenth of an inch (0.003 yd). The distance may then be described as

$$100.000 \pm 0.003 \text{ yd}$$

Note that the value 100.000 has a different significance from the value 100. It signifies that the observer has refined his measurement to provide against discrepancies of a few thousandths of a yard.

Finally, let us see what purpose could be served by diminishing still further the uncertainty in the measurement. The speed of sound through still air is about 370 yd/sec. Suppose we wanted to determine the speed as precisely as possible by timing the passage of a sound pulse over a 100-yd range. The question is: how closely should the distance be measured? This is a question which cannot be answered until the sensitivity of the timing device is specified. If time is to be measured with a stop watch which can be read to 0.1 sec, then the error in meas-

uring the distance can be anything less than 19 yd. For if one range were short of 100 yd by 18 yd, whereas another range exceeded 100 yd by 18 yd, the second range would be 36 yd longer than the first, and, although sound would require *almost* 0.1 sec to travel the extra distance, our watch would not record this additional time. Suppose, however, that a high-speed timing device were employed, capable of measuring a millionth of a second (0.000001 sec). During so short an interval the sound pulse could move only about 0.00037 yd, and the distance measurement should be reliable to the same extent, that is to about $\frac{1}{75}$ in. The surveyor's tape would not qualify for this purpose, but, assuming the distance to have been measured with a more sensitive device, it would be described as 100.00000 ± 0.00037 yd.

The foregoing illustrations are meant to emphasize the point that no measurement is ever exact but is always limited by the reliability and sensitivity of the measuring device. The operation of measuring is itself a physical experiment in which an error, or uncertainty, inevitably enters. The error may be diminished greatly, but it never vanishes. It is correct to say that there are exactly 12 inches in a foot and exactly 3 feet in a yard, because their relationship is *defined* by these numbers. It is also correct to say that a yard is exactly the distance between two marks on a bronze bar which is preserved in London because that particular distance has been agreed upon as being one English yard. Use of the word exact in connection with any copy of this distance, however, is incorrect (we might say inexact) because no copy can be made without at least some experimental error.

PROBLEMS

1. (*Home problem.*)   Using a globe to represent the earth, indicate with a pencil, and for various points on the earth, the following directions: up, down, vertical, horizontal, north, south, east, and west.   (Each student should possess a globe at least 6 in. in diameter.)

2. On your globe, observe the shortest route between New York and Le Havre.   Is it a straight line?   Is its geographical direction constant?   What is meant by the *great circle route?*

3. Why are globes representing the earth always made with the north pole up?

4. Calculate the apex angle in seconds at the sun of a triangle whose base is the whole diameter of the earth.
Ans.   17.7 sec.

5. Describe in detail how you would determine the height of a tall building by the method of triangulation.

6. In the problem of Aristarchus represented in Fig. 8, to what portion of the earth is an observer restricted?

7. Suppose the earth were a flat plane *A–E* as in Fig. 10. Would not the altitude of Polaris, even then, decrease as the observer moves toward *E*, through points *B*, *C*, and *D*?

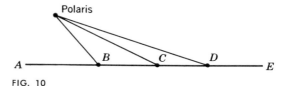

FIG. 10

8. On your globe trace the course of a plane which sets out from New York and moves constantly in a northeasterly direction.

9. Copenhagen and Milan are on approximately the same meridian and about 700 mi apart.   An observer at each place sights a star at the zenith and then turns his telescope toward the star which is at the other's zenith.   Through what angle must each telescope be turned?

. . . .

REFERENCE

1. *A Source Book in Greek Science,* Morris R. Cohen and I. E. Drabkin, McGraw-Hill Book Co., 1948, pp. 90–122.

The Solar System

The next step in our survey of the universe from the earth outward is more difficult because, apart from the sun and moon, celestial objects within the range of human vision appear to be small and exceedingly remote. Since we now have reason to believe that many of these objects are actually much larger than the sun, and that a few of them are not especially far distant, such beliefs must be the result of bringing logic to the aid of observation.

It might be supposed that modern instruments, such as the telescope, are solely responsible for man's present knowledge of heavenly bodies. This is not the case. A good deal of astronomical information, some of it remarkably accurate, had accumulated long before the invention of the telescope, and even those civilizations which flourished before the Christian era knew how to distinguish between the planets, which are all relatively close to the earth, and the stars, which are all very much further away. Moreover, by applying reason to their observations, the observers of antiquity had discovered the correct order of distance of the several planets from the earth. It is appropriate to resume our study of the physical components of the heavens with a review of these ancient arguments. In addition, let us become familiar with a few descriptive details which are facts of observation and which do not depend on any theory.

PLANETS AND STARS

The sky above us obviously contains a large number of bodies, most of which can be seen only at night, if at all. We differentiate among these bodies a small number of *planets* and an immense number of *stars*. To the naked eye there is no difference in appearance excepting that the planets Venus and Jupiter, and occasionally Mars, are brighter than the general run of stars. The fundamental distinction is that the planets shine only by the light which they reflect from the sun, whereas the stars are suns themselves and shine because they are extremely hot. This difference is certainly not apparent to the eye, however, and we seek a criterion by which the layman can decide with assurance: this is a planet, but that is a star.

There is no positive criterion which can be applied to a lone observation, unless the object is viewed through a telescope, for then most of the planets reveal their rounded contour, whereas stars still appear like bright points of light. The only way to recognize a planet with the naked eye is to watch it for several nights or weeks until it can be seen to have shifted its position with respect to the fixed pattern of stars beyond it. Stars and planets alike appear to rise in the east and set in the west nightly, but a planet will not maintain its position in the configuration of stars. If it rises tonight in company with a group of stars and its location among these stars is carefully noted, then on rising tomorrow night it will be seen to be displaced somewhat in the same group. On the next and following nights it will be still farther displaced, and soon

it will be located in quite a different group of stars.

RETROGRADE MOTION

A peculiarity of all planets is that their displacement against the starry background does not persist in the same direction. If a planet has been shifting eastward night after night, it will not continue to do so indefinitely but will presently appear to reverse its direction of shifting and will seem for a time to shift westward for a number of nights. Ultimately the planet will resume its eastward displacement and will continue to shift in that direction for a time until

PLATE II. Saturn and its ring system photographed with the 100-inch Mount Wilson telescope.

Mount Wilson and Palomar Observatories

a new reversal occurs. The path which it takes among the stars thus appears to be a circular one, with occasional closed loops. Figure 16 shows such a loop for the planet Jupiter.

PLANETS KNOWN IN ANCIENT TIMES

Surviving records indicate that long before the Christian era five celestial bodies had been distinguished as planets. The five were the planets known to us as Mercury, Venus, Mars, Jupiter, and Saturn. The order of their distances from the earth was inferred from their rates of displacement with respect to the stars. Since Saturn was observed to shift among the stars more slowly than Jupiter did, the ancient watchers concluded that Saturn must be farther away. Jupiter, in turn, shifted against the pattern of stars more slowly than Mars did and was accordingly believed to be more remote than Mars. The astronomers of antiquity did not know, however, how to estimate the actual distances of planets from the earth or from the sun, and the absence of such quantitative information not only left their factual data incomplete but it also hindered the development of any rational theory of the solar system. We shall postpone consideration of specific ways for estimating planetary distances at this time and proceed to classify the remaining celestial bodies as they are regarded by present-day astronomers.

Jupiter is notable for being far larger than any of the other planets excepting Saturn, which is itself an exceptionally large planet, having slightly more than one-half the volume of Jupiter. Both planets are accompanied by an unusually large collection of satellites—twelve in the case of Jupiter and nine belonging to Saturn. Saturn has, in addition, a peculiarity in the form of three flat, concentric rings which gird its equator like spinning quoits (Plate II). The rings can be seen plainly by a modern telescope and were so described by Huygens in 1655. They make the planet look like a gigantic head wearing a broad-brimmed hat. It is estimated that there is a difference of thousands of miles between the inner and the outer radii of each ring, and, inasmuch as the outer edges are known to revolve more slowly than the inner edges, it is obvious that the rings cannot be solid and continuous but must be made up of separate particles.

PLANETS DISCOVERED IN MODERN TIMES

In 1781 the British astronomer William Herschel (1738–1822) discovered a planet, more distant than Saturn, which he named Uranus (Plate III). This body, which is barely visible to the naked eye, had been seen several times previously, but it had hitherto been mistaken for a faint star. Prior to the recognition of Uranus, Newton's gravitation law had been published

Bettmann Archive

PLATE III. Herschel's largest telescope completed in 1789. The observer stood on the movable platform S to view with an eyepiece the image formed by a concave mirror four feet in diameter placed at the bottom of the tube. The huge telescope tube was raised and lowered by ropes and pulleys, and the observer reached the platform S by climbing around on ladders attached to the framework.

and by its aid astronomers now proceeded to plot in advance the path which Uranus should follow. As time went on, the actual path of Uranus was seen to depart more and more from the predicted one. This discrepancy implied that some other body must be affecting the motion of Uranus. On this assumption Adams in England and Leverrier in France worked out the location of a planet which could cause such a discrepancy. Their calculations led to the discovery in 1846 of a new planet farther out than

Uranus. This planet was named Neptune. A similar calculation by the American astronomer Lowell paved the way for the discovery in 1930 of the outermost planet, Pluto, by Tombaugh.

SATELLITES

Most of the planets have smaller bodies which revolve around them in relatively short intervals of time. Jupiter is known to have twelve such satellites or moons, four of which are so large

Bettmann Archive

PLATE IV. Galileo showing his telescope to the Venetian Senate. Fresco by Luigi Sabatelli. Natural History Museum of Florence.

that they were observed even by Galileo and described in his *Sidereal Message* in 1610. Galileo used his own telescope, home-made and rather crude by modern standards (Plate IV), but now we need only eight-power field glasses to observe these moons shifting in position in the course of an evening. Photographs of Jupiter occasionally show the shadows cast by these moons upon the planetary surface.

Saturn has nine moons, Uranus five, and Mars and Neptune each have two. No moons have yet been found around Mercury, Venus, and Pluto.

PLANETOIDS

More than a thousand small planetary bodies have been found between Mars and Jupiter within the last 150 years. These are known as planetoids, although some writers prefer to call

them *asteroids*. Most planetoids are quite small, ranging in diameter from a few miles to about 500 miles. Ceres, the largest, was also the first planetoid to be discovered. It was found accidentally by the Italian astronomer Piazzi in 1801. His discovery stimulated a search for others, inasmuch as the small size of Ceres suggested that it might be merely a piece of some larger planet originally situated between Mars and Jupiter and blown to fragments through some cosmic accident.

Three of the tiniest planetoids are of special interest because they come so close to the earth that their distance can be determined with sufficient accuracy by triangulation. These bodies, named Eros, Amor, and Apollo, approach to within 13 million, 10 million, and 3 million miles of the earth when they are nearest to us. By estimating the distance of any one of these planetoids when it is at several parts of its orbit, one can calculate all the dimensions of the orbit. This provides an indirect means of evaluating the astronomical unit, which is not accurately determinable by triangulation, as we pointed out earlier (p. 21).

ROTATION OF THE PLANETS

If a planet has conspicuous markings, it is easy to determine the time required by the planet to rotate on its axis. Essentially this task consists of noting the time elapsed between two successive appearances of a planetary marking in the same direction. The period of rotation of any planet, like the period of rotation of the earth itself, is remarkably constant. Mars has a rotational period, or day, only a little longer than the earth's twenty-four-hour day, but Jupiter, Saturn, and Uranus spin rapidly and complete a rotation in about ten hours. Moreover, the equatorial belts of Jupiter and Saturn rotate a little faster than their polar regions, from which we infer that the surfaces of these two planets are not rigid but yielding. Neptune spins somewhat less rapidly, although faster than the earth does.

When no markings can be seen on a planet, its period of rotation cannot be determined with assurance. Pluto is so small and so far away that only recently has its spin been observed, and Mercury is so close to the sun that observation of its surface is very difficult. Venus, on the other hand, is completely blanketed by clouds, so that no fixed markings, from which to determine its period, can be detected on its surface. Never-

(a)

Mount Wilson and Palomar Observatories

(b)

PLATE V. Mars (a) in blue light, and (b) in red light.

theless, by indirect evidence astronomers have concluded that Mercury and Venus undergo one rotation every time they pass completely around the sun.

ATMOSPHERES OF THE PLANETS

To all animals an atmosphere containing oxygen is a necessity for the maintenance of life. What of the atmospheres of other planets or their satellites? It can be shown that a celestial body cannot retain an atmosphere unless it is capable of exerting sufficient gravitational pull, and this capability requires that the body be sufficiently massive. The earth's moon has too small a mass for it to be able to hold an atmosphere, and the same is probably true of the planet Mercury. A gaseous atmosphere has the faculty of scattering light, so that the outline of a planet which possesses an atmosphere is not sharp but is dimly illuminated by the scattered light even if that part of the body itself is in shadow. Such twilight effects are missing from all views of the earth's moon or of Mercury, from which we con-

clude that these bodies lack any appreciable atmosphere.

That Venus has a thick and opaque atmosphere has already been mentioned. Mars also is surrounded by a gaseous blanket, which is much thinner, however, than our own atmosphere. Telescopic views of Mars (Plate V) show what are apparently ice-capped poles, and, since the caps increase and diminish in size periodically, it is fair to presume that some evaporation into the Martian atmosphere occurs.

The markings on Mars are especially interesting in view of the fact that, of all the planets, Mars is the only one which has climatic and atmospheric conditions at all similar to those on our earth. This has led to a great deal of speculation about the possibility of life on Mars. Because the surface coloring changes slightly at seasonal intervals it has been inferred that Mars has a kind of vegetation. Most interesting of all are the so-called canals which were so painstakingly observed and sketched by Lowell. Many have concluded that these are man-made projects de-

Mount Wilson and Palomar Observatories

PLATE VI. Jupiter, showing the large red spot. The shadow of one of Jupiter's satellites, Ganymede, is seen near the top.

signed to aid in the irrigation of the Martian fields. Unfortunately, much of the detail observed by Lowell has never been confirmed either by other visual observation or from photographs.

The atmospheres of Jupiter (Plate VI) and Saturn have been analyzed by means of the light which they reflect to us, and the analysis shows them to consist largely of ammonia and methane, two compounds which are gaseous under ordinary terrestrial conditions but which are believed to be solidified at the extremely low temperatures which must prevail on those planets.

UNIFORMITY OF MOTION

Although the moons revolve about their parent planets, they must also accompany those planets in a continual motion across the sky. Practically all these bodies, moons and planets alike, rotate on their axes in the same sense: from west to east. Observed from a point high above the north pole of the earth, these motions would be counterclockwise. Also, in almost every case, the moons would be seen revolving in a counterclockwise direction around their planets. Such remarkable uniformity in direction suggests a common origin for the entire solar system. This conviction is strengthened when we observe that the orbits of all these bodies lie very nearly in one plane: the plane of the ecliptic, i.e., the plane which includes the orbit of the earth.

METEORS AND COMETS

Inasmuch as any object which circulates around the sun is a member of the solar system, our brief description of the solar family must include two other types of body which participate in this general motion.

The universe seems to be littered with chunks of stone and metal which fly through space at high speeds. These chunks of solid matter are called meteors. Many of them apparently pursue orbits about the sun and so belong to the solar system. Millions of them strike the earth's atmosphere daily, and there, owing to the frictional resistance of our atmosphere, they are heated to incandescence. The familiar "shooting stars" are simply hot meteors. The vast majority of them are burned to ashes during their fall to earth, but occasionally large ones land without being consumed. Fallen meteors are called *meteorites*. Many tons of meteoric dust reach the earth every year.

Because of the protective action of the atmosphere, it is very rare to have a meteor reach the surface of the earth with enough mass and speed so that it leaves a permanent scar; less than a dozen such impacts are known. The most spectacular of them all has become a tourist attraction near Winslow, Arizona (Plate VII). It is a circular depression almost a mile in diameter and about 570 feet deep made by the impact of a large meteor which fell more than a thousand years ago. The frightening possibility exists that such an object might strike any spot on the earth at any moment, though the probability is extremely small.

Inasmuch as meteors frequently come in

PLATE VII. Meteor crater, near Winslow, Arizona.

Fairchild Aerial Surveys

showers, and from a definite direction in the sky, it is possible by triangulation to estimate their height when they first become visible. Two observers who are a known distance apart view the same shower at the same time, each one measuring the angle between the ground and his line of sight to the meteors, in addition to measuring the azimuthal angle (see Problem 1). By this means it has been found that meteors first make their appearance when they are about 75 miles above the earth. Such measurements provide one way of estimating the height of our atmosphere, which may thus be assumed to exceed 75 miles. At least one can say that at that height there is still enough gaseous material to make these projectiles red-hot.

Comets are enormous aggregates of gas and solid particles which follow very eccentric paths about the sun. When close to the latter, they develop very high speeds and acquire a huge, luminous tail of rarefied matter. The tail always points away from the sun even when the comet is receding from the sun. The head of a comet may be a collection of meteors. In the track of several comets which have disappeared after a number of periodic visits, unusually large swarms of meteors have been detected. More than a thousand comets have been recorded.

THE SUN

We conclude our preliminary sketch of the solar system with some data on the sun itself. This gigantic ball of incandescent gas is a star, but not an outstanding one as far as size or temperature are concerned. Its importance to life on earth, however, is beyond all reckoning, since the sun is our only significant source of energy. It is so large that, if all the plants were to fall into it, the increase in the sun's size would be negligible, the diameter of the sun being 109 times as large as that of the earth. The material in all the planets taken together makes up only about one-quarter of 1% of the matter in the sun. A direct view of the sun, especially through opera glasses or a telescope, is extremely harmful excepting *very* near sunrise or sunset, because at such times the greatly increased depth of atmosphere through which the sun's light must pass weakens the intensity of the radiation. Visual observations of the sun should be made only through very dark glass or dense photographic film.

SUNSPOTS

Dark spots on the surface of the sun are sometimes visible to the naked eye when the sun is very near the horizon. Their appearance was recorded by the ancient Chinese, although they first came to the notice of the western world as part of Galileo's telescopic discoveries. Sunspots are now known to be accompanied by violent magnetic disturbances on the sun, for, whenever the spots appear in large numbers there is a pronounced effect on magnetic instruments such as the compass. Extreme weather conditions are also noticeable on earth when sunspots are at a maximum.

The appearance of sunspots makes it possible to find out how the sun rotates, for, although most of the spots last only a few days, their displacement across the face of the sun gives a means of measuring the rotational rate. From such measurements one learns that the sun spins very slowly about an axis which is nearly perpendicular to the ecliptic plane (only 7° inclined as contrasted with the 23.5° tilt of the earth's axis), and also that the period of rotation varies considerably with solar latitude. Near the poles of the sun, about 34 days are required to complete a rotation, whereas the sun's equator turns once in about 25 days.

The great difference in rotational periods between the polar and the equatorial parts of the sun proves that the sun cannot be a solid body. Its incandescence, on the other hand, indicates that the sun is gaseous, at least at the surface.

The slowness of the sun's rotation could have been inferred without measurement from the almost perfectly circular shape of the sun's disk, for if this body were spinning rapidly, it would flatten out to a spheroidal shape somewhat like that of the earth. Note that the sun *does* appear to be flattened somewhat when it is seen near the horizon, but this distortion is illusory and depends on atmospheric refraction, which will be explained in a later section on light.

The sun's output of energy is prodigious, the earth alone receiving 126 million million horsepower (Plate VIII). Thus, in spite of the relatively small size of the earth—so small as to be a mere speck in the distance and the recipient of only one two-billionth of the sun's total radiation —our share is ample to promote life and growth over almost the entire globe. Whichever half of the earth happens to be facing the sun receives

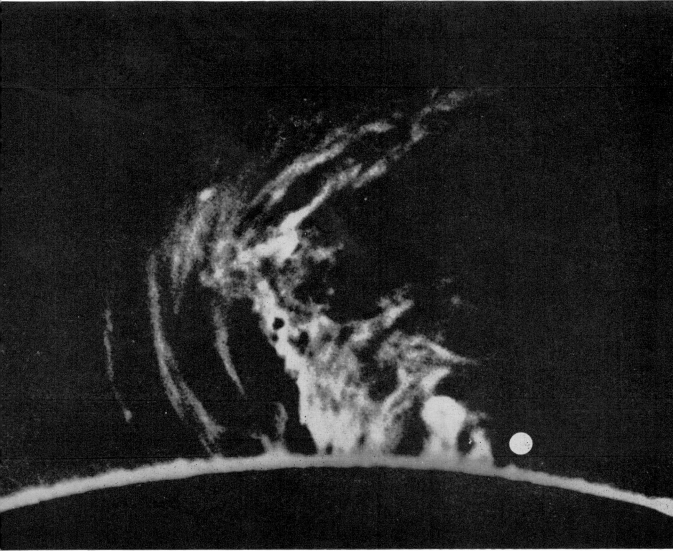

Mount Wilson and Palomar Observatories

PLATE VIII.   Solar prominence, observed July 9, 1917, which reached a height of 140,000 miles above the surface of the sun.   The white spot represents the earth in relative size.

radiant energy at an average rate of 1 hp per square yard, notwithstanding the fact that about half the solar radiation which strikes our outer atmosphere is reflected away again.

What is the source of the bountiful supply of energy which the sun and other stars emit so copiously and continuously? This question has puzzled scientists for centuries past and only within very recent years has a satisfactory answer been proposed. It is now believed that conditions within these incredibly hot bodies are such as to allow the spontaneous conversion of their matter into energy. The unleashing of atomic energy as an accomplishment of war-time research represents the same phenomenon on a modest scale. It will be shown later in this account that very large amounts of atomic energy can be liberated by the annihilation of very small amounts of matter, but the sun is so prodigal in its output that it loses a very considerable amount of matter every hour. Yet so great is the total mass of the sun that it should continue to be the powerhouse of the solar system for millions of years to come.

PROBLEMS

1. Figure 11 shows the essential geometry involved in determining the height *CD* of a meteor as observed from two arbitrary points *A* and *B* which are close enough together so that the surface of the earth may be considered a plane. Azimuthal angles are horizontal angles measured between a vertical reference plane, usually north and south, and some other vertical plane. Which angles must be measured? Describe the procedure for solving the problem.

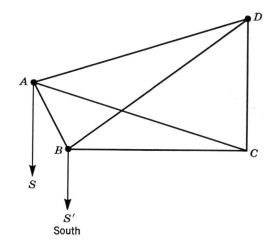

FIG. 11

2. If the sun has a diameter 109 times the diameter of the earth, how many times larger than that of the earth is its volume?

3. Which planets can now be seen in the night sky? Select one of them, and plot its position with respect to the background constellation. Continue to note its position for at least one semester.

· ·

REFERENCE

1. *Highlights of Astronomy,* Walter Bartky, University of Chicago Press, 1935, Chapter 6.

Hypotheses Concerning
the Solar System

THE PTOLEMAIC HYPOTHESIS

Long before the rise of the Greek civilization, the Babylonians and Egyptians were thoroughly familiar with the celestial motions of the more conspicuous stars and planets. They were restricted, of course, to naked-eye observations. Their explanation of the apparent daily passage of these bodies from east to west was the obvious one, namely, that the earth was the center of a gigantic rotational motion in which all heavenly bodies participated. This simplified concept was highly embellished with mystical accompaniments, for the astronomy of the ancients was closely connected with religious beliefs.

THE GEOCENTRIC THEORY

During the fruitful years of the Greek civilization, astronomy became an elaborate study which, although still steeped in mysticism, nevertheless contained the earliest rational attempts to account for celestial motions. Aristarchus (310–230 B.C.) supposed that the earth was merely one of many bodies circulating around the sun. The most prominent Greek philosophers, however, held that the earth was stationary and that the stars and planets really revolved around the earth, just as they appear to do. This point of view probably originated with Eudoxus in the fourth century B.C., but it is best known through the writings of Claudius Ptolemy (100–178). Ptolemy and others greatly elaborated on the original idea and their *geocentric theory,* as it came to be called, dominated scientific thought in Europe until the seventeenth century. The chief features of the Ptolemaic theory were these:

The earth was regarded as the center of a colossal, hollow sphere in which the stars were imbedded. This sphere revolved once in a little less than one day. Moving within the sphere were the seven heavenly bodies—the moon, the sun, and the five planets which were then known: Mercury, Venus, Mars, Jupiter, and Saturn. The sun and moon revolved in circular paths around the earth—the sun once every day, the moon once in about 24 hours and 50 minutes. Since the star-studded outer sphere revolved a little faster than the sun did, the sun appeared to be displaced progressively by a small amount each morning. In one year the stars gained a complete lap on the sun. Thus a different constellation of stars appeared in the background of the rising sun each month throughout the year. At the end of a year, the first of these twelve "zodiacal constellations" again appeared behind the sun and the succession repeated itself. The twelve constellations of the zodiac [1] are still used

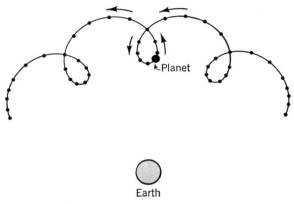

FIG. 12. Path of Jupiter, assuming the earth to be stationary.

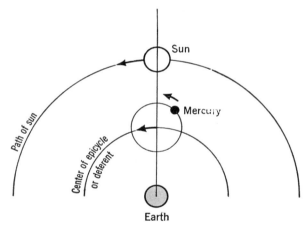

FIG. 13. Path of Mercury with respect to the sun and earth, according to the Ptolemaic hypothesis.

as convenient markers of the sun's position in the sky.

The planets also revolved about the earth, according to the geocentric theory, not in circular paths but in looped paths called epicycles. The combination of motions results in complex paths like those illustrated in Figs. 12 and 13.

This provision described the retrograde motion which all planets were known to undergo.

· · · · · · · · · · · · · · · ·

The paths of Mercury and Venus were interestingly explained. Both planets are clearly visible for a short time near sunrise or else for a short time near sunset. Thus, in order to see Mercury at all the observer must look toward the eastern horizon just before dawn or else toward the western horizon in early evening. This merely means that Mercury (as well as Venus) is relatively close to the sun at all times—a fact which the astronomers of antiquity fully realized. Ptolemy pictured the path of Mercury (and of Venus) as an epicycle which revolved around the earth at the same rate as the sun, while the two planets shifted progressively from point to point along their respective paths. Figure 14 is meant to show the positions of Mercury for a few months.

It must be stated emphatically that the geocentric theory accounted for all the facts known about the solar system at the time of Ptolemy.

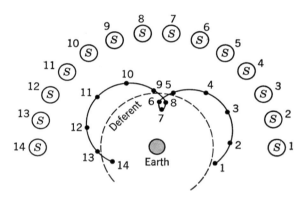

FIG. 14. The movements of the sun (S) and Mercury, according to the Ptolemaic system, assuming the earth to be stationary. The time intervals between successive positions of both sun and Mercury are identical.

Moreover, in the hands of persons with sufficient mathematical skill, it could be used to predict planetary positions correctly in advance. Correctness of prediction is at once the severest test of a theory and its most useful achievement. We can say with certainty that a theory is wrong if its predictions turn out to be contrary to observed data. However, it cannot ever be said that a theory or model is true in any absolute sense, since our knowledge of the ultimate mechanisms in nature will always be incomplete. The relative worth of a theory is judged, rather, by the amount of data it can efficiently correlate as well as by its successes in predicting new phenomena. Hence, the paradox that a scientific theory may be quite useful even though it is not completely true.   The observational evidence which doomed the Ptolemaic theory was not discovered until the seventeenth century; in fact, it could not have been discovered before the invention of the telescope.   Even Copernicus did not have this evidence; his argument was based on the fact that a simpler mechanism could explain the same movements if the sun, rather than the earth, were chosen as the center of the circular motions.

The invention of the telescope illustrates brilliantly the role played by inventive skill and refinement of instrumentation in the advancement of the natural sciences.   Suddenly, through the use of the telescope, Galileo revealed for the first time a wealth of information which doomed the Aristotelian and Ptolemaic cosmologies.   The moons of Jupiter, the mountains on the moon, the dark spots on the surface of the sun, the phases of Venus, the individual stars in the Milky Way, the rings of Saturn, all these were completely hidden from visual observation before this time.   When Galileo first peered into his telescope he truly saw a new world, and what he saw gave him intellectual power never before possessed by man.

THE HELIOCENTRIC COPERNICAN THEORY

The fundamental points in this explanation were published in 1543 by the Polish monk Copernik (Copernicus), and hence the basic idea is called the Copernican hypothesis.   In expanded form the Copernican hypothesis became our present *heliocentric theory,* so called because it considers the sun, not the earth, as the center of the solar system.

Copernicus suggested that the planets revolve in circular orbits around the sun, each planet moving at a speed which increases with its nearness to the sun.   Thus, Mercury, the planet nearest the sun, travels not only in the smallest orbit but also at the highest speed, whereas Saturn, the most distant planet then known, has not only the longest journey but the slowest rate of progress as well.

RETROGRADE MOTION OF PLANETS

By the Copernican assumptions the retrograde motion of all planets is easily explained.   Consider the motion of Jupiter, for example (Fig. 15).   Jupiter takes about twelve years to complete a cycle, i.e., to reappear among any particular group of stars.   According to the Copernican and to our own modern view, this means that Jupiter requires about twelve years to make a circuit about the sun.   Thus, every year Jupiter completes about $\frac{1}{12}$ of its orbital journey or about 30° of arc.   Figure 15a shows Jupiter's progress for a single year.

FIG. 15.   Explanation of retrograde motion of Jupiter by the Copernican hypothesis.

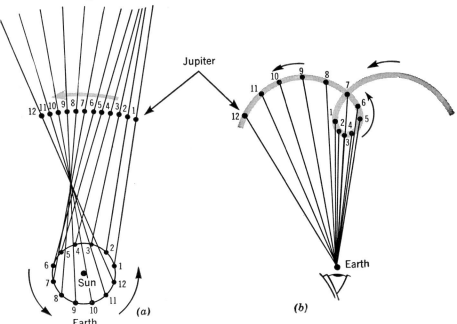

Let the earth occupy positions 1, 2, ···, 11, 12 at the end of each month of a given year, while Jupiter moves over 30° of its total path. The straight lines are lines of sight along which an observer on earth would look toward Jupiter at the end of each month. Figure 15b reproduces these lines of sight as coming to the eye of an observer who does not realize that he too is mov-

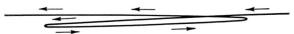

FIG. 16.   Actual path of Jupiter as seen from the earth.

ing through space, but who judges direction by the background of fixed stars. Note that the directions change in such a way as to make Jupiter appear to progress forward and then to retrogress.

It should be realized that, from the earth, the epicyclic paths are viewed edgewise, so that they do not appear to us as they are pictured in Figs. 12, 14, and 15b. Figure 16 shows the path of Jupiter as it actually appears to observers on the earth against the background of fixed stars.

OBJECTIONS TO THE COPERNICAN THEORY

The hypothesis of Copernicus met with strenuous opposition, much of it fantastic but some of it logical. The logical criticisms can be summarized as follows:

1. If the earth is merely another planet, it should shine as the other planets do.

The answer to this is that it does. When the moon is almost obscured in passing between the earth and the sun, the dark face of the moon can still be seen dimly by sunlight which is evidently reflected back from the earth's surface.

2. If the earth is a moving body, spinning rather rapidly as it revolves around the sun, why aren't all loose objects thrown off by centrifugal action and why do we not experience terrific winds as the solid earth rushes through the surrounding atmosphere?

It is now known that the earth's rotation does tend to make bodies fly off but that the tendency is small compared with their weight. As for the winds, the atmosphere is itself a part of the rotating system; it accompanies the spinning earth and does not lag behind to produce winds. It will be shown later that winds are indeed generated when parts of the atmosphere move from one latitude to another, and that the directions of these prevailing winds are consistent with the direction of spin of the earth about its axis.

3. Objects at different distances from the eye may appear in line when seen from one position but out of line when seen from another. From an airplane approaching Manhattan a passenger may see the Empire State tower in line with the Chrysler spire at one instant, whereas a few moments later the same tower is in line with Radio City. The observer explains this easily in terms of his own motion. This observational phenomenon we call *parallax;* it is the apparent change in

FIG. 17.   Stellar parallax.   Stars, *A, B,* and *C* appear to move with respect to one another as the earth moves in its orbit around the sun, *S.*

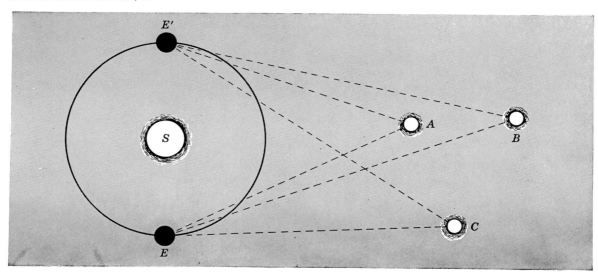

the relative positions of several objects when the observer moves and when the several objects are at different distances from the observer. Now if the earth moves around the sun, the stars should show such apparent displacements. Thus, when the earth is in position E (Fig. 17), star B appears to be between stars A and C, whereas at position E' star A appears to be between B and C.

The lack of any such noticeable change, i.e., the absence of stellar parallax, convinced the geocentric believers that the earth could not be moving in an orbit. On the other hand, if the objects viewed are extremely remote, their parallax may

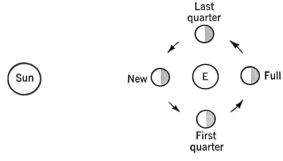

FIG. 18. Cycle of phases of the moon.

be so small as to escape notice. Stellar parallax is indeed so small, due to the excessive distances of the stars, that it was first detected only so recently as 1838 and then only after the invention of superior instruments.

4. Probably the most understandable argument for or against the heliocentric hypothesis of Copernicus concerned the phases of Venus and Mercury. It was known ages ago that these two planets lie closer to the sun than the earth does and that the directions in which they appear to an observer on earth never differ much from the direction of the sun itself. According to the Ptolemaic idea, with the sun and these planets revolving around the earth, the sun could never come between its two nearest planets and the earth. Hence, if they were lighted by the sun, the illuminated part must always be partly hidden from the earth. Accordingly, if seen in outline from the earth, Mercury and Venus would never appear as full disks but would always look like crescent moons or quarter moons. According to the Copernican idea, on the other hand, Mercury and Venus, as well as the earth and all other planets, revolve around the sun and, consequently, the sun will sometimes lie between them and the earth. In this situation the ob-

server on earth should be able to see the fully illuminated disk of the planet. When either planet is on one side of the sun or when it comes between the sun and the earth, the quarter and crescent phases respectively will be visible. The validity of this argument was freely admitted by both sides of the controversy, for precisely the same explanation of our moon's phases was generally admitted. There was never any doubt about the moon's monthly revolution around the earth, and the reason we see the moon waxing and waning is obvious from Fig. 18. Figure 19 shows why the interior planets, e.g., Mercury, should undergo the same cycle of phases if they move around the sun.

The answer to the crucial question as to whether or not Mercury and Venus do undergo a complete cycle of phases is sufficient to decide between the Ptolemaic and the Copernican hypotheses. Its answer depends upon the possibility of seeing these planets in clear outline. Since the phases could not be detected by naked-eye observation, the Ptolemaists concluded that they did not occur. It was not until 1610 that Galileo, with the aid of his crude telescope, observed

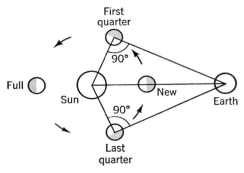

FIG. 19. Cycle of phases of Mercury.

Venus in what is called the gibbous phase (between quarter and full). This really started the downfall of the geocentric theory, for no theory is tenable when it is unable to account for observed facts. Later Galileo discovered the phases of Mercury also, yet it took a century or more before the geocentric theory of Ptolemy was abandoned. Telescopic photographs of today reveal not only the full phase cycle of Venus and Mercury but also the variation in their apparent size, for when these planets are "full," they are considerably more remote from us than when they are "new" and hence appear a good deal smaller.

This, of course, is additional confirmatory evidence in favor of the heliocentric theory.

TYCHO BRAHE

The method of science is to collect data, to derive, by the process of induction, such "laws" or "models" as will serve to correlate the data, to build theories which will rationalize the laws, and then to test the entire scheme through experiments suggested by the theories. Occasionally, as in the present case, a preliminary guess or *hypothesis* comes early in the sequence. Frequently the data are collected by observers who have no sympathy with the hypothesis which their findings help to support. The work of Tycho Brahe (1546–1601) is a striking example of this. Tycho was a Danish nobleman who devoted most of his life to improving the accuracy of astronomical tables.

This was made possible through the generosity of the Danish king, Frederick II, who presented Tycho with the island of Hveen and provided sufficient funds to build there a large observatory and laboratory with all the equipment he was able to design. The remnants of the old observatory are still to be seen on this little island in the narrow sound between Sweden and Denmark about half-way between Elsinore and Copenhagen. Here the tireless and colorful genius spent a little more than twenty years in skilled observation and painstaking recording of the positions of planets and stars. Although he had no telescope, his other instruments were excellent, and with them Tycho made an enormous number of highly precise observations. He did not accept the heliocentric hypothesis, however.

His tenure on Hveen terminated when the new Danish king, Christian IV, withdrew his support. Tycho then moved his instruments to Prague (1599), where Emperor Rudolph II provided him with a castle and funds for the continuation of his work. He lived only a little more than two years after his arrival in Prague, but this was long enough for him to begin to organize his data into the Rudolphine Tables, and just long enough for the fortunate meeting with Kepler, who became his assistant in 1600.

JOHANN KEPLER

To Johann Kepler (1571–1630) was entrusted the vast fund of data amassed by Tycho. It was an extraordinary legacy, and with it Kepler undertook the task of finding just what kind of path the planets actually follow. He was soon convinced that they move neither in circles nor in epicycles. After years of labor he proved that, by assuming each planetary orbit (including that of the earth) to be an *ellipse* of suitable dimensions, the accurate positions recorded by Tycho would fit these curves. These ellipses turned out to be very nearly circular, excepting those of Mercury and Mars.

KEPLER'S LAWS

The Copernican hypothesis had assumed circular orbits for all the planets in their motions around the sun. The data painstakingly collected by Tycho Brahe were precise enough to

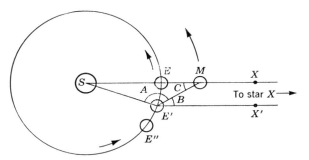

FIG. 20.   Determining the shape of the earth's orbit.

enable Kepler to check this point. The following geometrical discussion, though not exactly like that of Kepler, is designed to show how, after many years of observation, the orbits of planets may be plotted from data describing their exact positions throughout that time.

Let us begin our observations at a time when the sun, the earth, and Mars are lined up as in Fig. 20. Mars is at that moment at its maximum altitude in the night sky, and the time is midnight. In astronomical language, Mars is crossing the midnight meridian. Some fixed star, say X, is then also in line with Mars as seen from the earth. Both Mars and the earth now progress in their orbits in the direction of the arrows until Mars has completed its year and is back at M again. The Martian year would have to be determined from previous observations; it is now known to be 1.88 earthly years. During the Martian year the earth has made almost two complete revolutions and is now at E'. The angle A can now be measured; it is the angle through which a telescope would have to be turned from sighting the sun to sighting Mars. Again, the star X may be sighted, and, because of its great distance, EX is virtually parallel to E'X'. The telescope is turned from the star X to Mars, through the angle B. Now in the triangle SME' angles A and C are known because angle C equals angle B. Thus, all the angles of the triangle are known, and the ratios of all of its sides are determined. For example, SM/SE' is known. Now let Mars complete another circuit about the sun, returning after 1.88 yr to M. The earth will then be at E''. By a similar set of observations, the angles of triangle SME'' will be known and SM/SE'' will be known. Dividing SM/SE' by SM/SE'' gives SE''/SE' or the ratio of two distances of the earth from the sun. This argument may be repeated until enough ratios are known to describe the orbit of the earth with exactness. In 15 earthly years eight such positions could be calculated by using the distance of Mars from the sun as a fixed reference distance. Note that it is not necessary to know the distance of Mars from the sun in order to get this result. From calculations of this kind it is found that the orbit of the earth is not a circle but a closed curve called an ellipse. An easy way to draw an ellipse is to set two pins, f_1 and f_2, firmly into a board and, using a loop of string $f_1Pf_2f_1$ of constant length, let a pencil point, P, move in such a way

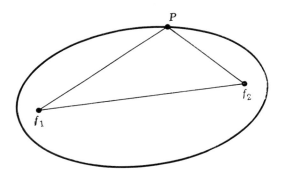

FIG. 21. How to draw an ellipse.

as to always keep the string taut (Fig. 21). The oval-shaped figure of the ellipse will then be traced out. It turns out that in the solar system the sun occupies one of the foci (f_1 or f_2) of such an ellipse, whereas the earth moves almost entirely around the elliptical path in a single seasonal year. The earth's elliptical orbit is nearly circular, the distance of the earth from the sun being about 3,000,000 mi less when the two bodies are nearest together than it is when the earth is farthest from the sun. The average distance ($\frac{1}{2}$ the sum of the maximum + the minimum distance) is 92,900,000 mi, so the total variation is roughly 3%. This conclusion is consistent with the known fact that the angle subtended by the disk of the sun varies throughout the year by 3% when viewed from the earth.

Knowing the orbit of the earth, we may now determine the orbit of Mars by applying the preceding argument to Mars when it is in positions other than M. It is found that the orbit of Mars is even more eccentric than that of the earth; the average distance from the sun being

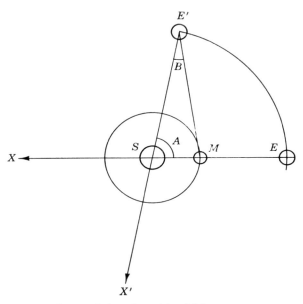

FIG. 22. Determining the orbit of Mercury.

141,000,000 mi and the total variation 26,000,000 mi or 18% during the Martian year.

All the planets whose orbits lie outside that of the earth may be similarly treated; their elliptical orbits are now known to a high degree of accuracy.

For the planets whose orbits lie within that of the earth (Mercury and Venus) the following geometrical argument may be used:

Consider the sun, Mercury, and the earth to be lined up as at S, M, and E (Fig. 22). The sun is then in the constellation X. Over a period of many years, the year for Mercury has been determined to a high degree of accuracy; it is about 0.24 earthly years. Now wait until Mercury has completed its circuit and returned to M. The earth will then have completed almost one-quarter of its year and will be at E'. The sun is then in the constellation X', and the angle A is accurately measurable. By sighting on the sun and then on Mercury, the angle B is measured. Since the orbit of the earth is now known, SE' is known and SM may be calculated. If this reasoning is repeated for other positions of Mercury, its orbit may be completely determined. It is found that Mercury has the most eccentric orbit of any of the planets with the exception of Pluto. Mercury is, on the average, 36,000,000 mi from the sun but varies 15,000,000 mi during its circuit about the sun.

By such reasoning as the foregoing we are able to determine the dimensions of the whole solar system with as much confidence as if we were surveying a plot of ground on the surface of the earth. In addition, the time required for any planet to make a complete circuit around the sun, with respect to the stars, is well known to us from reliable astronomical records kept through the centuries. Let us now summarize in Table 2 the knowledge we have established thus far.

What Kepler discovered about the orbits of the planets, he summarized in the following three laws:

Kepler's First Law. Every planet moves around the sun in an elliptical path, of which the sun occupies one focus.

Kepler's Second Law. If a line is imagined connecting a planet with the sun, the areas

traveling fastest on about January 3; it is at aphelion and traveling slowest on about July 4.

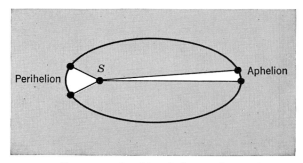

FIG. 23. Exaggerated orbit of the earth to illustrate Kepler's second law.

Kepler's Third Law. The time required for a planet to complete its orbit is related to its distance [2] from the sun in the following way:

The time squared is proportional to the distance cubed. Suppose planet A is at a distance of d_A miles from the sun and its time of revolution is T_A years, whereas the distance and time for planet B are d_B and T_B respectively. Then,

$$\frac{(T_A)^2}{(T_B)^2} = \frac{(d_A)^3}{(d_B)^3} \quad \text{or} \quad \frac{(T_A)^2}{(d_A)^3} = \frac{(T_B)^2}{(d_B)^3} = \text{Constant}$$

TABLE 2

	Mercury	Venus	Earth	Mars	Jupiter	Saturn	Uranus	Neptune	Pluto
Average distance from sun in millions of miles	36	67	93	141	489	886	1782	2793	3670
Distance from sun in astronomical units	0.39	0.72	1.00	1.52	5.20	9.5	19.2	30	40
Total variation in distance in per cent	42	1.3	3.2	18	9.6	12	9.4	1.7	49
Time of revolution in years	0.241	0.615	1.00	1.88	11.9	29.5	84	165	248
Satellites	0	0	1	2	12	9	5	2	0

passed over by this line are always equal for equal intervals of time.

It follows that the velocity of every planet is variable, for the focus of an ellipse is not equidistant from all parts of the curve. When a planet is nearest the sun it is said to be at *perihelion;* when farthest away at *aphelion* (Fig. 23). If a short line sweeps over an area just as large as that swept over by a long line, the short one must trace out a longer arc. In other words, the planet must move faster and cover a greater distance per day when closest to the sun than it does when farther away. Our earth is at perihelion and

The sense of this law can be realized from a simple example. Suppose that planet A is four times as far from the sun as planet B is.
Then

$$d_A/d_B = 4$$

and

$$(d_A)^3/(d_B)^3 = 64$$

hence

$$(T_A)^2/(T_B)^2 = 64$$

. . . .

[2] The distance in question is half the major axis of the elliptical path.

and

$$T_A/T_B = 8$$

If a planet four times as far from the sun as another takes eight times as long to complete a revolution, it is evident that the more remote a planet is the slower is its pace.

The same laws apply to planetoids, comets, and to moons. In the case of moons, the central body is not, of course, the sun but the parent planet. Kepler showed that the four moons of Jupiter which Galileo had discovered were consistent with his third law.

Taking a backward glance at Kepler's brilliant contributions, let us not fail to note the manner of reasoning and the nature of the evidence.

Kepler did not argue, as Aristotle would have, that the ellipse is a more perfect geometrical figure than the circle. Neither did he seek for recognized authorities, ancient or contemporary, to confirm his suspicions that the planetary orbits were not circular. He did not fall into a state of detached meditation, hoping for a description of the orbital figures to come to him by sudden inspiration or revelation. His reasoning was not subjective in the sense that he had a strong personal desire to have the orbits come out elliptical. On the contrary, he drew his conclusions objectively, using carefully assembled data obtained from observation and using freely the logic of geometry.

PROBLEMS

1. Using values from Table 2, draw the planetary orbits approximately to scale assuming them to be circular.

2. Draw the new, quarter, and full phases of Venus as you might expect them to appear on a series of photographs taken with a good telescope, using the same magnification for each.

3. Tycho Brahe assumed that the earth was stationary, but, unlike Ptolemy, he assumed that the planets revolved in circles around the sun while the sun itself revolved around the earth. Draw a diagram of the solar system to illustrate this hypothesis. Do you consider this an improvement on the Ptolemaic model of the solar system? According to this hypothesis, should Mercury and Venus show phases?

4. The mountains on the moon are estimated to have approximately the same heights as mountains on our earth. These are calculated from the lengths of the mountain shadows on the moon's surface. Explain in detail. (See Plate IX.)

PLATE IX. Portion of the moon showing shadows cast by its mountains.

Mount Wilson and Palomar Observatories

5. Using the average distances of Table 2, calculate the largest and the smallest distances between the earth and Mars. Does it matter a great deal at what time Mars is photographed by astronomers?

6. Using the information in Table 2, calculate T^2/d^3 for at least four planets. What do you conclude about Kepler's third law?

7. Suppose an asteroid to be 3 A.U. distant from the sun. What would be the length of its year?
Ans. 5.2 earth years.

8. Draw a diagram to illustrate the position Venus must have with respect to the sun and earth in order to seem half-illuminated (first or last quarter) to an astronomer on the earth (see Fig. 19). Knowing the distance between the sun and the earth, calculate the distance of Venus from the sun. Do you think this is a very precise method? Explain. Would the method be improved if the astronomer observed Venus and the sun just when the angle Venus-earth-sun is a maximum? Assume this angle to be 46°.

9. Do planets with orbits larger than that of the earth show phases just as Mercury and Venus do? Explain by diagrams.

10. If, anywhere in the United States, an observer at night sees a brilliant object in the northern sky, could this be one of the planets?

. . . .

REFERENCES

1. *Cambridge Readings in the Literature of Science,* Cambridge University Press, 1924, pp. 1–30.
2. *A Source Book in Greek Science,* Morris R. Cohen and I. E. Drabkin, McGraw-Hill Book Co., 1948, Chapter 3, pp. 122–143.

Motions of the Earth

The entire solar system is now known to be moving rapidly through a much larger group of stars called the galaxy. Besides taking part in this general drift, the earth has three distinct motions of its own:

1. It revolves around the sun in a counterclockwise sense as viewed from Polaris. The infinite plane which includes this orbit is called the *plane of the ecliptic.*

2. It rotates on its axis from west to east, again counterclockwise as seen from Polaris.

3. Its axis precesses very slowly in a clockwise sense as viewed from Polaris.

Some of the evidence by which these motions are proved and measured will now be offered and some of the practical consequences of the motions will be discussed.

REVOLUTION AROUND THE SUN

As the sun rises each morning, certain star groups can be seen in approximately the same direction as the sun, these rising slightly before the sun. A day by day observation would soon show the same stars rising progressively earlier, and a different group or constellation accompanying or slightly preceding the sun. Those star groups which form a background for the sun are known as *zodiacal constellations.* The name comes from a Greek root meaning animals, most of these star patterns having been named for animals (the ram, the bull, the crab, the lion, etc.) by the ancient Greeks. There are twelve zodiacal constellations forming a narrow belt stretching east and west across the sky, and extending above and below the ecliptic plane by 8 or 9° each way. The progressive change in the sun's background of stars is, of course, no certain proof that the earth is moving around the sun; the sun might be the body which makes the yearly journey.

However, *star parallax* is sound evidence that it is the earth that revolves around the sun. Star photographs taken at intervals through the years, as well as observations on individual stars, reveal the fact that some stars near the ecliptic plane seem to oscillate back and forth with respect to a background of seemingly fixed stars and that the periods of these oscillations are exactly equal to the sidereal year (to be explained on p. 62). Some stars viewed in a direction perpendicular to the ecliptic plane seem to pursue tiny circular orbits in the same yearly period. In other directions, some stars seem to pursue tiny elliptical orbits through a year of observa-

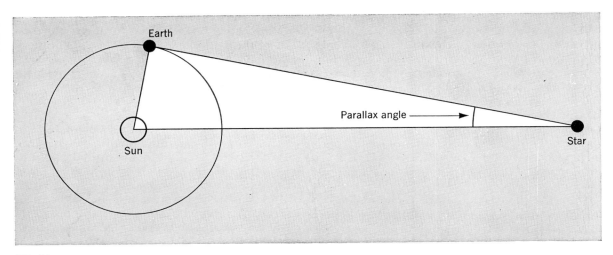

FIG. 24

tion. The conclusion is inescapable that these are *apparent* motions of relatively near stars with respect to a background of very distant stars as seen from an earth which makes a yearly circuit around the sun in an almost circular path (see Fig. 17). With the increased length of base line afforded by the radius of the earth's orbit, the parallax angles become, in fact, measures of the distances to those stars which show this effect.

ANNUAL PARALLAX

The angle which the radius of the earth's orbit subtends at any star is the *annual parallax* of the star (Fig. 24). For even the nearest star (Proxima Centauri) the angle is very small (less than 1 sec), and stars more than 300 light-years [1] distant have parallax angles too small to allow dependable calculations of distance. We cannot use a longer base line because all observations have to be made from the earth, which never gets farther from the sun than 1 A.U.

The *parsec* is a distance such that a star 1 parsec from the earth would have an annual parallax of 1 sec.

1 parsec = 3.26 light-years = 206,265 A.U.

ABERRATION OF LIGHT

Another excellent proof that Copernicus was right is recognized in the phenomenon of aberration of light. An analogy will help to clarify

. . . .

[1] The light-year is a unit of distance. It is the distance traveled by light through empty space in 1 yr. The velocity of light is 186,000 mi per second.

the effect. Suppose an observer in a closed car is watching raindrops coming in through a hole at B in the ceiling (Fig. 25). The drops splash on the floor at A, and, if the car is not moving, the observer correctly concludes that the path CBA represents the true motion of the drops. Suppose, however, that while the drops fall from B to the floor the car moves in the direction of the arrow through a distance AA'. The observer is then led to believe wrongly that the drops have come from the direction $C'BA'$ if he does not know that the car is moving. He has made a mistake equal to angle X whose tangent is AA'/AB, or the velocity of the car divided by the velocity of the raindrops. It is obvious that this mistake is made not merely because the car is moving but also because it is moving at right angles to the direction of rainfall.

This is the state of affairs when a star is being observed from our moving earth. Let the star's direction be at right angles to the direction being taken by the earth at the moment, this being the arrangement for which the aberration effect is greatest (Fig. 26). Then the light from the star will appear to come from a point slightly ahead of its true position. The observer must point his telescope forward in the direction of the earth's motion in order to get an image of the star at the center of his eyepiece. It is evident at once that no single observation will reveal this aberration of light, for the direction in which the star is observed might be its true direction. Actually, the apparent direction will change as the earth moves along its path. One-half year later, when the earth is again moving at right angles to the line connecting it with the star, the aberration will be just as large on the other side of the perpendicular, for the earth will then be moving in the reverse of its former direction. At points *A* and *B* there will be no aberration if the star lies in the plane of the ecliptic.

The aberration of light was explained by the British astronomer, Bradley, in 1727. The maximum angle of aberration, i.e., half the angle between the two extreme directions of the telescope, is very small—being about 20.5 sec for all stars so observed. This quantity is called the *constant of aberration*.

Since the effect is due to the compounding of velocities—that of the earth with that of light—measurement of the aberration angle enables us to determine the ratio of these velocities and from that to find either velocity if the other is known. A right triangle containing such a very acute angle as 20.5 sec will have one leg about 10,000 times as long as the other. The velocity of light must, therefore, be about 10,000 times that of the earth. If the earth is known to be moving at 18.5 mps (average), the velocity of light must be 10,000 times as much. Conversely, by using the best available value of the velocity of light (186,285 mps), the earth's average speed comes out as 18.49 mps.

It may be added that a very small daily aberration of starlight also occurs, owing to the rotation of the earth on its axis. This, of course, is corrected for in making the aberrational calculations. Incidentally, it may be taken as evidence that the earth does make a daily rotation.

DISTANCE FROM EARTH TO SUN

A result of the aberration measurement is to give us a unique way to determine our distance from the sun. Assuming the velocity of light to have been measured independently, this, taken with the aberration constant, leads to the value of 18.5 mps for the average velocity of the earth in its orbit. Assume further that this orbit is a circle, an assumption which is warranted for the present purpose. Then, at 18.5 mps, in 1 yr of about 31,557,000 sec the earth would traverse an orbit 583,804,500 mi long. The radius of this orbit, i.e., the distance of the earth from the sun, would consequently be this circumference divided by 2π.

$$\frac{583,804,500}{(2)(3.142)} = 93,000,000 \text{ mi}$$

THE EARTH'S ROTATION

If a camera is directed toward the North Star, Polaris, which is almost in line with the earth's

FIG. 25. Error in estimating direction of raindrop due to motion of observer.

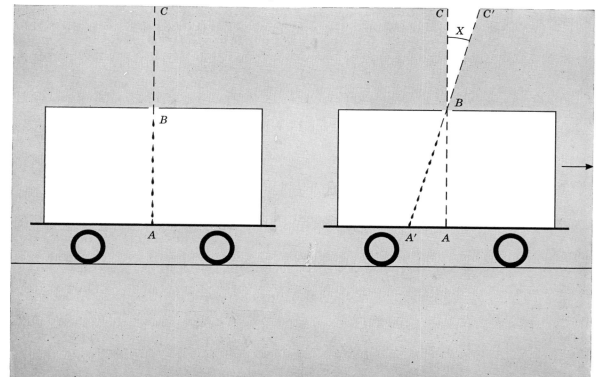

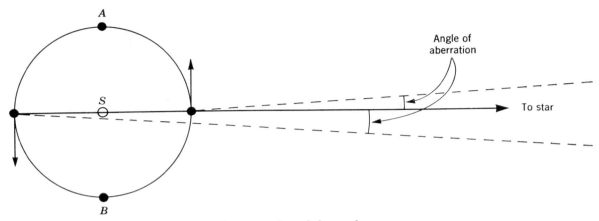

FIG. 26. Apparent displacement of star due to motion of the earth.

axis, and the camera's shutter is left open for several hours at night, the developed film will show a large number of concentric, though incomplete, circles around Polaris, these being the tracks of stars which occupy the northern sky (Plate X). The stars above the antarctic region produce similar trails. Over the temperate and tropical latitudes stars are seen to rise in the east and set in the west. These familiar motions indicate, though they do not prove, that it is the earth which is continually rotating on a practically fixed axis, thus causing the *apparent* revolution of luminous objects in the heavens.

EASTERLY DEVIATION OF FALLING BODIES; WINDS

Newton was the author of this proof (Fig. 27). Suppose in advance that the earth actually *is* rotating from west to east. Then the top of any tall tower must be moving faster than the base of the tower, just as a point on the rim of a rotating wheel must move faster than a point nearer the hub. Hence, a weight released from the top of the tower will have a greater easterly velocity than any part of the tower farther down. Aside from air resistance there is no reason why the falling weight should lose this easterly velocity; therefore, as it falls, the body continues to move eastward faster than the base is moving eastward. The base of the tower does not move quite as far east as the falling weight does and so the weight does not strike the ground just at the base of the tower but a little to the east of it. Experiment has shown this prediction to be true.

Additional proof that the earth spins about its axis is to be found in the directions of the *trade winds* and the *prevailing westerlies* over the sur-

face of the earth. Owing to the higher temperature along the equatorial belt, hot air rises there and spills over into the northern and southern hemispheres as shown in Fig. 28. These convection currents reach the ground again at about 30° N. and S. of the equator. Remembering that the earth moves from west to east, the equatorial air is moving eastward faster than the surface velocity of the earth at ±30° latitude. That part of the air which continues northward from 30° N. must then give the effect of a westerly wind, and the same will be true of the air currents which continue to move southward from 30° S. That part of the air currents which moves southward from 30° N., however, is slowed down by friction against the earth to form the relative calm of the horse latitudes and, inasmuch as the air movement continues southward, creates a northeasterly wind because these currents then meet surfaces of the earth which are moving eastward faster than the air currents. For the same reason there will be southeasterly trade winds just south of the equator.

FOUCAULT PENDULUM

Perhaps the most ingenious proof that the earth spins about a central axis is one furnished by Foucault in Paris in 1851. The principle of the experiment which he set up in the Pantheon can easily be demonstrated by the apparatus shown in Fig. 29. A simple pendulum is suspended at O from a frame mounted on a turntable which can be rotated in either direction. If we set the pendulum swinging in any direction, say AB, it will persist in that direction even if the table is rotated. The pendulum is

J. C. Smith, Colby College

PLATE X. Circular star trails obtained by pointing a camera toward Polaris and leaving the shutter open for several hours at night. The heavy arc near the center is due to Polaris, showing that this star is not exactly in the direction of the earth's axis.

unaffected by any change in the angular position of the table. Now imagine an observer standing on the table watching this pendulum as we rotate the table counterclockwise without his knowledge. The pendulum will truly continue to oscil-

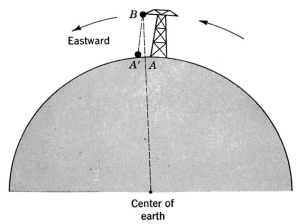

FIG. 27. Falling object strikes at A', east of the vertical BA.

late in its original plane of swing but the observer, unaware that he is rotating, will think that the plane of the pendulum is rotating clockwise. This is precisely what would happen if we set up such a pendulum at the North Pole. In 24 hr the plane of swing would seem to have rotated clockwise through a complete circle of 360°, although actually it has not changed its direction at all.

FIG. 28. Directions of winds which depend on rotation of the earth.

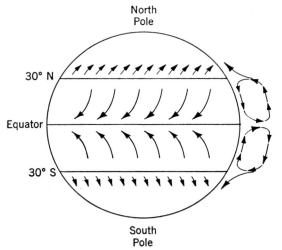

Returning to the experiment with the rotating table, the observer on the platform would see no change in the plane of swing if the table were displaced horizontally at uniform velocity. This would be the case with a similar pendulum set up at the equator. No change in the plane of swing would be observed there because, at the equator, the earth does not twist under the pendulum. As we move northward from the

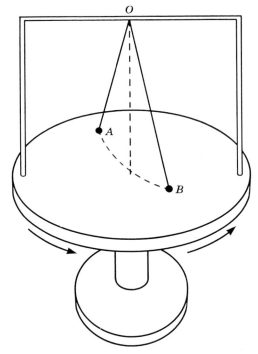

FIG. 29. The Foucault pendulum.

equator, the plane of the Foucault pendulum seems to change clockwise more and more rapidly until at the North Pole it seems to rotate 360° in 24 hr. The essential geometry is shown in Fig. 30. DAE and DBE are hour circles, i.e., they are circles passing through the poles and 1 hr apart in time. Let us imagine ourselves at latitude L, which intersects the hour circles at A and B. Tangents to these hour circles at the points A and B must intersect at some point C on the extended axis of the earth. At the latitude L, therefore, the plane of the Foucault pendulum will seem to turn through angle ACB in 1 hr. This is obviously a smaller angle than the 15° through which the plane of the pendulum would seem to turn during 1 hr if it were at the North Pole. At lower latitudes the point at which the hour circle tangents intersect moves out farther and farther from the earth, and the angle ACB becomes smaller and smaller; finally, when A and B lie on the equator, this angle becomes vanishingly small. In other words, the tangent lines are here parallel to one another. At Paris, where the latitude is approximately 49° N., Foucault observed an apparent hourly shift of a little more than 11° for his pendulum. In the south-

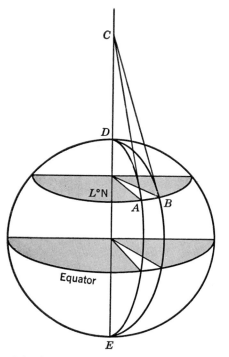

FIG. 30. The hourly change in angle for the plane of a Foucault pendulum varies with the latitude.

ern hemisphere the apparent rotation of such a pendulum is counterclockwise. A Foucault pendulum thus enables us to determine not only which hemisphere we are in but also our latitude in that hemisphere. All these facts, substantiated by numerous observations in many parts of the world, prove beyond doubt that the earth spins about its axis.

EFFECTS OF THE AXIAL TILT

The rotation of the earth on its axis produces night and day, but these are ordinarily unequal in length, the ratio of night to day being different in different latitudes. This is because the earth's axis is tilted with respect to the ecliptic plane by 66.5° or 23.5° from a line perpendicular to this plane. Figure 31 shows the disposition of

earth and sun in winter and summer. At the left the northern hemisphere is having winter and the southern hemisphere summer. From dawn to midday (lines DM and $D'M'$) is much shorter in the northern than in the southern latitudes, and of course the full period of daylight is correspondingly shorter also. For this position of the earth a region around the South Pole receives sunlight during the entire 24 hr, for this area is not in shadow during any part of the earth's rotation. The reverse happens around the North Pole at the same season where a certain area within the Arctic Circle is continually beyond reach of the sun's rays so long as the earth maintains the position shown. The

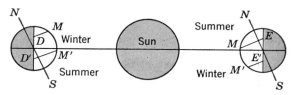

FIG. 31. Length of night and daylight varies with the seasons and with latitude.

right-hand part of the diagram represents the configuration for a northern summer. The earth is on the opposite side of the sun, and the period from midday to evening (lines ME and $M'E'$) is long in the northern hemisphere and short in the southern. An area around the South Pole is excluded from sunlight, while a similar area around the North Pole within the Arctic Circle is exposed throughout the 24-hr day.

SUMMER AND WINTER

This variation in the number of daylight hours due to the tilt of the earth's axis is one of the two principal reasons for our regular change of seasons. Since the axis always points in practically the same direction, it is clear that at one side of its orbit the earth will present more of the southern hemisphere to the sun and on the other side of its orbit more of the northern hemisphere. That hemisphere which enjoys more hours of daylight will accordingly receive more solar energy day after day, and the accumulation of heat will tend to produce what we know as summer. Figure 31 makes it apparent why regions south of the equator must necessarily have winter when the north is having summer and vice versa.

OBLIQUITY OF RADIATION

A second factor of great importance in the seasonal cycle is the angle at which the sun's radiation arrives on earth. Suppose, as in Fig. 32, two projectors are directing equal beams of light toward two parts of a sphere. For simplicity, let the light come from rectangular apertures. Then from the curvature of the sphere, it is apparent that a smaller area will be illuminated by the upper beam than by the lower. But, if the lower patch of light is larger, the amount of energy per square inch must be smaller; in other words, the *intensity* of the lower beam is diluted because the

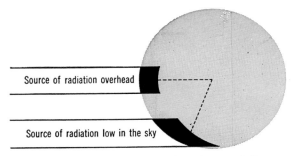

Source of radiation overhead

Source of radiation low in the sky

FIG. 32. Angle of incidence of sun's rays influences their heating effect.

radiant energy is spread over a greater surface. Similarly, those parts of the earth which are so placed as to have the sun overhead, or nearly so, are certain to receive more intense radiation than the regions where the sun is lower in the sky. In fact, this comparison may be made in a single place on any day by contrasting the relatively high intensity of sunlight around noon with its much lower intensity in the early morning or late afternoon—the times when the sun appears near the horizon. During the months of April, May, June, July, August, and September, it is the points north of the equator which have the noonday sun most nearly overhead; during October, November, December, January, February, and March, it is the points south of the equator which find the sun most nearly overhead at noon.

It should be remembered that all diagrams illustrating this topic are badly out of scale; the sun should really be far more distant than is shown.

EFFECT OF THE SHAPE OF THE ORBIT

At least two other factors contribute to the seasonal differences in climate.

One is the greater nearness of the earth to the sun at perihelion, which occurs on about January 3. The distance separating the two bodies is then about 3 million miles less than when the earth is at aphelion on about July 4. The intensity of radiation received from the sun increases as the earth gets closer to the sun. In consequence, the earth *as a whole* is in a more favorable position to receive solar energy in January than it is in July, and this circumstance mitigates the rigor of winters in the northern hemisphere. This effect is, however, much smaller than that due to the tilt of the earth's axis.

Another consequence of the distance factor is the changing speed of the earth in its orbit. When close to the sun, the earth moves most rapidly, and, as a consequence, winter in the northern hemisphere is the shortest of the seasons and summer the longest. In the southern hemisphere the reverse is true.

SEASONAL SHIFT OF THE SUN'S DIRECTION

A re-examination of the earth-sun diagram for winter and summer (Fig. 31, p. 54) shows that at the beginning of our winter in the northern hemisphere the direction of the rising sun is not east but considerably south of east, and to us in the northern hemisphere the sun appears to traverse an arc across the southern half of the sky, setting south of west. The farther north the observer, the nearer the sun is to the southern horizon during the day until, at the Arctic Circle, the sun is momentarily visible on the southern horizon at noon. Beyond the Arctic Circle the sun will not be visible at all. At the beginning of summer in the northern hemisphere, shown on the right in Fig. 31, the direction of the setting sun is north of west. The sun rises north of east, traverses an arc across the sky, and sets north of west. As we go northward, the sun again seems lower and lower in the southern sky, but when we reach the Arctic Circle, the sun rises and sets due north. Really, the sun does not set at all there during our summer but is visible throughout the 24 hours; at midnight, the sun just touches the northern horizon. At the North Pole, the sun then makes a large circle around the entire sky, always remaining 23.5° above the horizon. From the diagram, the student should now be able to imagine what happens as we go southward.

British Information Services

PLATE XI. Stonehenge monument. This monumental group of stones is believed to be almost 4000 years old, and seems to indicate an orientation with respect to the rising sun at the summer **solstice.**

SOLSTICES

That day on which the sun rises farthest south of east is called the day of the *solstice*. It is the winter solstice to all places north of the equator and the summer solstice to all places south of the equator. The word means "the stopping of the sun," and it originated with the circumstance that for several months prior to the solstice the sun has been rising at points which were daily farther and farther south of east, but on this morning its southward shift ends, and on the following day it will rise a little farther north.

At the time of our winter solstice the center of the sun is directly above the Tropic of Capricorn, 23.5° south of the equator. The winter solstice marks the day when the northern hemisphere is least favorably situated to receive solar energy. This occurs on about December 21. Notwithstanding the fact that on subsequent days the northern hemisphere receives progressively more and more energy than it did on that day, December 21 is scarcely ever the coldest day of the year; indeed, it is only the official *beginning* of winter. This is due to the fact that, on the days following, the ration of sunlight is only slightly larger, and the climatic effect of diminished radiation is cumulative.

On or about June 21, the summer solstice (winter solstice for latitudes south of the equator) occurs. The sun's rising direction is the farthest north it ever becomes; on the day following, its rising point is a little farther south again. At the time of the summer solstice the center of the sun is directly above the Tropic of Cancer, 23.5° north of the equator.

In order to recognize the occasions of the solstices one might watch the horizon for successive sunrises and sunsets. This was evidently the

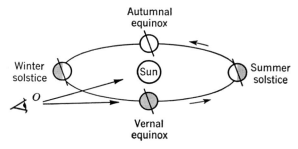

FIG. 33. Positions of earth through a seasonal year.

method of ancient Britons to guide them in the construction of the famous Stonehenge monument (Plate XI). There are some who interpret the orientation of arches and stones in its remaining ruins as an effort to mark the position of the rising sun on that morning when its progress northward came to a *standstill* and the southward retreat of the sun began. The need for fixing this date may have been religious as well as practical.

The solstices can also be recognized by the interval between sunrise and sunset, by the elevation of the sun above the horizon at noon, or by the length of shadow cast at noon by an upright pole. Let a pole several feet long be fixed vertically in the ground. When the sun is at its greatest altitude, i.e., at noon on the day of the summer solstice, the shadow of the pole will evidently be shorter than it is on any other day before or after. Conversely, at the winter solstice the noonday shadow will be at its longest.

THE EQUINOXES

Between summer and winter solstices are two other points of seasonal importance. They are called the equinoctial positions. At the two instants when the earth occupies these positions,

the sun is exactly above the equator, illuminating the northern and southern hemispheres equally so that the sun's rays just touch the North and South Poles. The axis of the earth is then exactly perpendicular to a line joining the centers of the sun and earth, and the sun at those times rises due east and sets due west all over the world. The spring (or vernal) equinox, occurring on about March 21, begins the spring season, and the autumnal equinox, occurring on about September 21, begins the fall season.

FIG. 34. Sun and earth at vernal equinox.

There is another way of recognizing the equinoxes by a property from which the word itself is derived. Figure 33 represents a perspective view of the earth occupying several positions in its orbit. Imagine an observer at O looking in the direction shown. His view ought to reveal something like Fig. 34, with the earth's axis perpendicular to a line from the sun. The earth's axis, however, does not lie in the plane of the page but makes an angle of 23.5° with it.

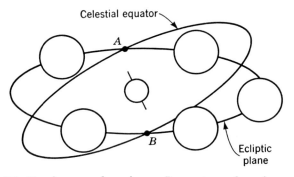

FIG. 35. A = vernal equinox. B = autumnal equinox.

The result is obviously an equal degree of illumination for both the northern and southern hemispheres. No one latitude will have a longer day or night than another; indeed, night and day will be equal in length all over the earth.

The equinoxes are actually defined as points in the sky at which the celestial equator (see Fig. 35) intersects the plane of the ecliptic. Reference has been made previously to the ecliptic plane. It is merely the plane of the earth's orbit, or better, the plane in which the earth's center moves in the annual journey around the sun. The *ecliptic is not the plane of the earth's equator,* which is tilted 23.5° to the ecliptic. For the present purpose it is simpler to regard the ecliptic as the plane in which the *sun's* center seems to move in the fictitious annual journey of the sun around the earth. If this nearly circular path is shown in perspective and then if a large circle whose plane contains the earth's equator is drawn as in Fig. 35, the two curves will intersect at the equinoxes. These points are identified by means of stars which may be seen in the same direction from the earth but, of course, at far greater distances from the earth.

The earth is spinning, however, and its axis *precesses* like that of a top (see Fig. 58). For a reason to be explained later (p. 103), this precession is such that the points *A* and *B* move clockwise as seen from Polaris. The motion is very slow, requiring 26,000 yr to complete a circle.

We are now ready to define more exactly the seasonal intervals in terms of the geometry of the earth's orbit. Reference to Fig. 36 shows why the seasons are not equally long. When the earth is nearest the sun (January 3), it moves

fastest and, in addition, has relatively less distance to cover; hence, winter is the shortest of our seasons. The earth moves most slowly

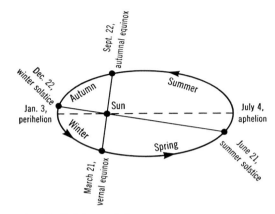

FIG. 36. Definitions of the seasons.

around July 4 and has a longer path to cover; hence, summer is the longest of our seasons— about 4.5 days longer than our winter. Autumn is almost a whole day longer than winter, and spring is almost 4 days longer than winter.

PROBLEMS

1. If the heat received from the sun is a maximum in the northern hemisphere on about June 21, why do we not have our hottest days at that time of the year?

2. Suppose that at the equator a camera is pointed at night toward the zenith and kept in a fixed position for several hours while its shutter is left open. Describe the picture you would expect to get from such an exposure.

3. Are there any planets which cannot ever be seen in the eastern sky immediately after sunset? Explain.

4. Show by a sketch where Venus has to be with respect to the earth and sun in order to be seen as an "evening star"; as a "morning star."

5. If two observations of a certain star taken 6 months apart revealed no aberration, what would you infer about its direction with respect to the earth and sun?

6. What would the seasons be like if the earth's axis were perpendicular to the plane of the ecliptic? If the axis lay in the plane of the ecliptic?

7. Since the earth's axis precesses, how will the apparent position of Polaris (the North Star) change through the coming centuries?

8. In approximately what direction would a New Yorker have to look in order to see the sun rise on August 21? Repeat for an observer in the Argentine.

9. Imagine yourself at the equator. Describe the motion of the sun you would see, from sunrise to sunset, as you went southward on December 22, March 21, June 21, and September 22.

10. In landscaping it is important to know the regions of shadow and sunlight. Calculate, for your latitude, the lengths of the longest and shortest shadows cast throughout a year by a vertical brick wall 10 ft high. Assume the wall runs east and west.

11. Houses are sometimes built so as to take advantage of the changing altitude of the sun throughout the year. An overhanging roof, projecting the right distance, may prevent direct sunlight from entering windows below it during the hot summer months, but allow the sun's radiation to enter the windows during the cold winter months. Make up reasonable dimensions for such a design, assuming the windows to face southward.

. . . .

REFERENCE

1. *Highlights of Astronomy*, Walter Bartky, University of Chicago Press, 1935, Chapter 1.

Measurement of Time

Our standards of time are defined in terms of astronomical motions. We may, of course, speak of time both subjectively and objectively. When we say that time "flies" or that time "drags" we refer to a subjective experience which cannot be defined with any absoluteness or universality, but when we speak of years or of days, we are really making use of the interval between the recurrence of the seasonal cycle or the rotation of the earth on its axis or its revolution around the sun. We are now prepared to study the mechanism which furnishes us with an objective and universal clock.

It is to be noted first that only certain subdivisions of physical time correspond to the interval between natural occurrences, whereas others are purely arbitrary. Thus, the year, the lunar month, the day, and the season have a basis in recurrent physical happenings; the week, hour, minute, and second are solely the products of human invention. There is, however, more than one kind of day, month, and year, and the following will now occupy our attention: the *sidereal day,* the *apparent solar day,* the *mean solar day,* the *sidereal year,* the *tropical year,* the *sidereal month,* and the *synodic month.* Their explanation will be facilitated by a knowledge of certain terms employed in celestial geometry.

THE CELESTIAL SPHERE

It is convenient for our present purpose to regard outer space as a huge hollow sphere with the earth at its center.

THE MERIDIAN

Any line running north and south along the earth's surface is a meridian of longitude—the whole spheroid being imagined as enveloped by these nearly circular curves which intersect at the poles. Imagine a plane passing through one such meridian and extending out to the celestial sphere. Its intersection therewith is a semicircle called the celestial meridian of all points on the earth directly below it.

THE ZENITH

An observer can look in many directions toward the celestial meridian, but only the direction vertically overhead pierces the celestial sphere at a point called the *zenith.* The vertical direction assumed by any suspended cord carrying a weight (a plumb line) points upward towards the zenith.

THE SIDEREAL AND SOLAR DAYS

As the earth rotates from west to east, the stars appear to cross the sky from east to west. Let us note the moment when any star is observed crossing our meridian. On the following night it will cross the meridian again. The interval between two successive crossings of the same meridian by the same star is evidently the time the earth takes for one complete revolution of 360° about its own axis. This interval is called one sidereal day. The sidereal clock is made to read from 0 to 24 instead of from 12 to 12.

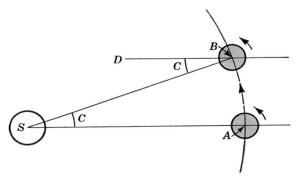

FIG. 37. Each day the earth must rotate through an additional angle C to repeat noon.

For any observer it is noon when the sun crosses his meridian. The time between successive transits of the sun across the same meridian is called the solar day. If it were not for the earth's orbital motion around the sun, this time would be exactly equal to the sidereal day. Actually, the solar day is a little longer than the sidereal day. Suppose that in one day the earth moves from *A* to *B* through the angle *C* (Fig. 37). This angle is greatly exaggerated in the figure to facilitate drawing of the essential geometry. Since the earthly year is about 365 days long, angle *C* is $\frac{1}{365}$ of 360° or approximately 1°. When the earth is at *A* the sun is sighted at noon in the direction *AS*, but when the earth is at *B* the sun's direction is *BS*. Within the interval between noon at position *A* and noon at position *B*, the earth has made one complete turn of 360° *plus* an extra partial turn through angle *DBS*, which equals angle *C*. Since a 360° turn of the earth requires 24 sidereal hours, the additional turn of about 1° consumes $\frac{1}{360}$ of 24 or $\frac{1}{15}$ of an hour, i.e., about 4 min. Thus the solar day is about 4 min longer than the sidereal day, and this is just the reason for the fact that

each night the stars rise 4 min earlier than they did the night before, according to our solar clocks. It should now be understandable also why any zodiacal constellation, along with the other stars, appears higher and higher in the night sky as the seasons progress, completing a cycle in one year.

Although the sidereal day is constant, the solar day varies in length throughout the year. Since we must, for practical reasons, set our ordinary clocks to keep step as closely as possible with the sun, our 24-hr day must then be an average or mean solar day. The fact that our clocks are not exactly in step with the sun can easily be verified by the following simple experiment.

Suppose that a hole in a roof allows a spot of sunlight to fall on the floor (Fig. 38). From day to day we shall mark the position of this spot just when our good practical clock reads 12 o'clock noon. If we persist in these observations throughout a year, we shall have traced on the floor a figure eight with its long axis running north and south. The figure eight is not quite symmetrical with respect to the north-south axis, and the south loop of the eight will be consider-

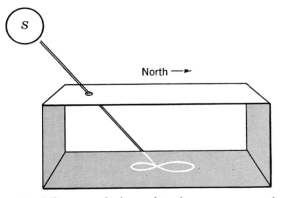

FIG. 38. When our clocks read twelve noon, we mark, from day to day, the spot made by the sun on the floor.

ably smaller than the north loop. The north and south movement of the spot of sunlight is, of course, due to the seasonal variation of the sun's elevation in the sky, for in winter, when the sun is farthest south, it is also at lowest altitude and so the beams which enter the hole must strike the floor relatively far north of the point beneath the hole. In summer, when the sun is farther north, it is also at higher elevations in the sky. Then its rays at noon will pass through the hole in a more nearly vertical direction. The east and west movement of the spot of sunlight represents the discrepancy between the sun and our clocks. Since the trace is a figure eight, there must be four times a year when our clock reads 12 noon exactly as the sun crosses the meridian. These times are about April 16, June 15, September 1, and December 25. Even the simplest of sundials, consisting merely of a central pin perpendicular to a horizontal plane, would therefore agree with a clock four times a year. On February 12 and November 2 it would be about 15 min in error at noon, and on May 15 and July 25 it would be about 5 min off. There are two reasons for this peculiar behavior of the sun.

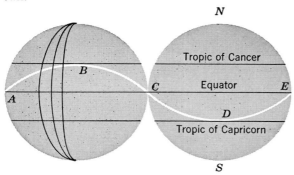

FIG. 39. The sun moves across the hour circles along the path *ABCDE* throughout a year.

Consider first the effect due to the elliptical orbit of the earth. It has already been shown that the solar day is longer than the sidereal day by about 4 min because the earth moves about 1° per day in its orbit around the sun. Moreover, this difference between the solar and sidereal day varies with the velocity of the earth. It is greatest at perihelion (January 3) and least at aphelion (July 4). The mean or average solar day would have some value between these two extremes, and twice a year our sundial would be correct. If this were the only effect involved, the figure on the floor would not be a figure eight. We must therefore seek some additional effect, and this is not quite so easy to describe or to visualize.

Because of the tilt of the earth's axis, the sun will be vertically overhead at latitudes ranging from 23.5° N. to 23.5° S. twice during each year. Figure 39 shows how the sun progresses across the hour circles in the course of a seasonal year. Each day the sun, in effect, moves eastward along this path. But the hour circles come closer together as the latitude increases so that the sun crosses more of them in a given time than it does

at the equator during an equal time. This effect is magnified because the direction of the sun's motion is more nearly perpendicular to the hour circles at high latitudes, whereas near the equator the sun approaches the hour circles at an angle. These effects change the length of the solar day, and they are not in step with the effect due to the variable speed of the earth in its yearly orbit. Together, they add up to a cumulative variation in the solar day which is summarized in Fig. 40. If the left side of the curve is folded over on the right half, using *AB* as an axis, the figure eight is evident. Plotted in that form, it is called an *analemma*.

THE SIDEREAL YEAR AND TROPICAL YEAR

When the earth has moved entirely around its orbit and the same star is visible in the original direction with respect to the sun, the elapsed period is *one sidereal year*. If the earth's axis pointed constantly in the same direction, this observation would also mark the end of a seasonal year, say, the recurrence of the spring equinox. That is not the case, however, for the slow precessing of the axis during this time has

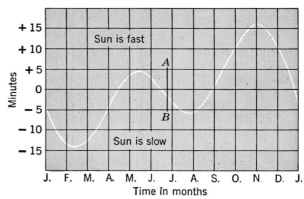

FIG. 40. Differences between the sun and our clocks throughout the year.

caused it to point in a very slightly different direction (see Figs. 57 and 58)—a shift which is enough to make the spring equinox observable about 20 min before the orbit has been completely traversed. The interval between successive spring equinoxes is the *tropical year*. It is the period which we commonly mean by the word year, and it is what our calendars attempt to record.

Summarizing: A *sidereal year* corresponds to one revolution of the earth around the sun. Its length is 365.25636 mean solar days.

A *tropical year* corresponds to the time between two successive spring equinoxes. Its length is 365.24220 mean solar days.

LEAP YEARS

By adding an extra day to our calendar year every 4th year, we assume tacitly that the tropical year consists of 365.25 mean solar days. This was, in fact, the assumption in the Julian calendar which was sponsored by Julius Caesar in 46 B.C. Since actually the tropical year is a trifle shorter than 365.25 days, we are evidently adding too much by inserting a full day in the fourth year and too much again by repeating the insertion four years later. In time the excessive increment becomes significant. The difference between the *assumed* tropical year and the *actual* tropical year is 365.25 − 365.2422 = 0.0078 day per year, or 0.78 day per century. Taking this last difference as approximately ¾ of a day per century, it follows that in four centuries the leap year insertion would add three days too many. In order to compensate for this, the advisers of Pope Gregory XIII proposed in 1582 the calendar reform which is now in use, namely, to drop three leap year days out of every four centuries. A convenient manner of doing so almost suggests itself: taking the first two digits of any century year, only one in four centuries will be divisible by 4; let this year have the extra day normally allotted to leap years, but omit the extra day from the others. Adoption of this policy made (or will make) the calendar lengths of certain century years as follows:

1600	366 days	2000	366 days
1700	365	2100	365
1800	365	2200	365
1900	365	2300	365

SIDEREAL AND SYNODIC MONTHS

There is, finally, the distinction between two lunar intervals. Our satellite, the moon, revolves in its orbit, i.e., sweeps through 360°, in an average time of 27.32166 days. This period is *one sidereal month*. This period is likewise the time required for one rotation of the moon on its axis, for the observer on earth always sees the same face of the moon, a condition which would be impossible if the moon did not rotate in the same period as the time of revolution.

In its elliptical orbit, the moon's distance from the earth's surface varies from about 221,000 to about 253,000 mi.

The *synodic month* is the time between successive identical phases of the moon, and this is longer than the sidereal month. The earth has moved about $\frac{1}{12}$ of the way, or 30° around the sun during the sidereal month, and the moon has accompanied it in the same journey. That is to say, the moon has to revolve about 30° more than 360° before again displaying the same phase to an observer on earth. At the rate of 27.3 days for 360°, this additional fraction of a revolution consumes about 2.2 days, making the synodic

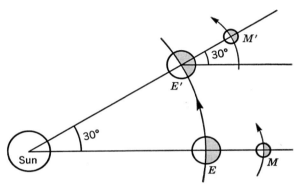

FIG. 41. Why the synodic month is longer than the sidereal month.

month 29.5 days long, more accurately 29.53059 days on the average (Fig. 41).

PHASES OF THE MOON

The moon is a globe like the earth, although much smaller. Its diameter is only 2160 mi, whereas the diameter of the earth is nearly 8000 mi. Light from the sun causes half the globe of the moon to be illuminated, but an observer on earth cannot see the entire illuminated half, no matter how favorably he is placed, except when the moon is in so-called *full* phase. The phases of the moon are readily understood from Fig. 42, which shows the moon occupying four positions in its elliptical path around the earth. In the "new" phase the moon stands between the earth and the sun, although it does not ordinarily prevent solar radiation from reaching the earth. This is because the moon's path lies in a plane which is tipped about 5° to the ecliptic, so that the new moon is usually above or below the ecliptic plane. When the moon happens to be *on* the ecliptic plane at the time it is in the new phase, the moon then intercepts the sun's light and a *solar eclipse* is observed. Otherwise only a small portion of the moon is visible from the earth because the illuminated half of the moon faces *away* from the earth, and only a thin bright crescent is seen as we look across the top (or bottom) of the satellite. Nevertheless, it is often possible to make out the whole circular silhouette of the moon in its new phase, as the dark side is faintly illuminated by sunlight which is reflected from the earth.

Figure 42 shows that in order to see the new moon an observer must look in the direction of the sun. Hence, the new moon seems to rise in the eastern sky in the morning and to set in the western sky in the evening. In about a week

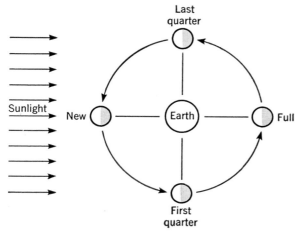

FIG. 42. Phases of the moon.

the moon has moved around to first quarter, where about half of its illuminated disk is visible to an observer on earth. The time schedule has changed, however, for at first quarter the moon can be seen by us only between noon and midnight. Evidently it will seem to rise in the east at noon and to set in the west at midnight.

A timetable for the full moon and for the last quarter moon can be worked out easily by studying the diagram. It may be noted also that only when the moon is in full phase can the light from the sun be intercepted by the earth to produce a *lunar eclipse*. Lunar eclipses are infrequent because the moon is not ordinarily on the ecliptic when it is full. However, lunar eclipses are more frequent than solar eclipses owing to the much smaller shadow cone cast by the moon than that cast by the earth.

TIME ZONES AND THE INTERNATIONAL DATE LINE

Time, as reckoned according to the sun, depends upon longitude. When the sun (or, rather, an imaginary sun whose progress is absolutely

uniform) crosses a meridian of longitude, the time is noon for all places on that meridian. It would be most inconvenient, however, if persons working a few miles east or west of one another actually abided rigorously by sun time. For example, *A* in New York has promised to telephone *B* in Boston at 12 o'clock. He does so, only to find that it is 12:12 in Boston and *B* has left. He then calls *C* in Buffalo to learn about the delivery of a consignment which was due there at noon. But it is only 11:41 in Buffalo, and the shipment has not yet arrived.

In the latter part of the nineteenth century, it was agreed internationally to partition the earth into 24 time zones, each zone bisected approximately by meridians of longitude 15° apart and each differing from its neighbor zones by 1 hr on the standard clocks. All places within a 15° time zone would employ the same time, and persons therein would know that in communicating with the next zone west of them they must subtract an hour from their own clock readings; with places in the next zone east they must add an hour. The prime or zero meridian runs through Greenwich, England, and Greenwich civil time is standard throughout the world.

The time zones in North America are as follows:

Longitude	When Greenwich Clock Reads Noon Local Clock Reads
Approximately 60° W., Atlantic (or Colonial) Time	8:00 A.M.
Approximately 75° W., Eastern Standard Time	7:00 A.M.
Approximately 90° W., Central Standard Time	6:00 A.M.
Approximately 105° W., Mountain Standard Time	5:00 A.M.
Approximately 120° W., Pacific Standard Time	4:00 A.M.

Owing to the convergence of the meridians, the distances separating them are much smaller in the extreme north and south than in the temperate or tropical latitudes. A difference in longitude of 15° at the equator corresponds to a separation of about 1000 mi. At latitude 60° this separation would be only about 500 mi.

Places on or near the 180th meridian of longitude are traversed by an imaginary irregular line known as the *international date line*. On either side of this line the calendar date differs by 1 day according to mutual agreement. In crossing the line westward, the date immediately becomes that of the next day, i.e., Wednesday becomes Thursday, etc.

CALENDAR REFORM

Only two major calendar changes have been made in the last 2000 years. The first was by order of Julius Caesar with the adoption of a twelve-month year of 365 days and one extra day every four years. The second, promulgated by Pope Gregory XIII in 1582, dropped the extra leap-year day in the century years which were not divisible by 400. The need for further reforms is apparent. Nothing much can be done about the year, since the tropical year is not equal to any rational number of days. The month, however, might well be altered. Most religious sects still reckon holy days on the basis of the lunar cycle. For example, the date of Easter is still set according to a decree issued in 325 A.D. as the first Sunday after the first full moon after the day of the spring equinox. If in a certain year the moon should be just past full when the spring equinox arrives, there is a period of practically four weeks before Easter is celebrated plus possibly another week if the full moon happens to occur on Monday. In another year the succession of spring equinox, full moon, and Sunday might occur nearly five weeks earlier. Such variable scheduling of significant dates is hardly desirable.

More serious are the facts (1) that our existing calendar year does not contain a whole number of weeks, and (2) that the length of the month is irregularly variable. These circumstances lead to the following difficulties:

1. The two halves of the year are unequal in length.

2. Months and quarter years do not contain equal numbers of weeks or days; hence, business transactions reckoned on a basis of time come out unequally according to the time of the year.

3. The present calendar is not perpetual in that a date falling on a certain day of the week in one year occurs on a different day the following year. Thus, holidays are not placed consistently.

The World Calendar Association has advocated a highly satisfactory reform by proposing a year of 364 days with one more day to end the normal year and one additional leap-year day to be inserted at the end of June every four years. These days would be holidays and would not belong to any week. The 364-day year is divisible by 7 and by 4; hence, it contains a whole number of weeks and a whole number of quarters. Each month would contain thirty days, except January, April, July, and October, which would have thirty-one days. The year would begin on Sunday and end on Saturday. So would each quarter year. Every date would always fall on the same day of the week year after year.

It is doubtful if this excellent and needed reform will be realized for a long time to come. People have always been extremely reluctant to accept calendar changes, being apparently under the impression that any existing system has a certain sanctity about it, even though that system was itself inaugurated for practical reasons over the staunch opposition of the public of its day.

PROBLEMS

1. During what season is the full moon highest in the night sky? Explain.

2. At what time will a full moon be seen to rise? To set? Repeat the problem for the moon at last quarter.

3. Does the moon rise earlier or later each day? By how much? Draw a diagram similar to Fig. 41 to prove your answer.

4. Draw the sun, moon, and earth in the positions necessary for a solar eclipse. Draw lines from the edges of the sun, touching the edges of the moon, to indicate the cone of total shadow cast by the moon. Assuming the sun's diameter to be 109 times that of the earth, and the moon's diameter to be 0.272 times that of the earth, calculate the length of the moon's shadow cone. (Assume the sun to be 93,000,000 mi from the earth.) Is this shadow cone long enough to reach the earth? What can you conclude about the frequency of solar eclipses? *Ans.* 232,000 mi.

5. If our moon revolved around the earth in a direction opposite to its present one but maintained its present average speed, what would be the length of the synodic month? Where would such a moon seem to rise? Would it rise earlier or later on successive days?

6. Phobos, one of the moons of Mars, is about 4000 mi from that planet, and it revolves about Mars in the same sense as our moon but with a period of about 8 hr. Remembering that the Martian day is about equal to our day of 24 hr, in what compass direction would a Martian look to see Phobos rise? Explain by diagram.

7. If the earth's axis made one complete precessional motion in 365 yr, instead of 26,000 yr, what would then be the difference between the sidereal and the tropical year?

8. In Act III, Scene 2, of *Hamlet* the following passage occurs:

> Full thirty times hath Phoebus' cart gone round
> Neptune's salt wash and Tellus' orbed ground,
> And thirty dozen moons with borrowed sheen
> About the world have times twelve thirties been. . . .

How long a time interval is described? Discuss the passage from the astronomical point of view.

9. In Fig. 38, what would be the shape of the figure on the floor if the earth's axis were perpendicular to the plane of the ecliptic, everything else remaining unchanged? *Hint:* Only the variable speed of the earth in its orbit need then be considered.

10. If the horns of the moon are turned toward the west, is it a waxing or waning moon?

11. The passengers on a plane cruising westward at 250 mph observe that the sun is stationary on the western horizon. At what latitude are they flying? *Ans.* Approximately 76°.

. . . .

REFERENCE

1. *Highlights of Astronomy*, Walter Bartky, University of Chicago Press, 1935, Chapters 2 and 4.

The Sidereal Universe

Let us imagine ourselves following a beam of light outward from the sun, traveling with a speed of 186,000 mps. In about three minutes we arrive at the orbit of the nearest planet Mercury. Five minutes more and we have reached the orbit of the earth. Between Mars and Jupiter we speed past swarms of small planets, or planetoids, some of which are only a few miles in diameter. Here and there we spot spectacular but harmless comets loafing along in their highly eccentric orbits, and all along the way we encounter small particles of matter and dust which we recognize as the stuff out of which meteorites are made. We pass Saturn, Uranus, Neptune, and finally in a total time of 5.5 hours we arrive at the outermost planet Pluto, having traveled a little more than 3.5 billion miles. This impressive system involving sun, planets, moons, comets, and meteoric dust we call with possessive pride our solar system, realizing that there may be many similar systems elsewhere in the universe.

The swarms of stars which we see scattered over the night sky are not to be found within our solar system, but suppose we set our course toward the nearest of these stars, still maintaining a speed equal to that of light. After hours and even days of travel we do not seem to be getting much closer to our star destination, but, if we persist, we shall finally, after 4.15 years, reach our goal: Proxima Centauri. Another star, Alpha Centauri, is about the same distance from the sun, and a very bright star, Sirius, is 8.6 light-years away from the sun. There are only about ten visible stars nearer than 10 light-years! On a clear moonless night the heavens seem very crowded, but in reality we find enormous patches of empty space, the celestial objects being separated by distances which overtax our restricted space perceptions.

In order to determine these stellar distances we again appeal to simple geometry. As the earth moves around the sun, the nearer stars show a measurable parallax with respect to very distant stars. Even though the nearest star has a parallax angle of only 0.785 sec, and all more distant stars have smaller parallax angles, modern telescopes make it possible to measure star distances up to 300 light-years by the parallax method. However, distances greater than this have been estimated in several other ways.

One of these methods involves what has come

to be called the *proper motion* [1] of stars, not to be confused with the apparent motion due to the revolution of the earth around the sun. When photographs of the heavens, taken at long intervals, are compared, it appears that stars are not truly "fixed" but that they move by small measurable amounts. This displacement is usually recorded in seconds of arc and, except for the very near stars, it amounts to less than 1 sec per year. An analogy will show how this proper motion is used to measure distance.

Imagine yourself on an elevated spot at night overlooking a densely populated region where you can see the lights of moving traffic over a wide

· · · · · · · · · · · · · · · · · · ·

[1] The proper motion of a star is the number of seconds of arc by which its direction changes each year.

area. Automobile lights near at hand appear to be moving rapidly through relatively large angles, whereas those far off in the distance appear to be moving more slowly even though the average speed of traffic is about the same everywhere. If we make a similar assumption about the motions of the stars, we have a way of calculating their distances. The distance should be inversely proportional to the proper motion. More specifically, the distance in light-years multiplied by the proper motion in seconds per year should be a constant. When we try this out on stars within 300 light-years, whose distances are known from their annual parallax, the result is gratifying. The product is a number which does not vary greatly; its average for some twenty of the nearer stars is about 12. This seems to indicate that stars are drifting around in the universe at

PLATE XII.   Two-hundred-inch Hale telescope at Mount Palomar, California.

Mount Wilson and Palomar Observatories

Mount Wilson and Palomar Observatories

PLATE XIII. Andromeda nebula. This nebula is a galaxy similar to the one of which our solar system is a part.

Mount Wilson and Palomar Observatories

PLATE XIV. Orion nebula.

roughly the same speeds. There are occasional strong departures from this rule, as in the case of Arcturus, whose speed is unusually high.

Having tried the method on stars of known distances, we apply it to more remote objects, taking care to use the results only statistically. The conclusions are startling! It appears that the solar system is just a tiny speck in an enormous disk-shaped structure which we call *our galaxy*. Since the boundary of this disk is not sharply defined, its thickness has been variously estimated at from 3000 to 30,000 light-years with a diameter from 30,000 to 300,000 light-years. We might have guessed at some such shape as this for, on a clear moonless night, we see many more stars in the direction of the Milky Way than in any other general direction. This is what we would expect as we look toward the

rim of our galaxy. It appears, too, that this immense disk rotates with a period of several hundred million years, carrying with it our sun and its family of planets somewhere between the center of the galaxy and its rim.

For determining the distance of very remote objects a method is used which depends on variable stars. These stars (Cepheid variables), scattered rather sparingly through the universe, vary their brightness at intervals of a few days and with surprising regularity. From the periods of their pulsations astrophysicists have been able to calculate the true brightness of these strange stars, and, with this knowledge, their distances can be estimated from their apparent brightness as seen from the earth. The problem is like that of estimating the distance of an automobile headlight if the actual or true brightness of the light is

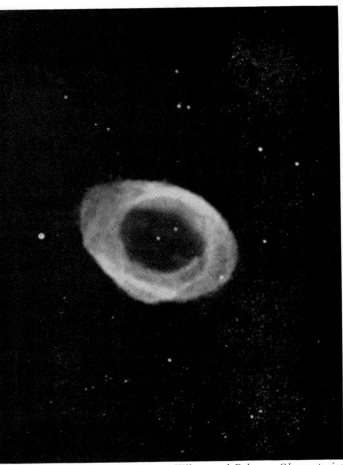

Mount Wilson and Palomar Observatories

PLATE XV. The ring nebula in Lyra.

Mount Wilson and Palomar Observatories

PLATE XVI. Globular star cluster in Canes Venatici.

known; the more distant the headlight, the lower the apparent brightness.

What lies outside our galaxy? Other galaxies, nebulous masses, and star clusters extend out and out as far as our telescopes can penetrate (Plate XII). Photographs can only suggest the grandeur of these remote and gigantic objects. In the constellation Andromeda, for example, there is a nebula which, to the naked eye, is just a point of light but which a telescope reveals to be a spiral-shaped system probably containing millions of individual stars (Plate XIII). It is a galaxy very much like our own and is estimated to be about two million light-years away. And there are millions of such galaxies within reach of our telescopes! Some of these objects are huge diffuse masses of gas like the nebula in Orion (Plate XIV); some are ring-shaped (Plate XV); some are clusters of stars decreasing in density of distribution from the center outward (Plate

XVI); some are dark patches seen only because there is something luminous behind them which they obscure (Plate XVII).

How far out does this universe extend? Is it finite or infinite? For that matter, what can infinity mean when applied to physical space? These are questions which do indeed lie within the realm of science and about which there has been much speculation, but they are beyond the scope of this discussion.

SUMMARY

It is now important for us to look back over our account to examine what has been accomplished and to note by what methods the information has been acquired.

Beginning with our position on the earth we were able to calculate the dimensions and describe the motions of the whole solar system with confidence and precision. What is even more impressive, we were able to reach out into the universe thousands, and even millions, of light-years beyond the solar system.

In achieving this we have certainly paid our respects to observed facts; without them our discussion would have remained as fruitless as the ancient astrology or the medieval alchemy.

Because we needed data, we were concerned with effective methods of measurement and special devices for sharpening their precision. Many phenomena, like the aberration of light or star parallax, could not be discovered until telescopes reached a certain state of refinement. Without the telescope Galileo could not have observed the clinching facts which made him support the Copernican theory.

We have made free use of the mathematical logic, mostly geometry. Without this logical machinery we should end up with stocks of unre-lated data which would neither aid us in understanding known phenomena nor enable us to predict new ones. Recognizing that circles and ellipses and even straight lines do not exist in nature, we have, nevertheless, used these geometrical abstractions to aid us in describing the shapes of objects and the paths of their motions through space.

Our attitude toward theories and hypotheses should be evident. No sentimental attachment to the Ptolemaic theory prevented us from discarding it as soon as the facts pointed out its inadequacy; it yielded to the Copernican system. Uncomfortable though it may be, we must accustom ourselves to the state of flux which exists in physical theories.

And so, by an effective combination of observation and logic we have arrived at least at a dimensional description of the physical universe which

PLATE XVII. Horsehead nebula in Orion.

Mount Wilson and Palomar Observatories

surrounds us.   Philosophically, a realization of the immensity of space would seem, at first glance, to shrink man into insignificance.   It was just this that earlier people feared; when the earth lost its position as the center of the universe, would not man also lose his position of importance?   But, strangely, it was about the time of Copernicus and Galileo that man as an individual began to assert his intellectual freedom. The loss was only a dimensional loss, far overbalanced by the feeling of strength and importance that comes with understanding.   Knowledge of nature and the physical universe was no longer esoteric and fearful, to be interpreted only by a chosen few who were initiated to the secrets.

PROBLEMS

1. Explain, by selecting your own analogy, how the proper motion of stars may be used to determine their approximate distance.

2. In the sixteenth and seventeenth centuries the Copernican theory was bitterly attacked by people outside the natural sciences. Can you think of a parallel case within the last 100 yr? Within the last 50 yr? What do you conclude from your answer?

.   .   .   .

REFERENCE

1. *Highlights of Astronomy*, Walter Bartky, University of Chicago Press, 1935, Chapters 4 and 7.

Mechanics

INTRODUCTION

USE OF DEFINITION IN THE NATURAL SCIENCES

In the aesthetic fields, accuracy of expression is, for the most part, not sought after and frequently it is avoided. In the realm where "beauty is truth" it is more important to excite the imagination than it is to achieve exactness in meaning. The whole field of art is strongly impressionistic, which means that it tries as much as possible to arouse the subjective reactions which people experience when confronted with works of art. It is not the function of the artist to inform, or to prove, or to establish facts, but to suggest and to stimulate, to recall memories and to arouse emotions, and it is just because of this that a good painting expresses more than a good photograph. Similarly, because poetry is meant to be read between the lines, many poets have expressed far more than perhaps themselves have realized.

But these are attributes of the subjective and the emotional. In the realm of the objective, in the natural sciences, precision in speech and exactness in written language are absolute necessities. Experiments must be described, and logical deductions must be expressed in unambiguous terms. That is why the natural sciences concern themselves so greatly with definitions.

It must be understood that a definition is not, in itself, a statement of a natural truth; rather, it is a logical necessity. Only two demands are made of a definition: it must not be logically inconsistent with other definitions, and it must be stated in the most efficient form possible. Consider, for example, the concept of "force." The popular meaning of the word is varied; people speak of the "force" of an argument, "force" of habit, economic "forces," and so on. The inference is that "force" must be some sort of coercive or constraining agency, and from the literary point of view this is sufficient, but in the discussion to follow we shall see how the natural scientist is able to define "force" with far greater rigor. To make the meaning of "force" clear, the physicist begins by defining "velocity" in terms of distance and time. Then "acceleration" is defined. Then the meaning of "mass" is made clear. Then "momentum" is defined. Finally, "force" is defined, as Newton did it, in terms of the rate of change of "momentum." Furthermore, one can then build on the now precise concept of "force" and define the terms "work" and "energy." The famous discovery, made about the middle of the nineteenth century, that energy can neither be created nor destroyed—the law of conservation of energy—could not even be stated without the sequence of definitions just described.

It is a tedious business to construct this logical pyramid of definition upon definition, and few people outside the natural sciences are willing to endure it, but in following such a procedure, laborious though it may be, the vocabulary of science is evolved. It is not easy to tell what the celebrated "man on the street" means by "democratic" or "liberal" or "reactionary," but those who have learned to speak correctly the language of science understand one another. No intellectual field deserves to be called a science until it has such a well-defined vocabulary.

THE ROLE OF MATHEMATICS IN THE NATURAL SCIENCES

The effort in making definitions is well rewarded; it results in an efficient and precise vocabulary. Some of these definitions are so simple that they can be stated verbally and their meaning visualized or comprehended in physical terms, but many of them must be stated in shorthand symbols which are borrowed from mathematics. Furthermore, the subtle logical relationships which exist among the many definitions could never be understood without the aid of the logical processes which mathematics furnishes. Apparently, the human mind is not able to follow through a long and intricate series of logical manipulations without some sort of aid. The mathematical processes of addition, subtraction, multiplication, division, differentiation, integration, expansion in series, and so on are logical aids without which the mind would be practically helpless. For example, it would be impossible for the average person to add a large number of items without benefit of paper and pencil (or adding machine), but with the aid of the written symbols of mathematics and the simple memory aids of addition the problem becomes elementary. Not even the great mind of Newton could have arrived at the law of universal gravitation without this logical aid, nor could Kepler have stated his three laws describing the planetary motions.

Again, as in the case of definition, it must be pointed out that the mathematical processes do not contain, in themselves, any natural truth.

There is not a single natural phenomenon which has been (or could be) discovered by mathematical methods alone. Mathematics is logic in its finest and most rigorous form. It must, therefore, be self-consistent within a given field, but no other demands are made upon it; it need not even be useful. This must be a difficult point to understand because so many famous people seem to have believed (and still believe) in what they like to call the "eternal verities" of mathematics. Leonhard Euler, a Swiss mathematician of the eighteenth century, thought he could prove the existence of God by means of a mathematical equation, and a rather simple one at that. The philosopher Kant thought that simple arithmetical statements like $2 + 2 = 4$ must be eternal verities which are not even sensory in origin. The error in this thinking is probably due to the difficulty in dissociating the concept of number from material objects. If numbers are taken to mean the masses of things, the statement $2 + 2 = 4$ is really no more than an example of the law of conservation of mass. It says that, if two objects are placed together with two other objects, none of them increases or decreases in mass and none of them disappears. This is commonly the case with masses on a large scale, but it is not true for the tiny particles which compose the nuclei of atoms. Suppose, on the other hand, the numbers are taken to mean volumes. Then $2 + 2$ will not always equal 4 even in very common cases—2 cu ft of water plus 2 cu ft of sugar will not equal 4 cu ft of sugar solution.

What about geometrical truths? Is it not an eternal verity that "a straight line is the shortest distance between two points"? That depends on where the distance is measured; it is not true on the surface of the earth, for example, because here the shortest distance is a part of a circle. The famous Euclidean axiom defines, in fact, a special kind of geometry, but in other geometries the axiom need not be true at all.

It is not true, as many people seem to believe, that a little clever mathematics can transform an erroneous or questionable statement into something reliable and rigorous. The mathematical processes, as applied in the natural sciences, always begin by making certain assumptions or by appealing to known physical laws, and any weakness or error in these initial steps will be transmitted to the result, however correct the mathematical machinery may be. Once again, any truth contained in the mathematical result must really be contained in the initial assumptions and postulates, though not always explicitly stated, and in the end that truth derives from an experimental observation.

NEED FOR A STUDY OF MECHANICS

A description of the components of the solar system, their distribution, and their motions is not completely illustrative of the scientific method even with the enunciation of Kepler's laws. Science demands a further step: the rationalization of all the known facts by means of a theory which shall account for them in a consistent and logical manner, besides suggesting avenues of thought which may lead to the discovery of additional facts. It is this department of science which challenges man's highest faculties of imagination and reasoning power, and genius among scientists is reckoned largely by their contributions to fundamental theory. The discovery of the law of universal gravitation is an excellent example of this final step in the scientific procedure.

However, we are not yet prepared to study the details of Newton's great achievement; we lack a vocabulary of precisely defined concepts in terms of which motion can be described. Even the brilliant writings of Galileo suffer from a lack of clearly defined terms; with all his physical insight, he never arrived at an adequate definition for the agent which causes the velocity of a body to change—the agent which Newton defined as *force*. Nevertheless, through a combination of experimentation and logical reasoning, Galileo may justly be said to have started the science of mechanics. The investigations of Galileo furnished the basis for Newton's later elaboration and development of mechanics into a rigorous department of knowledge.

A STUDY OF MOTION

Galileo is usually remembered by the general student of history for his astronomical discoveries. He it was who first saw four satellites moving around the planet Jupiter. He observed the jagged surface of the earth's moon; he detected spots on the sun; he noted that the Milky Way was a huge assemblage of separate stars. He was the first to see Mercury and Venus going through phases like those of the moon—a discovery which proved the essential correctness of the heliocentric theory.

Notwithstanding the importance of these sensational observations, they do not show Galileo's intellectual greatness so well as do his discoveries in mechanics. It may be assumed that anyone who was the first to look at the sky through a telescope would make many remarkable discoveries. Galileo's experimental study of motion, on the other hand, was an achievement which could be instigated and carried out only by a person of the highest intellectual caliber.

The most notable distinction between Galileo and the early Greek philosophers lay in the difference between their respective approaches to a problem of nature. Whereas the Greeks (with a few exceptions such as Archimedes) were primarily concerned with *why* a certain phenomenon occurred, Galileo realized that the first step toward understanding was to learn *how* the phenomenon occurred. It should be obvious that an accurate knowledge of *what* takes place must always precede any speculation about *why* it takes place, and, of course, the Greek thinkers believed that they knew the workings of those natural phenomena which they attempted to explain. What they failed to realize was the complexity of most natural occurrences, which is such that several laws are usually operating at once and it is difficult to sort out the workings of one of them from the general mixture. Only by experiment, in which extraneous influences are ruled out artificially, does the functioning of natural law usually approach simplicity.

For example, if a feather and a metal coin are allowed to fall through the air, the coin reaches the ground first and a casual observer might well assume that intrinsically the earth has less attraction for feathers than it has for metals. This was the belief of Aristotle, who even went further and said that the heavier an object is the faster it will fall. An experimentalist would have investigated the effect of air upon falling bodies by timing the descent of the feather and the coin in vacuum, or by selecting situations in which the air resistance played an unimportant part. The latter was actually achieved by Galileo when he placed the objects on an inclined plane, thus effectively reducing both the speed and the air resistance. The Greeks, of course, lacked the apparatus for producing a vacuum, but that is unimportant. In any event, Aristotle would not have performed experiments with falling bodies, preferring instead to deduce natural phenomena by logico-aesthetic reasoning. When, much later, a feather and a coin were allowed to fall in an evacuated glass tube, they were observed to fall identically and to do so even when their weights were widely different. The explanation that the resistance of the air furnishes an upward force which acts in opposition to gravity, and is greater for a bulky object than it is for a compact one, comes *after* the experiment has been performed.

There is a famous story that Galileo dropped two metal balls of different weights from the gallery of Pisa's leaning tower and showed before an assembled multitude that they fell in practically identical times. The truth of the story is now seriously questioned, but from Galileo's own writings it is clear that he did understand the behavior of falling bodies and the effect of air resistance on their rate of falling. He knew, for example, that, if air resistance is minimized by choosing rather dense materials such as metals, one can release two objects simultaneously from the same height and they will reach the ground together, even though one object may be much heavier than the other. He knew, moreover, that the vertical distance through which a body descends is proportional to the *square* of the time it has been falling and numerous other quantitative relations as well.

In order that these matters may be understood, it is advisable to define certain fundamental concepts which are susceptible of measurement. One of the most useful of these concepts is speed.

SPEED

When an object undergoes displacement from one location to another, the distance traversed divided by the time elapsed is called the speed of the object.

$$\text{Speed} = \frac{\text{Distance}}{\text{Time}}$$

Speed is thus the time rate of displacement. The object may move along any path—straight, curved, or zigzag. If the rate is constant, whether the entire displacement or any part of it is considered, the object has moved with *uniform* speed. If the object has not moved with uniform speed, the ratio of distance to time is its mean, or average, speed.

ANGULAR SPEED

The special case of rotational motion about an axis calls for modification of the above definition. Suppose a wheel is set spinning on a fixed axis, the observer having previously painted a radial stripe on the wheel so that he can tell whenever a rotation has been completed. If he counts the number of rotations that occur in a measured time and divides by the time, the quotient obtained is the rotational speed, or *angular* speed, of the wheel.

$$\text{Angular speed} = \frac{\text{Number of rotations}}{\text{Time}}$$

Again the speed may be uniform or not. If not, the indicated quotient gives the *mean* angular speed. A body may, of course, be traveling from one place to another and rotating at the same time; the wheels of a moving car or a football in flight are familiar examples. When it is necessary to distinguish between the two kinds of motion, we can identify the speed along the path of displacement as the *linear* speed.

VELOCITY

This term is frequently used as if it were synonymous with speed, but in rigorous usage velocity includes the *direction* of displacement as well as the speed. Thus, if a plane flies north for 200 mi in 50 min, its speed is 200/50 or 4 mi per minute, but its velocity is *4 mi per minute northward.* It follows that velocity cannot be uniform unless *direction as well as speed* is constant. For example, a car which is rounding a curve cannot possibly have uniform velocity, even though its speed be constant. We shall see the importance of this distinction shortly.

ACCELERATION

If the velocity of a body is continually changing, we say that the body's motion is *accelerated.* The same term covers decreases as well as increases in speed, for a body which is slowing down, or decelerating, may be said to have negative acceleration.

Acceleration is defined as the time rate of change of velocity.

$$\text{Acceleration} = \frac{\text{Change in velocity}}{\text{Time}}$$

To illustrate:

(*a*) Suppose that a car starts up from rest and, moving along a straight highway, attains a speed of 30 mph within 10 sec. It has thus undergone a *change* in velocity of 30 mph at an average rate of

$$\frac{30 \text{ mi}}{\text{hour} \times 10 \text{ sec}}$$

The acceleration of the car is therefore 3 mph per second. Note that a unit of time must appear twice in the denominator—once in connection with the change in velocity and again in connection with the rate at which this change occurs. It is usually convenient to employ the same subdivision of time in both cases, and since 3 mph equals 4.4 fps we may describe the foregoing acceleration as

$$\frac{4.4 \text{ ft}}{\text{sec} \times \text{sec}} \quad \text{or} \quad 4.4 \text{ ft/sec}^2$$

(b) Let the same car speed up uniformly from 30 mph (44 fps) to 45 mph (66 fps) during the next 10 sec. We shall assume that there is no deviation from the straight course so that the car is accelerated only by virtue of its change in speed. The new acceleration is

$$\frac{45 \text{ mi/hr} - 30 \text{ mi/hr}}{10 \text{ sec}}$$

or

$$\frac{66 \text{ ft/sec} - 44 \text{ ft/sec}}{10 \text{ sec}} = 2.2 \text{ ft/sec}^2$$

This second illustration emphasizes something which laymen often overlook in connection with acceleration, namely, that large velocities are not necessarily associated with large accelerations, or vice versa. If a body increases in velocity rapidly, its acceleration is large, even though its ultimate velocity be small; if the body increases in velocity slowly, its acceleration is small, even though its ultimate velocity be large. This point is worth illustrating by a numerical example:

(c) Car C starts up from rest and reaches a velocity of 7.5 mph (11 fps) in 2 sec. The acceleration is

$$\frac{11 \text{ ft}}{\text{sec} \times 2 \text{ sec}} = 5.5 \text{ ft/sec}^2$$

(d) Car D starts from rest and reaches a velocity of 60 mph (88 fps) in 40 sec. The acceleration is

$$\frac{88 \text{ ft}}{\text{sec} \times 40 \text{ sec}} = 2.2 \text{ ft/sec}^2$$

ANGULAR ACCELERATION

The interesting case of acceleration due to a change in direction will be considered later. Meanwhile let us note that, if a body which is spinning on a fixed axis increases its rate of rotation, its acceleration can be expressed in accordance with the definition already given. Here the acceleration is the rate at which the *angular* velocity increases. Thus, if a man who has been turning a grindstone at 1 rps increases his effort so that within 5 sec the stone speeds up to 3 rps, the average angular acceleration is

$$\frac{3 \text{ rev/sec} - 1 \text{ rev/sec}}{5 \text{ sec}} = \frac{2 \text{ rev}}{5 \text{ sec}^2}$$

THE ACCELERATION OF FALLING BODIES

Although the velocity of an accelerated body cannot be uniform, quite commonly the acceleration itself is uniform, so that the velocity changes by equal steps in equal intervals of time. One of the most familiar examples of practically uniform acceleration is that of a body falling freely toward the ground. Strictly speaking, it should be allowed to fall within an evacuated space, since the resistance offered by the atmosphere complicates its motion, but if the object chosen is a small metal ball, the air resistance does not matter greatly. Let us imagine ourselves conducting the following simple experiment, one which has been performed innumerable times and which has always yielded the data given below. We suppose that a metal ball is dropped from the roof of a building, while observers appropriately stationed at various floors record the distance which the ball has fallen at the end of each second. The figures for the first four seconds turn out to be as follows:

Time Elapsed	Distance Fallen from Rest
1 sec	16 ft = 16 × 1 ft
2 sec	64 ft = 16 × 4 ft
3 sec	144 ft = 16 × 9 ft
4 sec	256 ft = 16 × 16 ft

At the extreme right the distances are expressed as 16 times a factor which is evidently the square of the time elapsed. We could generalize at once, provided this same regularity persisted for subsequent seconds (and it does) by writing

Distance fallen (in feet)
= 16 × Time squared (in seconds)

or, using symbols, $h = 16t^2$.

It is easy to go further with the aid of a simple assumption. Obviously the missile is falling faster all the time. If we assume that its acceleration is uniform, its speed at any instant can be estimated. For example, an object which falls 16 ft in 1 sec has an *average* speed of 16 fps. But, if it started from rest and accelerated at a uniform rate, it must have attained a speed of 32 fps when the second ended in order to have an average speed of 16 fps for the entire second.

Next consider the ball at the expiration of 2 sec. By that time it has descended 64 ft, so that its average speed during the 2-sec interval must have been $^{64}\!/_2$ or 32 fps. But this average would be obtained by taking one-half the final speed, inasmuch as the initial speed was zero. Hence, the final speed must have been 64 fps. As a check on this result, we note that the falling body increased in speed from zero to 32 fps during the first second and, at uniform acceleration, it must have gained a like amount of speed during the next second. Its speed at the end of that time must therefore have reached the value of 64 fps. Thus, if we double the *average* speed found for any interval, we get the *momentary* speed which the body attained at the end of that interval. Applying the same argument to all the data, we get the analysis shown in Table 3.

TABLE 3

Time Elapsed, sec	Dis- tance Fallen, ft	Aver- age Speed, ft/sec	Momentary Speed at End of Interval, ft/sec	Gain in Speed during Successive Seconds, ft/sec²
1	16	16	32	32
2	64	32	64	32
3	144	48	96	32
4	256	64	128	32

THE ACCELERATION OF GRAVITY

Evidently the freely falling body gains in speed by 32 fps during every second it falls. This amount therefore represents its acceleration. With suitable care to minimize the effect of air resistance, one finds that *all* bodies falling toward the earth from moderate elevations experience a constant acceleration of (about) 32 ft per second per second.

If distances are measured in centimeters, the corresponding figure is about 980 cm per second per second.

This approximately constant acceleration is known as the *acceleration of gravity,* and it is customarily symbolized by the letter *g*. We may now insert this symbol into the equation which shows the height through which a body, starting from rest, will fall freely toward the earth in a specified time. That is

$$h = 16t^2$$

becomes

$$h = \tfrac{1}{2}gt^2$$

Furthermore, the vertical velocity attained at the end of t seconds is

$$v = gt$$

The relations between distance, time and velocity for a body moving with uniform acceleration were first elucidated by Galileo. He was unable to make reliable measurements on freely falling bodies because he lacked an instrument for determining very short intervals of time. In order to offset this handicap Galileo utilized an ingenious method of diluting the effect of gravity by using an inclined plane so as to lengthen the time of descent, and he was able to measure these longer time intervals with a crude water clock of his own manufacture. Galileo's apparatus consisted of an inclined plane having a smooth groove cut along the inclined surface.

A bronze ball was allowed to roll down the groove, and the time required for it to descend the entire slope or any part of it was determined as accurately as possible with the water clock. An object moving down an incline takes longer to reach the bottom than it would to fall through the same vertical distance because its acceleration is smaller. The diminished acceleration is nevertheless constant, and the relations between distance traversed, acceleration, time, and velocity are the same as those formulated above for a body undergoing free fall. It is necessary, of course, to replace the symbol *g* by the symbol *a*, inasmuch as the acceleration along the slope will be different from the acceleration of free fall.

Galileo noticed that, on reaching the bottom of the incline, the ball would continue to move horizontally in a constant direction and at nearly constant speed. Moreover, the smoother the horizontal track was the farther did the object travel and the more nearly constant was its speed. This experiment, many times repeated, convinced him that if a body could be set in motion and left entirely to itself—that is, be free of all outside interference—it should continue to move with constant velocity forever. This inference, which is derived from the evidence by extrapolation, is in flat contradiction to another fundamental belief of Aristotle's, namely, that a moving object requires the continual application of force to keep it moving. In familiar illustrations, such as the progress of a vehicle along a road, it is true that motion gradually ceases unless motive force is supplied, but the decay of motion is easily shown to be caused by resistances which the vehicle encounters. Its motion is opposed by roughness of the road, by friction in the wheel bearings, and by the large amount of air which it must push aside in order to move forward. All these are obstacles to its sustained motion, and, when anyone of them is diminished, the effort required to keep the vehicle moving diminishes also. It is therefore reasonable to suppose that, if all resistance to motion could be eliminated, a moving vehicle would persevere in its motion without any expenditure of effort upon it.

INERTIA OF MATTER

The postulate that moving bodies would continue to move forever if only they could be free of outside interference is very useful, in spite of the fact that nature does not offer any examples of such unrestricted motion. The postulate is intended to convey the idea that matter is incapable of changing velocity *of its own accord;* an independent agent is necessary to produce any such change. The agent has to act upon the matter, making it appear as if the matter had a reluctance or resistance to any change in its motion. The latter property, possessed by all matter, is called *inertia.* Hold a large book at arm's length and try to move it suddenly in a horizontal direction; you will feel the muscular tension involved in either starting or stopping its motion, that is, in acting against the inertia of the book. The larger the book, the larger will be the inertial resistance and the consequent muscular tension necessary to accelerate or decelerate the book will be larger also. In fact, we may use the property of inertia to introduce the meaning of a term which has already been used without definition, namely, *force.*

The agent which is always associated with every change in the velocity of a body is called *force.*

This is only a qualitative definition of force, yet it is preferable to the customary statement that force is any push or pull. All pushes and pulls are forces, to be sure, but intuitively we think of these words in connection with muscular effort, whereas most examples of force action are entirely independent of animate agents. Let us postpone a quantitative definition of force until we have investigated the property called inertia.

INERTIA AND MASS

Although every specimen of matter exhibits inertia, it is familiar knowledge that different specimens exhibit it to different degrees. Suppose that a wooden croquet ball and an iron shot of the same size are lying on smooth turf. Each sphere can be set in motion by striking it with a mallet, but to give them equal velocities requires a harder blow for the iron ball than for the wooden one. The iron ball displays the greater inertia. The difference is so marked that, even if the balls were painted identically, anyone could recognize the iron one by its greater inertial resistance. The relative amount of inertia possessed by a body is conveyed by the word *mass.* The iron ball is said to be more *massive* than the wooden one.

It is sometimes said that the mass of a body represents the *amount of matter* it contains. In a certain way this is true. The nutriment in foodstuff, for example, certainly depends on the amount, and a 2-lb mass of sugar is twice as nutritious as a 1-lb mass because the quantity is twice as great. But can we say that the iron shot contains more matter than the wooden ball? Both have the same size, i.e., both take up the same amount of space. Of course, they are made of different kinds of matter; yet two objects might easily be made of different kinds of matter and still be identical in both size and mass. A counterfeiter of coins or a manufacturer of paste jewels would be very careful to make the imitation resemble the genuine in mass as well as in size. If a skeptic demands to know why the iron ball is considered to contain more matter than the wooden ball does, we have to say that it is because the iron ball shows more inertia. This brings us back to the beginning of the argument: greater inertia signifies greater mass and greater mass is proved by greater inertia.

The ways of measuring inertia all involve comparison with some standard. It is first necessary to select a standard, say a block of metal, and to declare it to be of standard mass. Thus, a certain piece of precious metal has been preserved as the standard 1-kg mass, whereas another is a standard 1-lb mass. Carefully made copies of both are kept in all bureaus of standards. The original selection of such a standard is more or less arbitrary, although the standard metal pound was originally intended to have the same mass as that of a pint of water.

COMPARISON OF THE MASSES OF TWO BODIES

Let us suppose that we are conducting an imaginary experiment somewhere in outer space, far removed from the earth, the solar system or the stars, so that our experiment will be unaffected by any external influences whatsoever.

The materials for the experiment will be: two small, solid spheres, an assortment of light springs, a watch and a measuring stick (Fig. 43). We attach the spheres to opposite ends of one of the springs, stretch the spring, and then let go. Inasmuch as we are nowhere near the earth, the system will not fall but the spheres will move toward each other under the pull of the contracting spring. By means of the measuring stick and watch, we determine the accelerations of the two spheres at the same instant and discover that, although these accelerations differ in magnitude

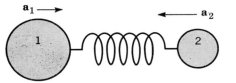

FIG. 43. Equipment for comparing masses.

and are oppositely directed, their *ratio* is constant for all repetitions of the experiment with the same spring as well as with stronger or weaker springs. This is to say that, although a weak spring gives each ball a smaller acceleration than a strong spring does, the ratio of the small accelerations produced by a weak spring is the same as the ratio of the large accelerations produced by a strong spring.

Representing any acceleration of sphere 1 by $\mathbf{a}_1$ and the simultaneous, oppositely directed acceleration of sphere 2 by $-\mathbf{a}_2$, the results may be summarized in the equation

$$\mathbf{a}_1/-\mathbf{a}_2 = \text{a constant}$$

Evidently there is some inherent characteristic of each object which is fixed in amount and which determines the response of the object to the spring. It is this characteristic which is called the inertia of the object, the amount of inertia being represented as so and so much mass.

If the accelerations of the two spheres turned out to be numerically equal at the same instant, we could conclude that both spheres had identical inertia—that is, that both had the same mass.

Alternatively, if the acceleration of sphere 1 were found to be twice that of sphere 2, we could reasonably infer that the first sphere had only half the mass of the second. In general, the amount of acceleration is defined as a measure of the mass, but in an inverse sense; the greater the mass, the smaller the acceleration.

If, therefore, we represent the mass of object 1 by m_1 and the mass of object 2 by m_2, the previous equation becomes, *by definition,*

$$\mathbf{a}_1/-\mathbf{a}_2 = m_2/m_1$$

If the reader is puzzled at having such a categorical result derived from an experiment which was described as imaginary, he may now be assured that a quite similar experiment yielding the same result can actually be conducted at any place on the earth. The objects, connected by a stretched spring, may be allowed to accelerate along a smooth, horizontal surface like a table top. In this way any complication resulting from the effect of gravity will be largely avoided.

FORCE

In an earlier paragraph it was proposed that the term force be used to denote the agent which can impart acceleration or deceleration to a body. In our imaginary experiment it was the contracting spring which caused the two spheres to accelerate; hence, the contraction of the spring supplied the force. Since the same spring acted simultaneously on both bodies, we may presume that it exerted the same force on each sphere, although in opposite directions. By cross-multiplying in the equation

$$\mathbf{a}_1/-\mathbf{a}_2 = m_2/m_1$$

we get

$$m_1\mathbf{a}_1 = -m_2\mathbf{a}_2$$

which represents an equality between two oppositely directed quantities. If we were to define the product $m_1\mathbf{a}_1$ as the *force exerted on sphere 1* and $m_2\mathbf{a}_2$ as the *force exerted on sphere 2,* letting $\mathbf{F}_1$ and $\mathbf{F}_2$ stand for the respective products, the last equation would read:

$$\mathbf{F}_1 = -\mathbf{F}_2$$

This relation would then adequately symbolize the foregoing statement that the contracting spring exerted equal and opposite forces simultaneously on the two spheres.

Extending this definition of force to any case whatsoever, we may now state that:

(*a*) Whenever a body experiences accelerated motion, the acceleration is due to the application of force to the body.

(*b*) The mass of the body multiplied by the amount of acceleration it receives determines the magnitude of the force

$$\mathbf{F} = m\mathbf{a}$$

(*c*) The acceleration and the force causing it have the same direction.

BALANCED FORCES

It is not to be supposed that all cases of force application result in accelerated motion. Very commonly the same body may be subject to two

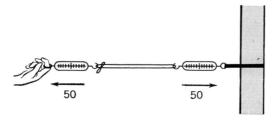

50   50

FIG. 44. Action and reaction forces are equal.

equal and opposing forces. Under these circumstances the body, if at rest, will remain at rest; if it is in motion, it will continue to move at uniform velocity. Thus, a book lying on a shelf is subject to the downward force which we call its weight and also to an equal upward force exerted on it by the shelf. Again, a sled may be pulled along the road with a forward force just equal to the backward force of friction on the runners. The sled continues in motion but not in accelerated motion. Only an *unbalanced* force will produce acceleration, and as long as the unbalanced force persists the velocity of the body will change *continually*.

Isaac Newton, who made an exhaustive study of motion during the second half of the seventeeth century, was the first person to recognize that force action is always mutual. This means that when one body exerts a force on another, the second body simultaneously exerts an equal but opposite force on the first. For example, one cannot exert force on a rope unless it is attached to something which can pull back. If two teams are pulling equally hard in a game of tug of war, the members of each team are aware of the force which opposes their own pull. But one team could disband after tying its end of the rope around a tree, and the tree would exert as

great a pull as the remaining team is exerting. If there is a doubt of this, let a pair of spring balances be inserted anywhere along the stretched rope and the balances will indicate identical forces oppositely directed. Referring to the sketch in Fig. 44, if a person pulls to the left with a force of 50 units, as registered on the spring balance near his hand, the other balance

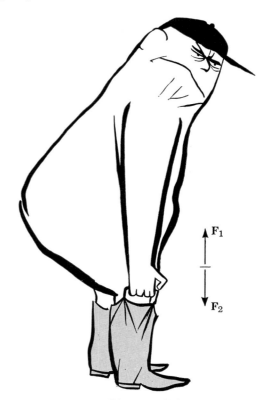

FIG. 45. You cannot lift yourself by your bootstraps.

will show that the tree is pulling to the right with a force which is also 50 units.

The act of walking consists of successive backward pushes against the ground by the feet of the walker. He would not advance, however, if the ground did not push forward against his feet. If the surface is so smooth that frictional force between his feet and the ground is negligible, he cannot walk at all. A close approach to this predicament is experienced by a person attempting to walk on a waxed floor or on wet ice. One body (the walker) cannot act if the other body (the ice) cannot react.

If a person standing in the bow of a rowboat tries to jump a very short distance to the shore, he may be surprised to find himself in the surf instead. The water offers very little resistance, and the backward push which he tries to exert in jumping becomes a very feeble force due to the absence of sufficient reaction by the boat because the water in turn is unable to react to the boat's thrust. The person's judgment, gained from his experience in jumping on land, is worthless under these conditions.

The equality of mutually acting forces supplies the reason behind the old adage "a man cannot lift himself by his own bootstraps" (see Fig. 45). He can exert an upward pull on the straps, but if he does so the straps merely pull down with equal force and no motion results. Both pulls are really applied to the same body (his own), whereas, if lifting is to result, the *action* must be performed on another body in order that the *reaction* may affect his own. Thus, he can clutch a horizontal bar above his head and by pulling downward on the bar, cause himself to rise in consequence of the upward reaction of the bar.

Nor is this truth restricted only to a static system. If a magnet and an unmagnetized iron bar are placed near each other on movable platforms, it is immediately apparent that both bodies are subject to forces, for each one begins moving toward the other—the magnet being attracted toward the bar with a force equal to the one by which the bar is attracted toward the magnet.

THE LAWS OF MOTION

It was Newton who summarized the behavior described in the foregoing paragraphs by three concise statements which have come to be known as the *three laws of motion*. Expressing the laws in modern language, we have the following:

FIRST LAW OF MOTION

Every body which is at rest remains at rest and every moving body persists in its motion *at uniform velocity* unless an unbalanced force acts upon it.

SECOND LAW OF MOTION

Every body which is acted on by an unbalanced force is accelerated in the direction of the force. The amount of acceleration is directly proportional to the magnitude of the force and inversely proportional to the mass of the body.

THIRD LAW OF MOTION

Whenever one body exerts a force on another body, the second body exerts an equal and opposite force on the first body.

If forces always occur in pairs, it follows that accelerations always occur in pairs also. It must be remembered, however, that, just as the two opposing forces act on different bodies, so too are the resulting accelerations the accelerations of different bodies. Thus, although a horse pulling forward on a wagon is thereby subjected to an equal pull backward by the wagon, this does not mean that the horse-wagon combination will remain stationary, for not only are the two forces acting on different bodies but they are not the only forces in operation. The wagon is acted on by several frictional forces as well as by the forward pull of the horse, and its acceleration depends on the net force forward. The horse is pushed forward by the reaction of the ground against his hoofs, and this force may exceed the backward pull of the wagon on him. If it did not, the combination would, indeed, fail to accelerate.

WEIGHT

It is now appropriate to point out that, since bodies fall toward the earth with accelerated motion, they must do so in response to force which the earth exerts on them. The general name given to this force is the force of gravity, but it is more commonly called *weight*. If two bodies experience the same amount of gravitational force, they are said to be equal in weight. Weight is thus the *measure* of the force of gravity. All bodies on or near the earth are subjected continually to this force of gravity, which tends to pull them downward toward the center of the earth, that is, vertically downward. And this is true whether they are at rest or in motion. If a body is stationary, it is only because a force equal to its weight and directed upward is also acting on it continually. The upward force necessary to support a body is not noticeable when this force is supplied by a shelf, or a suspending cord, or by the surface of the earth itself. But when a man or beast furnishes the upward force, as he does in holding up a heavy burden, the attendant muscular fatigue gives convincing proof that the opposing force of gravity is acting continually.

What of the unsupported body whose weight is not balanced by an equal force exerted upward? Such a body falls toward the center of the earth with accelerated motion in accordance with the second law of motion. It should be borne in mind that this downward acceleration manifests itself independently of any other motions which the body may have. For example, if the body is given an impetus horizontally or vertically by being *projected* away from its position of rest, it will fall nevertheless, receiving the same downward acceleration as it would have acquired if it had merely been dropped. The impetus, if horizontal, will displace the body horizontally while it falls, but the horizontal impetus cannot alter the time required for the body to reach the ground. If applied vertically, the impetus will add a constant velocity upward or downward to the variable downward velocity which the body gets in consequence of falling. No momentary initial force affects the downward acceleration.

THE (NEARLY) CONSTANT ACCELERATION OF GRAVITY

Let us consider now what seems at first thought to be a mystifying feature of falling bodies. All bodies, great or small, acquire the same acceleration when they are free to fall toward the earth's center. Yet the gravitational force which the earth exerts on a massive body is greater than the gravitational force which it exerts on a light body. In other words, massive bodies *weigh* more than light ones do. To be specific, if body A is twice as massive as body B, the earth's gravitational pull on A is twice as great as its pull on B and we wonder why body A does not experience twice as much acceleration as B does. The answer is that body A has twice the inertia of body B; hence, even though A does experience double the pull that B does, the *effect* of double the pull on double the mass is the same as the effect of unit pull on unit mass. In the symbolic language of the second law, since $\mathbf{a} \propto \mathbf{F}/m$, this ratio must remain constant if both $\mathbf{F}$ and m change from body to body in equal proportion. This is true of all bodies which are situated within the range of the earth's gravitational force; their masses and their weights are proportional to each other, so that the ratio of weight to mass is constant and all experience the same acceleration when they fall. This acceleration is not precisely the same for bodies falling from high elevations as it is when the elevation is low, but the variation is so slight for ordinary heights that it can be safely disregarded.

FALLING BODIES AND THE THIRD LAW OF MOTION

Students are sometimes puzzled in attempting to apply the third law to falling bodies. If a body falls in response to gravitational force exerted on it by the earth, how is the equal and opposite force which is called for by the third

law manifested? We conclude that the freely falling body exerts an upward force on the earth equal to the body's weight. If we detect no evidence of this upward reaction, that is undoubtedly because the earth's mass is enormous compared to the mass of the falling body. Hence, although the earth may be thought to be falling upward at the same time that the body is falling downward, the earth's upward acceleration must be negligible. Only when the falling body is something of comparable mass, as, for example, the moon, can any oppositely directed acceleration on the part of the earth be detected.

MOMENTUM

Newton utilized another concept which he called "quantity of motion," but which is now better known as *momentum*. Some effects which a moving body is capable of producing depend on its mass and its velocity. The product of the two, $\mathbf{mv}$, is called the momentum of the body (more precisely, the *linear* momentum).

Suppose that a body whose mass is representable by m is moving at a uniform velocity $\mathbf{v}_1$. Let an unbalanced force be applied to the moving body for a brief time designated by t. The velocity of the body will change in consequence of the force action, attaining a value, let us say, of $\mathbf{v}_2$. The momentum has evidently changed by the amount $\mathbf{mv}_2 - \mathbf{mv}_1$, and the *rate* at which it has changed is

$$\frac{\mathbf{mv}_2 - \mathbf{mv}_1}{t}$$

This fraction is nothing else, however, than

$$\frac{m(\mathbf{v}_2 - \mathbf{v}_1)}{t}$$

otherwise $m\boldsymbol{a}$, which we have already seen to be equivalent to the unbalanced force $\mathbf{F} = m\boldsymbol{a}$. It appears, therefore, that we can express the value of a force by giving the rate at which the force can change the momentum of a body.

$$\mathbf{F} = \frac{\mathbf{mv}_2 - \mathbf{mv}_1}{t}$$

This is, in fact, the way in which Newton originally dealt with the concept of force.

CONSERVATION OF MOMENTUM

Let us suppose that two objects having different masses m and M are moving horizontally toward each other, each with its own uniform velocity. Let the momenta of the two objects be $\mathbf{mv}_1$ and $\mathbf{MV}_1$. When the bodies collide head on, each one will exert a force on the other, the force on the right-hand ball tending to drive it toward the right and the force on the left-hand ball tending to drive it toward the left. The third law of motion tells us that these two forces will be equal, although oppositely directed.

$$-\mathbf{F}_l = \mathbf{F}_r$$

where $-\mathbf{F}_l$ is the force on the left-hand body, and $\mathbf{F}_r$ is the force on the right-hand body. Note that the minus sign signifies a force directed toward the left. After colliding, the objects will take on new velocities, say $\mathbf{v}_2$ for the left-hand one and $\mathbf{V}_2$ for the right-hand one. The changes in momentum are respectively

$$\mathbf{mv}_2 - \mathbf{mv}_1 \quad \text{and} \quad \mathbf{MV}_2 - \mathbf{MV}_1$$

Suppose that the collision lasts for a very short time, which we shall designate by t. Then the average force applied to the left-hand object is

$$\frac{\mathbf{mv}_2 - \mathbf{mv}_1}{t} \quad \text{or} \quad \mathbf{F}_l$$

and the average force applied to the right-hand object is

$$\frac{\mathbf{MV}_2 - \mathbf{MV}_1}{t} \quad \text{or} \quad \mathbf{F}_r$$

Hence, if $-\mathbf{F}_l = \mathbf{F}_r$ we may write

$$-\frac{\mathbf{mv}_2 - \mathbf{mv}_1}{t} = \frac{\mathbf{MV}_2 - \mathbf{MV}_1}{t}$$

or

$$-\mathbf{mv}_2 + \mathbf{mv}_1 = \mathbf{MV}_2 - \mathbf{MV}_1$$

or

$$\mathbf{MV}_1 + \mathbf{mv}_1 = \mathbf{MV}_2 + \mathbf{mv}_2$$

Put into words, the last equation tells us that the total momentum of both objects after the collision is the same as the total momentum they had before the collision.

This result is the statement of a profound and useful generalization known as the *conservation of momentum*. A fuller statement of this universal principle is the following:

If a system of two or more bodies is isolated from all outside influences, then, even though the members of the system react on one another, the total momentum of the system remains constant.

On or near the earth, of course, bodies which can react on one another do not form isolated systems; there are always the gravitational pull of the earth and usually frictional forces to interfere with the momentum of such a system. Yet, when such outside interference is small, the conservation principle can be demonstrated to hold almost exactly. If, for example, two billiard balls collide on a level table, their velocities after the collision are rather accurately predictable with the aid of the conservation principle.

CENTRIPETAL ACCELERATION

Heretofore we have considered only such accelerations as involved change in the *magnitude*

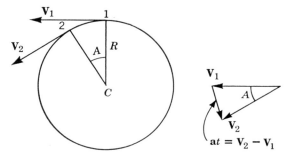

FIG. 46. A body moving with constant speed in a circular path is accelerated toward the center C.

of velocity. It is now time to evaluate the acceleration of a body which undergoes a change in the *direction* of its motion. For simplicity we shall confine the treatment to uniform motion in a circular path where the direction changes continually but the speed remains constant. Such motion affords the most familiar example of centripetal acceleration, or acceleration *toward* the center of a path of motion. Our problem is to find the rate at which the velocity changes when a particle moves at constant speed around the circumference of a circle (Fig. 46).

The arc connecting positions 1 and 2 is the distance traversed during the time t. Its length is therefore $\mathbf{V}t$.

We imagine the motion to be clocked between position 1 where the velocity was $\mathbf{V}_1$ and position 2 where the velocity was $\mathbf{V}_2$, the time elapsed between the two positions being t. $\mathbf{V}_1$ and $\mathbf{V}_2$ are equal in magnitude, but they differ in direction; hence, we can conveniently represent them in the diagram at the right by arrows which are equal in length but pointed in the directions which these arrows have in the left-hand diagram.

The angle A between $\mathbf{V}_1$ and $\mathbf{V}_2$ is evidently equal to the angle A at the center of the circle, for $\mathbf{V}_1$ and $\mathbf{V}_2$ are respectively perpendicular to the radii bounding angle A. The arrow drawn from $\mathbf{V}_1$ to $\mathbf{V}_2$ represents the magnitude and direction of the change in velocity. But the change in velocity divided by the time taken to make the change is, according to definition, the acceleration of the particle.

$$\frac{\text{Change in velocity}}{t} = \mathbf{a}$$

Hence, we may let the product, $\mathbf{a}t$, stand for the change in velocity.

The final step in this demonstration requires that we assume the two positions 1 and 2 to be so close together that the arc connecting them is not sensibly different from a straight line. With this assumption the sector enclosed by the tiny arc and the two radii may be regarded as an isosceles triangle similar to the isosceles triangle shown at the right of the diagram. By the familiar property of similar triangles, the short base of this triangle bears the same relation to the radius of the circle that the arrow $\mathbf{a}t$ does to either $\mathbf{V}_1$ or $\mathbf{V}_2$. That is

$$\frac{\text{Distance 1, 2}}{R} = \frac{\mathbf{V}t}{R} = \frac{\mathbf{a}t}{\mathbf{V}}$$

canceling t and solving for the centripetal acceleration, we find that

$$\mathbf{a} = \mathbf{V}^2/R$$

Note that the arrow, or vector, $\mathbf{a}t$, points toward the center C when the angle A becomes extremely small.

CENTRIPETAL FORCE

The second law of motion states that the acceleration of a body multiplied by the mass of the body gives the force by which the acceleration is produced. The law applies to centripetal as well as to all other types of acceleration. Here the force which deflects the body from a straight path to a curved one is called a centripetal force, and it has the magnitude

$$\mathbf{F}_c = m\mathbf{V}^2/R$$

Centripetal force has to be applied in the familiar experience of steering an automobile around a turn. The diagram of Fig. 47 illustrates two curves on a highway, the second having a shorter radius of curvature than the first. At each bend in the road the moving car tends to continue in its straight course because of its inertia. When the forward wheels are turned so as to direct the car around the curve, a centripetal force, due to friction between the tires and the road, comes into play and, if this force is large enough, the turning will succeed. The magnitude of the required centripetal force is $\mathbf{F}_c = m\mathbf{V}^2/R$. It is obvious that m and R in this equation are not subject to the will of the driver. Nor can he materially influence the maximum value of the friction fixed by the condition of

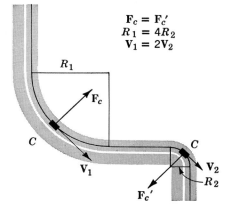

FIG. 47. The car C must decrease its speed in going around the turn of smaller radius.

the tires and the condition of the road. All that the driver can really control is $\mathbf{V}$, and this he must make small enough so that $m\mathbf{V}^2/R$ will not exceed the available frictional force. He must realize too that a small increase in the speed $\mathbf{V}$ calls for a much larger increase in the requisite force, inasmuch as $\mathbf{F}_c$ depends on the *square* of $\mathbf{V}$. Furthermore, if the road happens to be slippery, the maximum centripetal force available to him through friction is sharply decreased and the speed must be decreased accordingly. Finally, it must be remembered that, if the radius of the second curve is, let us say, $\frac{1}{4}$ the radius of the first curve, then the maximum speed to be used in rounding the sharper curve can be only $\frac{1}{2}$ as large as the maximum speed permissible around the larger curve. There are other factors which influence the turning of vehicles around curves, but those mentioned are the major ones.

CENTRIFUGAL FORCE

We have seen that the term centripetal force refers to any force which pulls a moving body toward the center of a curved path, thereby defeating the inertial tendency of the body to continue along a straight line. But, according to the third law, the centripetal force which acts on the body must be accompanied by an equal, outwardly directed force exerted *by* the body. This opposing force is known as the centrifugal reaction of the body. It is most simply illustrated in the example of a stone which is whirled in a circular path at the end of a cord. The cord is stretched because of two opposing radial forces —an inward, centripetal force exerted by the operator, and an outward, centrifugal force exerted by the stone. The outward force continues to act only so long as the inward force does, for, if the cord is cut, both radial forces vanish simultaneously and the stone flies, not outward but tangentially, i.e., in the direction in which it was moving at the instant when the cord was severed.

A planet such as the earth in revolving around the sun must be subject to an inward centripetal force exerted on it by the sun. This is no small force, inasmuch as the mass of the earth amounts to billions of billions of tons. At the same time the earth exerts an outward centrifugal force just as large on the sun. That the sun fails to exhibit any marked acceleration as a result of this outward pull upon it is due to the enormously greater mass of the sun.

What is the source of this enormous mutual force between the sun and its planets? How is it able to reach out through millions of miles of empty space to hold the planets captive in their elliptical orbits around the sun? How must the force vary with the distance so as to make Kepler's laws valid? Questions of this kind led Newton to speculate on the possible existence of a truly universal force, the gravitational force, which would act between masses everywhere in the universe.

PROBLEMS

1. Discuss the statement: "There is not a single natural phenomenon which could be discovered by logic alone."

2. Looking back to the happy days of high-school geometry, did you believe then that the truths of Euclid's propositions were independent of the physical world? Has your belief changed since then?

3. Turn back to the explanation of prevailing winds on p. 53 (Fig. 28). What part does the inertia of the air play in the explanation?

4. On p. 80 the suggestion was made to hold a large book at arm's length and to accelerate it horizontally. If this were done on Mars or some other planet, how would the muscular tension compare with that you would feel on earth?

5. Which one of Newton's laws suggests that a rocket can propel itself in a vacuum?

6. Could you set up a powerful blower in a sailboat and propel the boat by blowing on its sails? Explain.

7. If two identical bullets are fired at the same speed, one at a steel target and the other into a bale of cotton, will they strike with equal force? Explain.

8. About the middle of the seventeenth century, Otto von Guericke performed his famous experiment with the Magdeburg hemispheres. To make the demonstration as dramatic as possible, he hitched eight horses to each of the opposite halves of his evacuated sphere in order to pull the hemispheres apart. Would the total force have been just as large if only eight horses had been used, all on one side, and the other hemisphere had been tied to a tree? Why?

9. A 2-lb mass and a 3-lb mass lying on a smooth frictionless surface are connected by a spring. When the two masses are pulled apart and released, the initial acceleration of the 2-lb mass is observed to be 5 cm per second per second. What must be the initial acceleration of the 3-lb mass?

10. Explorers frequently make use of the simple trick of timing the free fall of a pebble down a cavern or crevasse to determine its depth. In such an example, a pebble was heard to strike the bottom just 2.5 sec after its release. How deep was the crevasse?
Ans. 100 ft.

11. An east-bound and an identical west-bound train, both having the same speed, pass each other on a railroad which runs along the equator. Which train presses down harder on the tracks, and why?

12. A driver finds that he can go around a certain turn safely at a maximum speed of 40 mph. What would be his highest safe speed around a turn with twice the radius?
Ans. 56.6 mph.

13. Imagine that the time has come to set up a research laboratory on an artificial satellite encircling the earth. In such a laboratory objects cannot be *weighed* because their weights will be practically zero. How do you suggest measuring the masses of objects under these conditions?

14. Discuss the meaning of the statement: "Circles, ellipses, or even straight lines do not exist in nature; they are geometrical abstractions."

15. Photographs of falling smokestacks reveal that frequently such structures break into sections which are turned at different angles with respect to the earth, as shown in Plate XVIII. Explain this in terms of Newton's laws.

Wide World Photo

PLATE XVIII. Photographs showing stages in the fall of a smokestack. Note the manner in which the structure breaks.

. . . .

REFERENCES

1. *Dialogues concerning Two New Sciences,* Galileo, translated by Henry Crew and Alfonso de Salvio, Northwestern University, 1939, Chapter III.
2. *A Source Book in Physics,* W. F. Magie, McGraw-Hill Book Co., 1935, pp. 1–30.

The Theory of Universal Gravitation

Sir Isaac Newton (1642–1727), whose numerous scientific discoveries were so frequently momentous, is honored most for devising the theory of gravitation, which he published around 1685. It is one of the brilliant examples of insight and rationalization in scientific history.

There is a popular belief, derived from the story of Newton's contemplation of a falling apple, that he was the first man to explain that objects fall downward because the earth pulls them downward with gravitational force. Like many common traditions, this one is erroneous. The falling of unsupported bodies was attributed to gravitation long before Newton's day. What Newton did was to conceive of the hypothesis that this same familiar force of gravitation was also responsible for the curved paths pursued by the planets and moons in the solar system.

In following the steps of Newton's reasoning it is necessary to show first that, when planets revolve about the sun, they are perpetually falling toward the sun, even though they never strike it. Imagine a rifleman stationed on top of a very tall tower from which he can shoot projectiles horizontally and at various speeds (Fig. 48a). For low speeds every such projectile would fall to the ground in the same time that it would take an object which was merely dropped from the tower, but the paths of the projectiles would be parabolic, and the greater the horizontal speed imparted to any projectile, the farther from the base of the tower it would land.

Now imagine the horizontal speed of the projectile to become very great so that it lands very far from the base of the tower, and let us remember that the surface of the earth is curved (Fig. 48b). Eventually a horizontal speed may be tried which is so great that the projectile will follow path OBD and will not reach the earth at all, in spite of its constant fall toward the earth. The path of the projectile will then have become a circle, and the centripetal acceleration will have reached a value of 32 ft/sec², the value for a freely falling body. This possibility can be made clear in the following way:

Suppose that the force of gravity suddenly ceased to act, so that a bullet on leaving the rifle horizontally were to continue moving in its initial direction OAA'. Then, owing to the curvature of the earth, this bullet would get farther

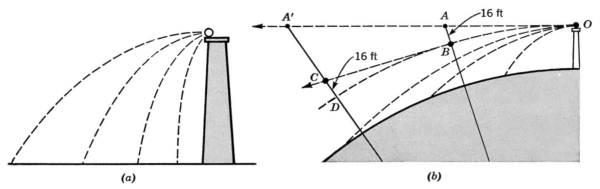

FIG. 48. With sufficient horizontal velocity, a body may fall steadily toward the earth without ever reaching it.

and farther away from the earth. On the other hand, with gravity acting on it, the bullet could fall just as all other bodies do and yet remain at a constant distance above the earth, provided its horizontal speed were great enough. We recall that a freely falling body drops 16 ft during the first second of its fall. Suppose the distance AB in Fig. 48b to be just 16 ft, whereas OA is the distance which the bullet would move in 1 sec if gravitational force were absent. Then, inasmuch as it *does* respond to the force of gravity, the bullet will not arrive at A 1 sec after its horizontal projection but, instead, it will be at B, which is 16 ft nearer the ground. The falling will be continuous, and the path of the bullet will be the arc OB. At the instant of passing B, the bullet is moving in the direction BC, and it would reach C at the end of the next second if gravity were not operating. But under the influence of gravity it falls to D instead, CD being 16 ft as before. Incidentally, $A'D$, which is the vertical distance through which the bullet has dropped in 2 sec, turns out to be 64 ft, as expected from Table 3 on p. 79. It is assumed that, in this discussion, OB and BD are very small compared to the radius of the earth.

The horizontal velocity which a projectile must have in order to behave in the manner just described amounts to about 5 mps. If we were able to project bodies at this speed, neglecting friction of the air, we could produce any number of artificial satellites. For that is just what they would become—a system of bodies traveling in orbits about the earth and always falling toward the earth but never striking it.

The foregoing illustration enables us to understand that, although the force of gravity acts in the same way on all unsupported bodies, causing them to fall whether they are moving hori-

zontally or not, yet for the body which is moving horizontally gravity is a *centripetal* force and the resulting acceleration must be regarded as a centripetal acceleration.

It follows that bodies which fall toward the earth in consequence of their weight need not actually hit the earth at all. If they have tangential speeds within certain critical limits, they may follow a circular (or an elliptical) orbit about the earth indefinitely, whereas, if their tangential speed is too high, they may leave the earth without completing even a single trip around it. Planets likewise, in their revolutions about the sun, are actually falling toward the sun, but their tangential speeds are such as to prevent them from either falling into the sun or leaving the solar system.

UNIVERSAL GRAVITATION

We can now transfer our attention to the planets, regarding them as bodies which are continually falling toward the sun, although never getting significantly closer to the sun. The same statement applies to the moon as a body continually falling toward the earth, and it was the moon's motion which Newton first studied as an example of universal gravitation. Although, of course, we cannot be certain of the procedure in Newton's mind, the several steps in his reasoning may conveniently be *studied* in the following order:

IS GRAVITATION UNIVERSAL?

The weight of a body on earth undergoes very little change even when the body is transported to extremely high altitudes. In other words, the earth's gravitational force is almost undiminished even when the objects on which this force is exerted are miles above the earth's surface. Contemplation of this fact led Newton to wonder if there were any limit to the distance over which the force of gravity could be felt. Perhaps the moon itself might be influenced by the earth's gravitational pull—indeed, it might be this very pull which causes the moon to fall toward the earth. And if the moon is attracted toward the earth by gravity, why should not the earth and all other planets be attracted toward the sun by the sun's gravity? In short, could the familiar terrestrial force which we call gravity and which we are conscious of as weight really be a universal force operating between celestial bodies as well? Specifically, could it be the force of gravity that keeps the parts of the solar system together?

RELATION BETWEEN MASS AND GRAVITATION

What is it that makes the earth pull other bodies toward it so that they fall with accelerated motion unless prevented from so doing by the application of an upward force equal to their weight? This is a question which cannot be answered if the sense of the query is "why?" No one knows *why* specimens of matter attract one another. The best that can be done, after acknowledging that all matter *is* mutually attracting, is to associate the attractive force with some property of matter. Kepler believed that magnetism caused gravitational attraction. Apparently the property responsible for the gravitational force exerted by matter is *mass*. In assuming that the gravitational force between two bodies is due to their masses, we realize that this does not explain the *cause* of gravitation. It merely specifies the *seat* of gravitation. Somehow the possession of this property of mass by any two bodies causes them to attract each other with a force whose magnitude is rigorously determined by the law we are about to derive.

That gravitational force stems from the mass property of matter is suggested by the way in which weight depends on mass. Suppose that we have determined the relative masses of two bodies by measuring the accelerations they receive from the contraction of a stretched spring. Let us say that the experiment shows one body to have 3 times the mass of the other. Then, on *weighing* the two, we find that the first body also *weighs* 3 times as much as the second. Thus the force of gravity which the earth exerts on any object within range of its influence is directly proportional to the mass of that object.

What of the earth's mass, however? Does that also contribute to the magnitude of the force of gravity? The answer is that it must, since in all independent measurements of gravitational attraction the mass of *every* interacting body plays a part. In a modern laboratory we could establish this point by an idealized experiment which, although never performed, yet seems possible but extremely difficult to carry out. Imagine two massive, identical spheres of metal which are suspended by cords so that they hang very near to each other (Fig. 49). The suspending cords will be found to deviate slightly from their nor-

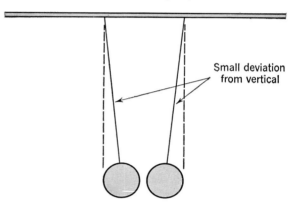

FIG. 49. Two suspended masses attract each other with a force proportional to their masses.

mally vertical direction, thus indicating that each ball is exerting a horizontal force of attraction on the other ball, although the force is very small. By measuring the extent of the deviation of the cords from the vertical direction, we can calculate the gravitational force between the two masses. On replacement of the two spheres by others having twice as much mass, but with the same radius as before, the inclination of the cords toward each other becomes greater and it could be shown that the force of attraction is 4 times as large as before, provided the distance between their centers remained the same.

Clearly the gravitational attraction between the spheres is proportional to the product of the masses, since doubling the mass of each quadruples the total force effect.

Newton generalized this point by asserting that every particle of matter in the universe attracts every other particle with a force which is proportional to the product of their masses.

EFFECT OF DISTANCE ON GRAVITATION

It is not enough to realize that gravitational force diminishes with increasing distance between bodies. What we need to know is the quantitative relation between the force and the distance. Newton determined this relation with the aid of Kepler's third law in an analysis like the following.

Suppose a planet to be moving around the sun in a circular path of radius R. Let the mass of the sun be m_S and that of the planet m_P. Then the gravitational force between the bodies may be written tentatively as

$$\mathbf{F} = G \frac{m_S m_P}{R^x}$$

where G is a constant introduced to convert the *proportional* dependence into an *equality*. The symbol R^x in the denominator means that there is an inverse relationship between the force and the distance but that its exact character is so far undetermined. The denominator may be R, R^2, R^3, or some other power of R. But, inasmuch as the revolving planet is attracted toward the sun at the center of the circle, the attracting force $\mathbf{F}$ is really a centripetal force, and the form of any centripetal force is known to be $\mathbf{F} = mV^2/R$. Here V represents the speed at which the planet moves in its orbit.

This speed can be expressed differently, for if the circumference of the circular orbit is $2\pi R$ and if a period of time, T, is required for the planet to traverse its orbit, the planet's speed is evidently $2\pi R/T$. The centripetal force may therefore be written

$$\mathbf{F} = \frac{m_P V^2}{R} = \frac{m_P}{R} \frac{4\pi^2 R^2}{T^2} = \frac{m_P 4\pi^2 R}{T^2}$$

Now let us equate the two expressions for force

$$G \frac{m_S m_P}{R^x} = \frac{m_P 4\pi^2 R}{T^2}$$

and, after canceling m_P, the relation may be written

$$\frac{R^{x+1}}{T^2} = \frac{m_S G}{4\pi^2}$$

All quantities on the right are constants, and so the right-hand fraction as a whole is constant. But Kepler's third law, as confirmed by observation, is

$$R^3/T^2 = \text{Constant}$$

By comparison of the two last equations, which refer to the same situation, it must be true that

$x = 2$. With this knowledge of the correct power by which distance affects gravitational force, Newton was able to state the quantitative dependence of gravitational force on mass and distance by the formula

$$\mathbf{F} = G \frac{m_S m_P}{R^2}$$

A TEST OF THE GRAVITATIONAL LAW

The simplest test that occurred to Newton in attempting to verify the foregoing relation was a comparison between the earth's gravitational attraction for the moon and the earth's gravitational attraction for any object near the surface of the earth. Such a comparison would eliminate the need for knowing G, for if the equation is written once for the moon and again for the terrestrial object and the first equation is then divided by the second, G cancels.

However, before this could be done, a difficult problem had to be solved. In the preceding derivation of the inverse square law of gravitation, it could be assumed that the sun and planets were very nearly point masses, since their diameters are so small with respect to the distances between them; but suppose this were not true. If we are to consider the earth's attraction for an object at its surface, this assumption is certainly not valid. Each particle of the earth attracts each particle of the other body, and the distances between particles vary greatly, so that the calculation of the total force evidently poses a very difficult problem. Actually, the solution involves the summation of an exceedingly large number of small forces. Newton was finally able to solve the problem for the case of two homogeneous spheres, and this was no small achievement at a time when calculus methods of summation were unknown. The solution can be stated in terms of a point, defined for each body, called the *center of mass*. For every body there exists a point such that, if a single force is directed toward that point, the body is accelerated without any accompanying rotation. In other words, as far as simple acceleration along a straight line is concerned, all the mass of the body might be concentrated at the center of mass. For homogeneous spheres, this point coincides with the geometrical center of the sphere. What Newton discovered was that, for any two homogeneous spheres, the gravitational attraction is exactly the same as if all the mass of each body were concentrated at its center of mass or geometrical center. For the earth and the moon, or for the earth and an object at its surface, R in the inverse square law becomes simply the distance between centers. This is an enormous simplification.

Figure 50 indicates the arrangement of the bodies. Let m_E be the mass of the earth, m_M the mass of the moon, and m_o the mass of the

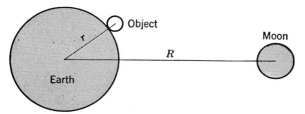

FIG. 50. Comparison between the moon's acceleration toward the earth and the acceleration of an object near the earth.

object on the earth. Also, let r be the radius of the earth and R the distance between the centers of the earth and moon. Then the gravitational force between the earth and the moon is

$$\mathbf{F}_{EM} = G\frac{m_E m_M}{R^2}$$

and the force between the earth and the object is

$$\mathbf{F}_{Eo} = G\frac{m_E m_o}{r^2}$$

whence

$$\frac{\mathbf{F}_{EM}}{\mathbf{F}_{Eo}} = \frac{m_M r^2}{m_o R^2}$$

But, according to the second law of motion, any force which accelerates a body is proportional to the mass of the body times the acceleration, or $\mathbf{F} \propto ma$. With this substitution the last equation becomes

$$\frac{m_M a_M}{m_o a_o} = \frac{m_M r^2}{m_o R^2}$$

where a_M and a_o are the respective accelerations acquired by the moon in falling toward the earth and by the terrestrial object in falling toward the earth.

The masses can now be canceled, and, since r is about 4000 mi, whereas R is about 240,000 mi,

$$\frac{r}{R} = \frac{4000}{240,000} = \frac{1}{60}$$

and

$$\frac{r^2}{R^2} = \frac{1}{3600}$$

The final relation thus becomes

$$\frac{a_M}{a_o} = \frac{1}{3600}$$

Then, if the earth's gravity is what causes the moon to fall toward the earth, the moon should fall with an acceleration amounting to only $\frac{1}{3600}$ of 32 ft/sec², or 0.0088 ft/sec².

Expressed in larger units this lunar acceleration becomes 21.8 mi/hr².

Now, the distance h fallen by an accelerated body is given by $h = \frac{1}{2}at^2$. Using one hour for t and 21.8 mi/hr² for a, we obtain 10.9 mi as the distance which the moon falls toward the earth every hour.

Here at last is a specific figure to be verified. We may do so by calculating h in the exaggerated

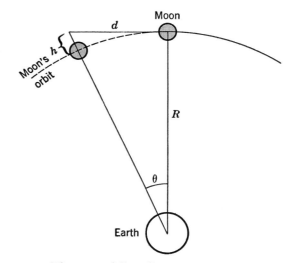

FIG. 51. The moon falls a distance h toward the earth every hour.

diagram of Fig. 51, where d is the distance which the moon would traverse in one hour if it were not deflected by the earth's gravity, h is the amount of deflection which we are trying to calculate, and R is the known radius of the moon's orbit. The angle θ is the central angle subtended by the arc which the moon actually traverses in 1 hr. We shall first estimate θ and then look up its sine. Knowing that the moon completes its 360° orbit in 27.3 days (one sidereal month), the arc and the angle corresponding to one hour's journey are obtained from the relation

$$\theta = \frac{360°}{(27.3)(24) \text{ hr}} = 0.55°/\text{hr}$$

The sine of 0.55° is 0.00958.
Next we note that

$$\sin \theta = \frac{d}{h + R}$$

and therefore

$$h = \frac{d}{\sin \theta} - R$$

The distance covered by the moon in a single hour is obtained on dividing the moon's orbit, $2\pi R$ miles long, by the number of hours in a sidereal month, and this distance is nearly the same as d in the diagram.

Hence

$$h = \frac{2\pi R}{(27.3)(24) \sin \theta} - R$$

$$= 240,000 \left[\frac{2\pi}{(0.00958)(27.3)(24)} - 1 \right]$$

$$= 10.8 \text{ mi}$$

The agreement between this figure and the value of 10.9 mi which we calculated from the law of gravitation is so close as to confirm the law satisfactorily as far as the earth-moon system is concerned.

We may also calculate the acceleration of the moon toward the earth from the relation $a = V^2/R$, where V is the speed of the moon in its orbit and R is the distance of the moon from the center of the earth. This calculation yields a value for a equal to 0.0089 ft/sec². This is in good agreement with the value 0.0088 calculated from the gravitation law.

Newton, however, did not get the excellent agreement which has just been obtained here. At that time the moon's distance was not very accurately known, and, besides, Newton was troubled by the difficulty described on p. 93. As a result, he delayed publication for more than twenty years—until 1687.

It should be emphasized that a single confirmatory illustration is seldom sufficient to establish a scientific theory. The numerical agreement between speculation and observation in one instance merely provides incentive to the search for additional verification. When Newton's gravitational theory was at last sufficiently confirmed,

the equation relating force, mass, and distance attained the status of a scientific law.

THE GRAVITATIONAL CONSTANT, G

The equation for gravitational force contains a constant of proportionality which we have designated by G. Newton did not himself undertake the determination of this constant, although he described how the measurement could be performed. The actual determination has been made numerous times and by several methods.

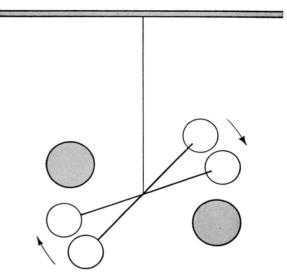

FIG. 52. Cavendish method of determining G.

We shall consider two of these methods, which were followed by the English scientists, Cavendish and Poynting. Any such experiment is one of the greatest delicacy because the gravitational force between two bodies is very small unless one or both of them has an enormous mass. It is only because the earth's mass is very great that the gravitational force between the earth and terrestrial objects is considerable.

It is evident from the equation

$$\mathbf{F} = G \frac{m_1 m_2}{r^2}$$

that if the force of attraction between two known spherical masses were measured, as well as the distance between their centers of mass, G would be the only missing quantity and it would be found by substituting the numerical values of m_1, m_2, and $\mathbf{F}$ and r in this relation.

Cavendish took a long rod carrying a ball of known mass at each end and suspended it at the center by a fine thread (Fig. 52). Two additional massive balls were then moved close to those at the ends of the rod, one on each side. Gravitational attraction drew the movable system nearer to the stationary masses, thus causing the rod to assume a new direction and putting a slight twist in the thread. It was a simple task to find out how much force was needed to produce the same amount of twist independently. Determination of the distance between the centers of the movable and stationary spheres was the only additional measurement required.

Poynting constructed a large but delicate balance and suspended a massive lead sphere from

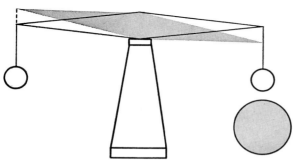

FIG. 53. Poynting method of determining G.

each end of the beam (Fig. 53). The spheres were balanced, and then a much larger sphere was rolled into place beneath one of them. Only that sphere which hung immediately above it was sufficiently close to experience a perceptible effect. This side of the balance consequently tipped downward, and a small mass had to be attached to the opposite sphere in order to restore equilibrium. The weight of the small extra mass was equivalent to the gravitational pull between the lower and the upper spheres, whose masses had been determined previously. The distance between centers of the suspended and stationary spheres provided the final datum.

THE DYNE OF FORCE

Thus far we have avoided mentioning any of the units in which force may be expressed. The determination of G as a numerical magnitude, however, requires the adoption of a force unit. Of the several units in which forces may be stated we shall confine ourselves to only one, the *dyne of force*. This unit is defined with the aid of the second law. Recalling that, when a body is accelerated the force responsible for this effect is directly proportional to the amount of acceleration and to the mass which is accelerated, it is logical to define unit force as that force which will give unit acceleration to unit mass. Thus,

if a mass of 1 gram acquires an acceleration amounting to 1 cm per second every second, the force which produces this acceleration is called 1 dyne.

If force, mass, and acceleration are equal to 1, then F is not merely *proportional* to m and to a but is *equal* to their product; whence the second law of motion can be written as

$$F = ma$$

THE NUMERICAL VALUE OF G

A specimen determination reveals that if two bodies, each having a mass of 6000 grams, are near enough together so that their gravitational attraction for each other can be measured, this force amounts to 0.024 dynes when the centers of the bodies are 10 cm apart. Let these values be substituted into the gravitation equation written as follows:

$$G = \frac{Fr^2}{m_1 m_2} = \frac{(0.024)(10)^2}{(6000)^2}$$

and G turns out to be 6.67×10^{-8} dynes cm²/gm². It is important to point out that this value of G is believed to be the same everywhere in the universe.

THE MASS OF THE EARTH

Besides the proportionality constant G, the gravitation equation contains four variable quantities, any one of which can be calculated if the other three are known. If the mass of the earth is responsible for the force by which terrestrial bodies are held to the earth, this mass can now be calculated from the law of gravitation.

Let M be the mass of the earth, which is to be found. If a body whose mass is 1 gram rests on the surface of the earth, the gravitational force on this body is the same as it would be if the earth's mass, instead of being distributed, were all located at the earth's center 4000 mi below the body. The force on the body is its weight, amounting to about 980 dynes, for weight is given by the equation $W = mg$, and, if $m = 1$ gram, and $g = 980$ cm/sec², W must be 980 dynes.

Using suitable conversion factors, let us substitute these figures into the equation

$$F = \frac{GMm}{r^2} \quad \text{or} \quad M = \frac{Fr^2}{Gm}$$

$$M = \frac{(980)[(3960 \text{ mi})(5280 \text{ ft/mi})(30.5 \text{ cm/ft})]^2}{(6.67 \times 10^{-8})(1 \text{ gram})}$$

$$= 6 \times 10^{27} \text{ grams} \quad \text{or} \quad 13.2 \times 10^{24} \text{ lb}$$

The earth's mass is truly very great in comparison with the masses of familiar bodies on the earth. It is very small, on the other hand, when compared with the masses of stars like the sun.

THE DENSITY OF THE EARTH

Inasmuch as the earth is very nearly spherical, we can calculate its volume to a good approximation by means of the spherical formula, $V = \frac{4}{3}\pi r^3$. Insertion of suitable numerical values yields the result

Volume of the earth $= 1.09 \times 10^{27}$ cc

From the mass-volume data we can now estimate the earth's average density, and we discover a remarkable implication in the result.

Density is the ratio of mass to volume. In the case of water, for example, a specimen which occupies the volume 1 cc has a mass of 1 gram and so the density of water is 1. When we divide the mass of the earth by the volume of the earth, we get the overall density of the earth as

$$\text{Density of earth} = \frac{6 \times 10^{27} \text{ grams}}{1.09 \times 10^{27} \text{ cc}}$$

$$= 5.5 \text{ grams/cc}$$

What makes this result surprising is the fact that the rock materials which make up the bulk of the earth's outer crust have densities of about 3 grams per cubic centimeter or less! The inference which these dissimilar figures invites is plain enough. If the density of the earth as a whole is notably more than the density of its surface materials, then the interior of the earth must be composed of much more dense matter than the crust is. Most common metals have densities of 8 or more grams per cubic centimeter. If the earth's core consisted of solid iron and related metals (densities 7.9 to 8.9 grams per cubic centimeter), such a composition would be consistent with the rather high average density of the earth calculated from the total mass and volume. Meteorites are found in many cases to be chunks of nearly pure iron and nickel, and if we make the plausible assumption that our earth is de-

rived from similar cosmic stuff a high density is entirely reasonable.

DEDUCTION OF KEPLER'S LAWS FROM THE LAW OF GRAVITATION

It is now apparent that Kepler's laws led to the law of universal gravitation. Kepler's laws thereupon become consequences of this greater law. In the first place, Newton proved that, if a planet is attracted by a central force which diminishes in proportion to the square of its distance from the sun, then the planet will follow an elliptical path around the sun with the sun at one focus of the ellipse. (Note that a circle is

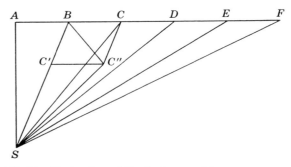

FIG. 54. Derivation of Kepler's second law.

merely a special ellipse having both foci coincident.) This was the type of planetary path discovered by Kepler and specified in his first law.

The law of gravitation also leads to Kepler's second law of equal areas as the following proof indicates.

Imagine a body moving with uniform speed along a straight line, AF (Fig. 54), the small, equal subdivisions of this line being the distances traversed each second. Then the triangles drawn are all equal in area, since they all have equal bases (AB, BC, etc.) and the common altitude AS.

Next suppose that at the end of each second a central force pulls the body in toward S. Then, at the end of 1 sec, with the body at B and due to reach C a second later, it is pulled inward toward S by the central force. If the body were stationary at point B, this force would displace it to C' during that second. But the body is not stationary at B. Instead it has two velocities—its original horizontal velocity as well as a radial velocity resulting from the pull toward S. These two velocities combine to transport it neither to C nor to C', but to C'', along the diagonal BC''

of the parallelogram $BCC''C'$. This is the familiar behavior of all bodies having velocities in two directions at once; they actually move in an intermediate direction with a speed related to the component speeds as the diagonal of the parallelogram is to its sides.

By elementary geometry we can see that the areas of triangles SBC'' and SBC are equal, for both have the same base SB, and their altitudes are equal because CC'' is parallel to BC'. But if triangle SBC'' equals triangle SBC it also equals triangle SAB, as already pointed out. Hence, the area swept over by the line from S to the moving body is the same in two successive seconds. It will, of course, be the same in subsequent seconds as long as the same factors prevail.

Now, instead of supposing the central pull to be exerted only at the *end* of each second, imagine it to occur at much shorter intervals. The foregoing proof remains unchanged, the triangles merely becoming much narrower and the path, which was a series of short straight lines, approaching a curve. If the central pull is *continuous,* the path *does* become a curve and the areas swept over in equal times by the lines to S are all equal. This is what Kepler's second law states for the planets moving around the sun, and the foregoing demonstration shows that the sun alone is the seat of the attracting force.

With regard to Kepler's third law, $T^2 = KR^3$, there is no need to prove that it is consistent with the gravitational law, since the latter was actually derived from it (see p. 93). It is true that in taking this step Newton assumed the orbit of the celestial body to be circular, but he proved later that the same relation holds when the orbit is elliptical.

APPLICATIONS OF THE LAW OF UNIVERSAL GRAVITATION

CALCULATION OF THE MASS OF THE SUN

If the earth is considered, for simplicity, to be whirling about the sun in a circular orbit, the centripetal force which the sun exerts on it may be expressed by the equation

$$F = m_E V^2 / R$$

where m_E is the mass of the earth, V is the speed of the earth in its orbit, and R is the radius of this orbit.

But the speed is also given by the ratio between the length of the orbit and the time required for the earth to traverse it. Thus

$$V = \frac{2\pi R}{T} \quad \text{and} \quad V^2 = \frac{4\pi^2 R^2}{T^2}$$

so that

$$F = m_E \frac{4\pi^2 R}{T^2}$$

The law of gravitation gives this same force as

$$F = G \frac{m_S m_E}{R^2}$$

where m_S is the mass of the sun.

By equating the two expressions for F we get

$$\frac{G m_S m_E}{R^2} = \frac{m_E 4\pi^2 R}{T^2}$$

whence

$$m_S = \frac{4\pi^2 R^3}{G T^2}$$

Inasmuch as m_E, the mass of the earth, cancels out, it is evident that the calculation of m_S could be accomplished equally well by reference to any planet at all by mere insertion of the appropriate period for T and of the appropriate orbital radius for R. The calculation is very slightly in error not only because we have assumed the mildly elliptical orbits to be circular but also because each planet is subject to additional gravitational pulls by the neighboring planets. These latter effects are very minute, however, in comparison with the pull exerted by the sun.

CALCULATION OF THE MASS OF A PLANET HAVING A SATELLITE

Any satellite which revolves about a planet may be treated in the same way that we have just used in dealing with a planet which revolves about the sun. It is necessary to know the distance between the centers of the satellite and planet and also the time required by the satellite to traverse its orbit. Calling these values r and t, respectively, we obtain from the last equation

$$m_P = \frac{4\pi^2 r^3}{G t^2}$$

The power of this reasoning is evident in the fact that the masses of all the planets except Mercury, Venus, and Pluto are known to a high degree of accuracy. The masses of Mercury and Venus, which have no moons, are not unknown, however; their masses are less accurately known because they are calculated from their gravitational attractions on neighboring planets.

Since the volumes of the planets can be calculated from their observed diameters, the densities of the planets are also known. In the following table the densities of the planets are compared to that of water, taken as 1 (from Bartky, *Highlights of Astronomy*, Chapter 4).

Mercury	3.8 (uncertain)
Venus	5.1 (uncertain)
Earth	5.5
Mars	4.0
Jupiter	1.3
Saturn	0.7
Uranus	1.4
Neptune	1.3
Pluto	unknown

These interesting variations in density pose very difficult problems for anyone desiring to explain the orgin of the solar system.

GRAVITATION AND TIDES

It is well known to all that the ocean waters in any locality gradually pile up to produce high tides and then fall away to give low tides in an orderly sequence which occurs about twice a day. Thus, a high tide is succeeded about six hours later by a low tide, which in turn is followed about six hours later still by another high tide, and so on. Small bodies of water exhibit minor tidal changes also, and weak tidal fluctuations are detectable even within the solid earth itself.

A detailed explanation of tides is exceedingly complex, for local topographic peculiarities strongly influence tidal magnitude and the tidal timetable at any one place. We shall discuss here only the elementary features of the oceanic tides insofar as they are controlled by purely gravitational factors.

The fact that tides are caused primarily by the moon and secondarily by the sun must have been known in ancient times. Early peoples can hardly have failed to note that each month, when the moon is either new or full (i.e., when it is in a direct line with the sun and the earth), high tides are exceptionally high and low tides are exceptionally low. Such tides are called "spring tides." When the moon is at either quarter and the difference between high and low water is a minimum, the tides are called "neap tides." Perhaps the most striking indication of the moon's preponderant role in tidal alternations comes from the time schedules. Since the moon completes a 360° revolution in 27.3 days it must advance about 13.2° in its orbit every day. The earth also advances in its orbit around the sun,

but only about 1° per day. The moon's net advance is therefore about 12.2° per day. This means that the earth must rotate on its axis about 372.2° between successive appearances of the moon over any one meridian. The earth requires about 24 hr and 50 min to rotate through 372.2°, and so it happens that, if the moon crosses a particular meridian at 8 o'clock tonight, it will not cross the same meridian tomorrow night until about 8:50.

Returning to the tidal schedule, high tide at a given place is followed by another high tide 12 hr and 25 min later and by still another 24 hr and 50 min later. The interval between successive high tides is thus half the period between successive appearances of the moon over the meridian.

It is one thing to observe a connection between the moon's apparent motion and quite another thing to explain the connection. In the *Principia* Newton showed that high tides occur because the ocean waters are heaped up into a huge mound by the gravitational attraction of the moon and to a smaller extent by that of the sun. Considering only the influence of the moon for the moment, it should be remarked first that two tidal bulges form simultaneously—one in the waters of that hemisphere which faces the moon and one in the waters of the opposite hemisphere. Put crudely, it may be stated that the moon pulls the nearer waters toward it to make a tidal bulge and that it also pulls the solid earth away from the remoter waters, thereby causing a tidal bulge on the opposite side.

Effect of the Earth's Rotation. The explanation given up to this point would suggest that a pair of permanent wave crests, or humps in the ocean, should form along the line joining the centers of the earth and moon. As the solid earth rotates beneath this distorted layer of ocean, an oceanside locality should pass successively through conditions of high water and conditions of low water at approximately 6-hr intervals. As the moon advances in its orbit, so do the tidal bulges, and, therefore, a place which has passed a high-water point at a certain time today will not reach the new position of high water tomorrow until nearly 25 hr later. That is, high tide at a given locality occurs approximately 1 hr later each day than it did the day before. It must be realized, however, that the spinning earth tends to carry the tidal wave crests around with it, and, because of friction between the ocean and the ocean bottom, this tendency is partially fulfilled. In consequence, the tidal crests never lie on a line passing through the centers of the earth and moon but always considerably in advance of it.

The gravitational effect of the moon alone is to raise the level of ocean water about 3 ft; that of the sun alone raises the level about 1 ft. Hence a spring tide is about 4 ft above normal water level, whereas a neap tide is only about 2 ft above normal level. Numerous factors besides those we have considered make a full explanation of tides extremely complex, especially along shore lines where the coastal contour, ocean currents, and merging river water may cause large variations from place to place. Moreover, the earth's distance from the sun and the moon is continually changing, and the moon also changes in its inclination to the ecliptic plane. All such changes make the gravitational effects of the sun and moon variable, so that no two successive tides could be quite the same, even if seasonal and topographical features played no part.

If, as astronomers believe, the moon was closer to the earth in early geologic times, it must then have produced much higher tides than we have now with eroding effects on the coast lines far greater than any tidal effect now observable.

THE MASS OF THE MOON

It is instructive to watch a hammer thrower practicing for an athletic meet. The hammer is a heavy ball attached to one end of a thin cable which has a handle at the other end. In preparing to hurl the hammer, the athlete swings it around in a circle before letting go, and we notice that he too must revolve in a smaller circle in order to accomplish this feat. In other words, he does not rotate in one spot but is himself swung around in a small orbit by the revolving ball. This mutual action is merely an example of the third law of motion for, as the man exerts centripetal force on the ball, so does the ball exert an equal centripetal force on the man. Two circles are thus described by the man and the ball about a common center, and, since the man's mass is much greater than the ball's mass, his circle is much smaller than the circle traversed by the ball. This statement will be proved presently. The earth and the moon comprise just such a system as the hammer thrower and the ball. Each body attracts the other and causes it to revolve about a point situated somewhere between their centers. Let us suppose that this

point is X in the diagram of Fig. 55. By the third law

Force by earth on moon = Force by moon on earth

or

$$F_E = F_M$$

Inasmuch as both forces are centripetal in character, we may replace each F by its equivalent, getting

$$\frac{m_E V_E^2}{R_E} = \frac{m_M V_M^2}{R_M}$$

where the m's stand for masses, as usual, and V_E and V_M are the respective speeds with which the

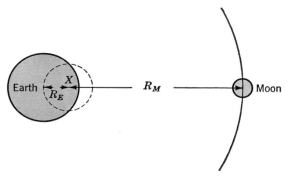

FIG. 55. The earth and the moon revolve around a common center X.

earth and moon move in their orbits. If we take these orbits to be circular, which is nearly the case, their circumferences will be $2\pi R_E$ and $2\pi R_M$, and if each body completes its orbit in the same time, T, the two speeds can be written as follows:

$$V_E = \frac{2\pi R_E}{T} \qquad V_M = \frac{2\pi R_M}{T}$$

Substituting these quantities in the last equation, we obtain

$$\frac{m_E 4\pi^2 R_E}{T^2} = \frac{m_M 4\pi^2 R_M}{T^2}$$

or

$$m_E/m_M = R_M/R_E$$

This result provides a means of finding the relative masses of the earth and moon, provided we can locate the common point about which the two bodies revolve. It is really this point, the center of gravity of the earth-moon system, rather than the center of the earth itself, which remains in the ecliptic plane as the earth and moon travel around the sun. The centers of the earth and moon slowly oscillate from one side of the ecliptic plane to the opposite side, as if they were joined together by a rigid bar.

Although the earth's center is never more than slightly off the ecliptic plane, its displacements from one side to the other are enough to be measurable. By observation of the nearer planets when the earth's center is above the ecliptic plane and again when it is below this plane, it is possible to locate the point which actually lies in the ecliptic plane, and this is the center of gravity needed for our calculation. It is found that the center of gravity of the earth-moon combination is situated about 1000 mi below the earth's surface. This point is thus about 3000 mi from the center of the earth and about 240,000 mi from the center of the moon. Inasmuch as the latter distance is 80 times the former, it follows that the moon is about $\frac{1}{80}$ as massive as the earth is.

THE SHAPE OF THE EARTH

It has already been stated in this account that the earth is not truly spherical. Its shape is more correctly that of a spheroid whose diameter from pole to pole is about 27 mi shorter than its equatorial diameter. No spinning body can remain spherical unless it is infinitely rigid, and undoubtedly the earth has acquired its equatorial bulge in consequence of its rotation. In Newton's day the size of the earth was known but its precise shape was not. A calculation of this shape was one of his accomplishments, and, although the difference between polar and equatorial radii which he obtained was somewhat in error, his recognition that there is such a difference led him to an explanation of the precession which the earth's axis undergoes. This was an achievement of very high order.

The weight of a body anywhere on the earth's surface depends on the acceleration of gravity ($W = mg$), and g is a quantity which can be measured with great precision by means of a pendulum. Gravitational acceleration and, hence, weight are less at the equator than at the poles for two reasons: (1) the centrifugal effect due to the earth's rotation is a maximum at the equator, and (2) a point on the equator is farther from the center of the earth than either pole is. We have learned how to calculate the centrifugal effect on a whirling body, and, by applying this calculation to a body lying on the equator, we find that the earth's rotation on its axis diminishes the weight of the object by about 0.35%. But experimental determinations of g at various

places indicate that an object at the equator actually weighs about 0.52% less than it would at either pole. It should accordingly be true that a loss in weight at the equator amounting to $0.52 - 0.35$ or 0.17% is due to the fact that points on the equator are farther from the center of the earth than points near the poles are. A double application of the equation of universal gravitation might be expected to give the amount of this difference in distance. It does not do so with any satisfactory degree of correctness for a number of reasons, chief among them being, probably, the fact that the density of the earth's interior is nowhere near uniform.

THE PRECESSION OF THE EQUINOX

We have already remarked that the earth does not quite encircle the sun between any one spring equinox and the next. In other words, at successive spring equinoxes the earth is not in exactly the same part of its orbit. This fact was first observed by the Greek astronomer Hipparchus around 150 B.C. What he did was to record the sun's position against the background of stars over many annual recurrences of the spring equinox and to note that this position advanced a little each year, so that about 20 min had to elapse between the moment of the equinox and the arrival of the sun at the equinoctial position it had occupied the year before. Copernicus, in the sixteenth century, rightly attributed this slight displacement to a corresponding shift in the direction of the earth's axis. This explanation can be understood by a study of the diagram in Fig. 56. Recall that the sun stands vertically

FIG. 56. The precession of the equinox.

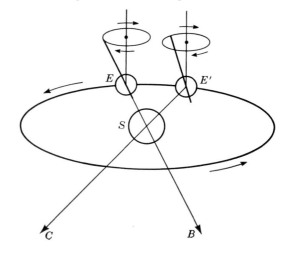

above the equator at the time of either equinox. The position of the earth in its orbit at, say, the spring equinox can be marked by means of a line *ESB* passing through the centers of the earth and sun to a distant star. If the earth's axis really maintained a fixed direction, then 1 yr later the earth would again be in the same position and the same line would extend to the same star.

Let us suppose, however, that the earth's axis were to undergo a change in direction during one incomplete revolution about the sun. Figure 56 illustrates this supposition. Starting at *E*, the earth is at spring equinox and the sun is directly above the equator. The earth moves around its orbit, passing through the summer solstice, the autumnal equinox, and the winter solstice a little sooner than it did before and eventually reaching *E'*, where the sun is once more above the equator owing to the shift in direction of the earth's axis. Arrival at *E'* marks the recurrence of spring equinox and the termination of the tropical year. A line *E'SC* through the centers of the earth and sun now extends to a different star. Astronomers use the word equinox to denote such points in the sky as *B* and *C*, and the shift from *B* to *C* is called a *precession of the equinox*. The motion described is a greatly exaggerated version of the earth's actual behavior. If the earth's axis could be prolonged far out into the heavens and its direction observed for several centuries, we should find this extended axis to be slowly tracing out a cone. Almost 26,-000 years would elapse before the line would sweep out a complete cone, yet the slow change in axial direction is sufficient to require the selection of a new polestar every few centuries.

It was Newton, as stated, who discovered the reason for the gradual change in the earth's axial direction. In order to make this reason clear, we shall describe a more familiar example in which the same type of motion is exhibited. Picture a top spinning about an axis which is inclined to the vertical as shown in Fig. 57. A stationary top so inclined would topple over, but a spinning top, although it *tends* to fall, does not succeed in doing so. Instead, its axis gyrates about a vertical line passing through the peg, thereby describing a conical figure whose apex is at the peg. This conical motion of the spinning top's axis is called *precession,* and it is due to the compounding of two angular velocities, the velocity of falling and the velocity of spinning.

The earth, too, is like a spinning top, whose spheroidal shape gives rise to forces which tend to diminish the axial tilt. These forces result from the sun's, and especially the moon's, gravitational pull on the equatorial bulge. Picture the earth, as in Fig. 58*a* with the moon on one side of the ecliptic plane. For convenience let us regard the earth as a true sphere which is girdled by a distinct mound along the equator. Then we can disregard the moon's attraction for the spherical core, since that force will act along a line through the earth's center, and confine our

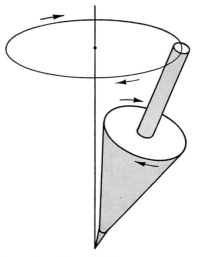

FIG. 57. Precession of a spinning top.

attention to the mound alone. Half of this mound is above and half below the ecliptic plane. Evidently the moon pulls on the nearer parts of the mound with greater force than it does on the remoter parts. In consequence, the resultant pull must act along a line which does not pass through the earth's center. This eccentric pull tends to right the earth by turning its equator into the ecliptic plane. As we have seen with the rotating top, this tendency is not fulfilled in the expected manner so long as the body is spinning. Instead, the earth's axis maintains its inclination to the ecliptic plane but slowly changes its direction in space. It is the gradual shifting of the axial direction that is called precession, and it takes place in a sense which is clockwise when viewed from above the North Pole.

In consequence of the very slow change in direction which the earth's axis undergoes, it follows that Polaris will not always be the earth's polestar. Indeed, it is not exactly that now, being about 1° away from the direction in which the earth's axis points.

Figure 58b attempts to show the change over a span of 4000 years. Looking upward along line CO of Fig. 58a, we see a portion of the northern sky with Ursa Major (Big Bear), Ursa Minor (Little Bear), and Draco (the Dragon) roughly outlined for ready reference to their constituent stars. Note that, since the precessional motion of the earth's axis is clockwise if seen from above point O (Fig. 58a), it must appear to be counter-clockwise if seen from the earth looking upward toward O (Fig. 58b).

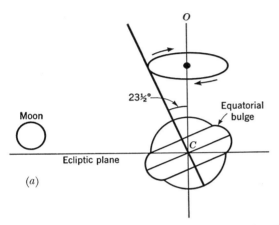

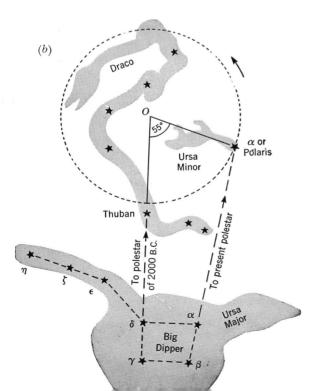

FIG. 58. (a) The moon, exerting a gravitational pull on the earth's equatorial bulge, causes the earth to precess. (b) 4000 years ago the polestar was not Polaris but Thuban. After Sir Oliver Lodge, *Pioneers of Science*, The Macmillan Co., 1928, p. 29.

Star α in Ursa Minor is our present polestar, Polaris. The pointers by which we locate Polaris are Dubhe and Merak (also designated α and β) in the Big Dipper of Ursa Major. But if we go back in time, say 4000 years, the direction of the equinox must have been about

$$\frac{4000}{26,000} \text{ of } 360 \quad \text{or} \quad 55°$$

away from its present one. On the diagram this would make the polestar of 2000 B.C. Thuban in the constellation Draco, otherwise known as α Draconis. At that time the pointers must have been those stars marking the other side of the Big Dipper, namely Phecta (γ) and Megrez (δ).

DISCOVERY OF URANUS AND NEPTUNE

One of the most dramatic consequences of the theory of gravitation was the discovery, long after Newton's time, of the planet Neptune. In 1781 William Herschel had discovered Uranus, the planet next more remote than Saturn. It has about 60 times the volume of the earth but is so far away that it can barely be seen by the naked eye. Its recognition as a planet was sensational in that this was the first planet to be discovered in modern times. Mercury, Venus, Mars, Jupiter, and Saturn had all been familiar objects to the earliest civilizations. Another surprising circumstance connected with Uranus is that the planet had been seen at least twenty times previously, as a re-examination of earlier records proved. All previous observers, however, had mistaken it for a faint star.

To the scientific world Uranus offered an opportunity for testing the gravitational law. Its complete orbit was soon calculated from the positions in which it had already been seen. Yet, as time went on, the new planet was found to be making small but measurable departures from its calculated path. After many alternative suppositions, Adams in England and Leverrier in France came independently to the conclusion that the deviations of Uranus were due to its attraction by some undiscovered planet. In our earlier consideration of planetary paths no mention was made of the effect one planet has upon another. For simplicity's sake it was assumed that the sun was the only body attracting them. It is indeed the principal source of attraction because of its enormous mass, but, if the law of universal gravitation is valid, the individual planets must certainly attract one another to some extent. Such attractions, called *perturbations,* were apparent to Newton and his successors and were duly allowed for in their calculations. Adams and Leverrier reasoned that the additional perturbing influence on Uranus must be *outside,* not inside; otherwise Saturn and even Jupiter would have been perturbed also. The problem of locating an unknown body of unknown mass and position merely from the slight, unaccounted deviations of Uranus was one of the greatest difficulty. Yet both Adams and Leverrier solved it, each unaware of the other's employment in this matter. Both placed it at about a billion miles from Uranus. Leverrier, in 1846, sent his estimate of the new planet's location to the German astronomer, Galle, who promptly observed the actual planet, Neptune, by telescope. No greater triumph of prediction for any scientific theory has ever been realized.

DISCOVERY OF PLUTO

Even Neptune does not account for all of the small deviations of Uranus, and Neptune itself deviates very slightly from its calculated path. From these small deviations, the American astronomer, Lowell, predicted the existence of another still more remote planet, which was discovered by Tombaugh at the Lowell observatory in 1930. This planet, Pluto, is very small and very distant. Its gravitational effects are not comparable with those of Neptune, and so its position could not be estimated with certainty. The actual sighting and identification of Pluto required many years of patient search.

THE EVOLUTION OF A THEORY

The sequence of contributions leading to the discovery of the law of universal gravitation furnishes an excellent example of how a theory evolves and ultimately yields new laws. Too many people believe that a complete theory suddenly comes into existence in a fit of inspiration, or clairvoyance, or revelation, like a bolt from the blue. Nothing could be farther from the truth. A theory is a completed logical structure resulting inductively from a sequence of contributions, some of which are logically derived and some of which are experimental and empirical. Note the following sequence in the discovery of the gravitation law:

1. Accumulation of data by Babylonian astonomers.
2. Refinement and addition of data by Tycho Brahe.
3. Announcement of the Copernican hypothesis.
4. Organization by Kepler of Tycho Brahe's data into three laws of planetary motion.
5. Statement by Newton of the law of gravitation.

This sequence does not present a picture of sudden inspiration but of slow evolution. The final theory was preceded by long years of painstaking observations and careful correlation of data by scientists before Newton. Only after these initial contributions had been made was the moment opportune for Newton, with great physical insight, to make his generalization.

The sequence above is a fine example of what we have called the inductive method. We are now in a position to show how the deductive method is applied. Let us add the following statements to the five above;

6. Prediction of the existence of Neptune by Adams and Leverrier.
7. Consequent discovery, by observation, of Neptune by Galle.
8. Prediction of the existence of Pluto by Lowell and Pickering.
9. Discovery of Pluto by Tombaugh.

These last additions to the sequence are obviously deductive in nature; the position of Neptune was almost exactly predicted by gravitation theory. The discovery of Pluto may be said to have been deductive also in the sense that its existence was suspected from what Lowell thought to be true perturbations.

It must now be noted that, without the inductive procedure which preceded Newton, the last deductive steps would have been impossible, and so it always is in the natural sciences; induction must come before deduction.

PROBLEMS

1. Calculate the acceleration of a body which is acted on by a single force equal to three times its weight.
Ans.   96 ft/sec².

2. Suppose that on some future week end on Mars you are invited to play a game of billiards. Remembering that Mars has only one-half the diameter of the earth and only one-tenth its mass, would you expect the game of billiards on Mars to be very different from one on earth? Assume that you would use the same equipment.

3. Using the data in Problem 2, compare the density of Mars with that of the earth. Would you conclude that Mars is made up of much the same material as that of the earth?

4. When a moving billiard ball collides head on with an identical stationary billiard ball, the first stops and the second suddenly acquires the velocity of the first. Show that this is consistent with the law of conservation of momentum.

5. Using Newton's second law and the law of universal gravitation, explain why a planet changes its speed as it moves in its elliptical orbit.

6. If a man weighs 175 lb on the earth, how much would he weigh on Mars?
Ans.   70 lb weight.

7. A car weighing 2400 lb is guaranteed by its manufacturer to accelerate from 30 mph to 50 mph in 15 sec with one 150-lb driver in the car. Calculate the maximum acceleration when six people of average weight 150 lb are in the car. How long will it then take to accelerate from 30 to 50 mph?
Ans.   Acceleration =1.03 mi/hr/sec.   Time =19.4 sec.

8. Neglecting air resistance, a bullet projected horizontally near the surface of the earth and with a velocity of about 5 mps will not reach the earth at all but will become an artificial satellite. Confirm this statement by calculation.

9. In Fig. 48*b* the lengths *OB* and *BD* are exaggerated to make the geometry clear. Calculate the true lengths of *OB* and *BD*. Are they really small with respect to the radius of the earth? Is the general proof weakened by the assumption that *OB* and *BD* are small?

10. At what point on a line between the moon and the earth would each of them exert the same gravitational pull upon a third body? Assume the mass of the earth to be 80 times that of the moon.
Ans.   24,000 mi from the moon.

11. One of the moons of Mars, Phobos, is about 6000 mi from the center of Mars and has a period of revolution of about 7.6 hr. From these data calculate the mass of Mars.
Ans.   About ¹⁄₁₀ the mass of the earth.

• •

REFERENCES

1. *A Source Book of Physics*, W. F. Magie, McGraw-Hill Book Co., 1935, pp. 30–46.
2. *The Autobiography of Science*, Forest R. Moulton and Justus J. Schifferes, Doubleday, Doran & Co., 1950, Part IV.

Work and Energy

We have deliberately postponed until now a consideration of the concept of energy because a satisfactory comprehension of energy is hardly possible without an understanding of such concepts as mass, force, and velocity. Nevertheless, in its popular usage, when we speak of food energy or the energy of fuels, it is the heat derivable from the food or fuel that we usually have in mind.

It is not to be supposed from this statement that heat and energy are entirely synonymous terms, for, although energy is very commonly manifested in the form known as heat, it may also take various other forms. Indeed, energy may be available without being manifested at all, as in the case of foods and fuels. If we compare a piece of coal with a piece of slate, there is nothing in their outward characteristics to indi-

PLATE XIX. Erection of an Egyptian obelisk in the Piazza di San Pietro in Rome in 1586. It is said that the operation required 800 workmen and 140 horses.

cate that one is a plentiful source of available energy, whereas the other is not. The coal might be described, somewhat inaccurately, as having energy stored up in it, awaiting the release which will occur if the coal is burned.

More careful consideration of the effects of eating food or burning fuel reminds us that they can do more than merely supply heat. Given a suitable mechanism, such as an automobile engine, fuels like gasoline can set resting bodies in motion. If the fuel tank goes dry, an automobile not only cools off; it also stops running. The human engine likewise consumes food in order to keep it running, as well as to keep it warm. Furthermore, manual laborers require more food than sedentary people do and in amounts dependent on the strenuousness of the labor. Since it can be shown that fuels and food do not suffer any loss in mass when they are consumed, there is apparently some non-material constituent latent in such substances which can be transformed into heat and which is also necessary for the performance of work. It is this latter activity which enables us to arrive at a simple and rigorous definition of energy once we have rigorously defined the term *work*.

WORK

Of the numerous meanings associated with this common word, only one is valid in the mechanical sense, namely:

Work is performed when a body is moved against a resisting force.

To illustrate, if an object at rest on the floor is lifted to a table top, the operation involves work. The resisting force in such a case is the weight of the object, and an upward force equal to the weight must be applied to the object in order to perform the work. The *amount* of work is described as the product of this force by the height through which the object is raised.

$$\text{Work} = \text{Weight} \times \text{Height}$$

Suppose, on the other hand, that the object were pushed or pulled along the floor by application of a horizontal force. The minimum force needed to accomplish such a displacement is usually very much less than the weight of the object, its magnitude depending on the smoothness of the surfaces in contact. If both object and floor are smooth, a small force will suffice to move the object, for only a slight frictional resistance has to be overcome. If either the object or the floor is rough, there will be considerable fric-

tional resistance and the force needed to move the object is greater. In any case the product of the applied force and the distance through which the object is moved expresses the work.

A third example points up the fact that force and distance must be measured in the same direction. A boy pulling a sled along a horizontal surface is likely to pull obliquely on the rope so that he does not have to bend over. But an oblique pull, as pictured in Fig. 59, is partly a lifting force, and only the component $F \cos A$ is effective in moving the sled horizontally. Hence, the work done for a displacement amounting to s units is no longer Fs but $Fs \cos A$. For gener-

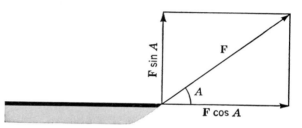

FIG. 59. Work done in pulling the sled is equal to distance times $\mathbf{F} \cos A$.

ality, therefore, it is best to symbolize work by $Fs \cos A$ and then, for cases in which F is actually applied in the same direction as s, A becomes zero, $\cos A$ becomes 1, and the expression $Fs \cos A$ reduces to Fs. Hence, greater generality is achieved by the introduction of $\cos A$.

Let us now summarize the definition of work by stating:

If a body is displaced from one position to another by the continuous application of a constant force, then the force performs work on the body in amount expressed by Fs cos A, where F is the magnitude of the constant force, s is the distance traversed by the body, and A is the angle between the direction of the force and the direction in which the body moves.

In the event that the applied force is not constant, the work may be computed by taking the product of the distance traversed and a suitable *average* force.

UNITS OF WORK

Since work is the product of force and distance, any force unit multiplied by a distance unit makes an acceptable unit of work. Thus, 1 dyne-centimeter expresses the work done when 1 dyne of force displaces a body through 1 cm of distance. This amount of work is better known, however, by the name especially coined for it—the *erg*.

$$1 \text{ erg} = 1 \text{ dyne-cm}$$

so that, for example, a force of 1000 dynes which moves a body 50 cm in its own direction accomplishes 50,000 ergs of work.

Inasmuch as the erg is an inconveniently small amount of work, it is customary to employ a larger unit—the joule (pronounced jool)—as a more practical standard.

$$1 \text{ joule} = 10,000,000 \text{ ergs, i.e., } 10^7 \text{ ergs}$$

POWER

Another concept which is very useful in solving mechanical problems is called *power*. It is simply the time rate of doing work, that is, the total work done divided by the time required to perform the work. There are a great many units for power, since any of the common work and time units may be selected. For example, if 550 lb of mass were lifted vertically through a distance of 1 ft every second, the rate of doing work would be called *one horsepower*. In the metric system, a very common power unit is so defined that the rate of doing work is 1 joule per second. This power unit is called the *watt*.

ENERGY

Anything which is capable of performing work possesses energy, and the *amount* of energy it possesses is determined by the amount of work it can perform. Energy is expressed in the same units as work, e.g., in ergs or joules.

Furthermore, although work cannot be performed without the expenditure of an equivalent amount of energy, it does not follow that the expenditure of energy must result in the performance of equivalent mechanical work. The fuel intended for operating the hoisting engine might be used merely to feed a bonfire and its latent capacity for work dissipated as heat. It is thus apparent that energy and work are related in a way which is roughly parallel to the role of money in human affairs. A person may have savings which represent potential spending capacity. He may hoard the savings; he may spend them for necessities; he may squander all or any part of them. In like manner energy represents potential work, and it may be hoarded, converted into useful mechanical work, or squandered in the sense of being transformed into some less useful form of energy such as heat.

It may now be noted that the mere supporting of a burden, that is, the exertion of force without a consequent displacement, is excluded from the category of mechanical work. A porter who holds a trunk on his shoulder does no mechanical work, even though the task tires him. The trunk could be supported equally well by the floor without the expenditure of any energy and a feat which does not require the spending of energy cannot be regarded as work.

KINETIC ENERGY

The criterion by which energy is recognized as such is its ability to be transformed into work. The simplest example of work is undoubtedly

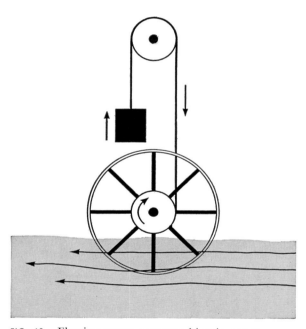

FIG. 60. Flowing water possesses kinetic energy.

the lifting of a load. But matter in motion can be made to lift a load, as shown in Fig. 60, where water flowing along a river causes a water wheel or turbine to rotate and thereby lift a weight. Because of its ability to perform work, any body in motion possesses energy. The energy of a moving body is called *kinetic energy*.

POTENTIAL ENERGY

An elevated body can also do work, for, when its support is removed, the body falls with continually increasing speed. Thus, it acquires kinetic energy in falling, and, by means of a suitable mechanism, this kinetic energy can lift a load or perform other kinds of work. The energy of an elevated body is called *potential energy*.

Similarly, a spring or other elastic body under tension is said to possess potential energy because it can do work when the tension is relaxed. An unburned fuel contains potential energy by virtue of its chemical structure. Finally, we must not neglect to mention the most spectacular example of all, the atomic nucleus, which releases enormous amounts of energy in disintegrating, and sometimes in forming. Potential energy is therefore *stored* or *latent* energy.

CONSERVATION OF MECHANICAL ENERGY

When an elevated body is allowed to fall toward the earth, it steadily loses the potential energy which it had at its greatest elevation; but its speed of descent increases progressively, so that it continually gains kinetic energy. We wish now to show that the decrease in potential energy is exactly compensated by the increase in kinetic energy. In other words, the total mechanical energy of a falling body remains constant throughout the fall. In order to prove this point, we need a mathematical expression for kinetic energy as well as one for potential energy.

Imagine a very smooth object lying on a very smooth horizontal surface so that there is practically no frictional resistance to be overcome in moving the object. The application of a constant horizontal force, F, will cause the object to move with continually increasing velocity. Suppose that the object has attained the velocity, v, by the time it has covered the distance, s. The work done on the object is Fs or, since $F = ma$,

$$\text{Work} = mas$$

Recalling now that acceleration is the time rate at which velocity changes, if the object gained the velocity, v, in t seconds, its acceleration can be written as $a = v/t$. Also, if the object had no velocity at the start but it gained the velocity, v, during t seconds, its average velocity throughout the interval must have been $v/2$. Hence, the distance, s, can be expressed as the average velocity multiplied by the time.

$$s = \frac{v}{2}t$$

On replacing a and s in the work equation by these expressions, we get

$$\text{Work} = m\frac{v}{t}\frac{v}{2}t = \tfrac{1}{2}mv^2$$

Since friction was disregarded in this experiment, it is evident that all the work was spent in speeding up the object and giving it kinetic energy equal to $\tfrac{1}{2}mv^2$.

The foregoing expression is general enough so that, whenever we have occasion to evaluate the kinetic energy of any moving body, we shall do so by writing

$$\text{Kinetic energy} = \tfrac{1}{2}mv^2$$

Only the magnitude of velocity (i.e., speed) is considered in reckoning kinetic energy.

The relation between work and kinetic energy is so important that a numerical illustration will be profitable at this point. Let us suppose that the object in question has a mass of 1 kg (i.e., 1000 grams) and that a steady horizontal force of 50,000 dynes acts on it for 12 sec.

Assuming friction to be negligible, the constant acceleration of the object is

$$a = \frac{F}{m} = \frac{50,000}{1000} = 50 \text{ cm/sec}^2$$

and the speed attained at the end of 12 sec is

$$v = at = (50)(12) = 600 \text{ cm/sec}$$

The *average* speed ($\bar{v}$) must therefore have been 600/2 or 300 cm/sec, and the horizontal distance covered in 12 sec was

$$s = \bar{v}t = (300)(12) = 3600 \text{ cm}$$

We can now compute the work which the force has accomplished in moving the object 3600 cm from its starting position and getting it up to the speed of 600 cm/sec.

$$\text{Work} = Fs = (50,000)(3600)$$
$$= 18 \times 10^7 \text{ ergs} = 18 \text{ joules}$$

Let us find also the amount of kinetic energy possessed by the object when its speed has reached 600 cm/sec.

$$\text{K.E.} = \tfrac{1}{2}mv^2 = \tfrac{1}{2}(1000)(600)^2$$
$$= 18 \times 10^7 \text{ ergs} = 18 \text{ joules}$$

This result confirms our previous assertion—that, if none of the applied force has to be used to overcome frictional resistance, all the work done on the object becomes kinetic energy.

Suppose now that the moving body is brought to rest by the application of a constant horizontal force opposing its motion. Let this force be 25,-000 dynes. The resulting deceleration is

$$a = \frac{F}{m} = \frac{25,000}{1000} = 25 \text{ cm/sec}^2$$

and the time required to stop the moving object is

$$t = \frac{v}{a} = \frac{600}{25} = 24 \text{ sec}$$

As before, the average speed during the reduction of motion to zero is 300 cm/sec, so that the distance which the object traverses in coming to rest is

$$s = \bar{v}t = (300)(24) = 7200 \text{ cm}$$

But the work done in stopping the object is the constant force times the distance traversed or

$$\text{Work} = Fs = (25,000)(7200)$$

$$= 18 \times 10^7 \text{ ergs or 18 joules}$$

the result being that as much work is done by the object in stopping as was done in the first place to bring the object to its maximum speed. This work in both cases equals the maximum kinetic energy which the object acquired.

Note that, inasmuch as work is the product of two factors, force and distance, the same work may always be done by a small force acting over a large distance as is done by a large force acting over a proportionately smaller distance.

We can now calculate the potential and the kinetic energies of an object which is falling toward the earth. If the object has the mass m grams, its weight is mg dynes, and to raise it to a height, h, above the ground would require work amounting to mgh ergs. Consequently, mgh is the amount of potential energy possessed by the elevated object.

The object is now allowed to fall, and we consider its energy at the instant when it has descended y centimeters. By then it has evidently lost mgy ergs of potential energy. On the other hand it has gained kinetic energy to the amount of $\frac{1}{2}mv^2$. Here v is the vertical velocity acquired during the time the object has been falling, and it can be expressed by $v = gt$, whence $v^2 = g^2t^2$; whereas the distance fallen is given by $y = \frac{1}{2}gt^2$. Eliminating t^2 from the two equations,

$$v^2 = g^2 \frac{2y}{g} = 2gy$$

It follows that the kinetic energy gained is

$$\tfrac{1}{2}mv^2 = \tfrac{1}{2}m2gy = mgy$$

But this is just the amount of potential energy lost in falling through the height, y. Therefore the potential energy lost equals the kinetic energy gained. Another way of stating this result is that the sum of the potential energy and the kinetic energy at any point in the descent is constant. We emphasize this statement by a numerical example.

Let an object of 2000 grams mass be allowed to fall from a height of 7840 cm. In the absence of air resistance it should take 4 sec for the object to reach the ground, inasmuch as $g = 980$ cm/sec^2 and $h = \frac{1}{2}gt^2$,

$$7840 = \tfrac{1}{2}(980)(4)^2$$

The kinetic and potential energy of the object at the end of each second are given in Table 4.

TABLE 4

Time, Elapsed, sec	Height, cm	Velocity Attained, $v = gt$, cm/sec	Kinetic Energy, K.E. = $\frac{1}{2}mv^2$, joules	Potential Energy, P.E. = mgh, joules	Total Energy, K.E. + P.E., joules
0	7840	0	0	1537	1537
1	7350	980	96	1441	1537
2	5880	1960	384	1153	1537
3	3430	2940	865	672	1537
4	0	3920	1537	0	1537

It may be concluded from these results that a body falling through empty space has a constant amount of mechanical energy at all points on its downward journey.

The question now presents itself: what becomes of this energy when the body strikes the ground? For the moment let us explain the situation qualitatively. If the body rebounds, it evidently reacquires potential energy, although never in the amount which it had originally; the height of rebound is always less than the height from which the body fell. It is observed, moreover, that when bodies collide with each other their temperatures rise. This observation suggests that the mechanical energy lost when a moving body comes to rest may have been converted into the form of energy which we call *thermal energy* or *heat*.

It should be noted that the mere detection of heat in a body whose motion has been reduced to zero is not proof that a conversion of mechanical energy into heat has occurred. Only by the establishment of a *quantitative* relation between the kinetic energy which disappears and the thermal energy which is generated simultaneously can we safely assert that such conversion has taken place. Many delicate and painstaking experiments have been conducted during the past century for the purpose of confirming the suspected relation between kinetic energy and heat. The outcome of this protracted work has convinced all scientists that mechanical and thermal energy are transformable into each other in a fixed ratio. When a moving body is brought to rest and its kinetic energy vanishes, heat energy in equivalent amount develops in its stead. Granting the correctness of this result, it may now be asserted that in such operations as we have described energy is *conserved* in amount, altering only in its form. An object is raised to an elevated position. This requires the performance of a definite quantity of work. The elevated object now has this amount of potential energy. When it is allowed to fall to the earth, the object steadily loses potential energy but gains an equal amount of kinetic energy, and this in turn is transformed into heat energy when the fallen body imbeds itself in the ground.

Extensive experimentation with energy in other forms (magnetic, electrical, radiant) has shown that this same principle of energy conservation appears to be universal. No exception has yet been found to the general statement:

Energy may be converted from one form into other forms, but it cannot be destroyed. The total amount of energy in the universe remains constant.

It may be objected that this statement is altogether too sweeping to be warranted by the known facts. What if scientists have tested the claim a few thousand times without contradiction? Does that rule out the possibility that exceptions may occur? To be sure it does not. The principle that energy is always conserved has not been established by any general proof; one can only record the persistent failure of all attempts to disprove it. Assertion of the energy conservation principle aptly exemplifies the inductive method of science, whereby a very broad generalization is derived from numerous specific cases and is then assumed to hold for myriads of untried cases. But, even after the inductive generalization has been established, it is thereafter continually exposed to challenge. Every subsequent confirmation of its correctness strengthens the likelihood that still further tests will also confirm it.

The conservation of energy principle, which was first stated by the German physiologist Helmholtz (1821–1894), is generally regarded as the cornerstone of physical science. It is the basis of numerous derived laws, and it frequently simplifies the solution of complex problems. We shall take suitable occasions to invoke the principle as new topics are considered.

PROBLEMS

1. Suppose that in a tug of war the sides are so evenly matched that neither is able to move the rope. How much mechanical work is done? Is your answer consistent with the personal feelings of the participants in the tug of war? Explain.

2. Inasmuch as the sun exerts gravitational force on the earth as the earth revolves around the sun, is it correct to say that the sun does work on the earth? If so, what is the source of the energy required for the performance of such work? Explain.

3. How much momentum has a body of 500 grams if it is moving with kinetic energy amounting to 100 joules?
Ans. 1,000,000 gram-cm/sec.

4. At a speed of 30 mph the brakes of a particular car can bring it to rest in 100 ft without skidding. (*a*) Assuming that the brakes are applied in the same way, how long a distance is needed for stopping at 60 mph? (*b*) How many times larger is the kinetic energy of the car at 60 mph?
Ans. (*a*) 400 ft. (*b*) 4 times.

5. In an experiment, a moving steel sphere was allowed to collide head on with a stationary steel sphere having only one-half the mass of the first. It was found that after collision the velocity of the large sphere had been reduced to one-third of its original velocity, whereas the smaller sphere had acquired velocity equal to 4/3 the original velocity of the large sphere. Are these facts consistent with the law of conservation of momentum? With the law of conservation of energy? Ignoring the law of conservation of energy, might there be other velocities after the collision which would satisfy the law of conservation of momentum?

6. A ball made of soft clay collides head on with an identical clay ball so that the two stick together. It is a fact that after collision the two balls will then move with a velocity equal to one-half the original velocity of the first ball. Are these facts consistent with the law of conservation of momentum? With the law of conservation of energy? Ignoring the law of conservation of energy, might there be other velocities after the collision which would satisfy the law of conservation of momentum? The second clay ball is assumed stationary before collision.

7. From your answers to Problems 5 and 6, would you conclude that the law of conservation of momentum and the law of conservation of energy are derivable from each other?

. . . .

An Experiment in Mechanics

DEFINITION OF EXPERIMENT

A good deal has been said up to this point about the method of experiment, but we still lack a detailed answer to the question: "what is meant by an experiment in the natural sciences?" Such an explanation is all the more necessary because the word "experiment," like many scientific terms, is not unique to science but one which has meanings in popular language rather different from the restricted meaning which the term conveys to the scientist.

For example, an experiment, in popular usage, is anything hitherto untried. If the government issues a new coin of unusual denomination, say, a $12\frac{1}{2}$ cent coin, this is immediately labeled an experiment in currency. If a person who seeks to improve his health begins the practice of drinking ten glasses of water a day or of eating lettuce at every meal, he believes this to be an experiment in dietetics. By the same token a child who mixes all the condiments in the pantry to see what the concoction will taste like is performing an experiment. In a certain sense any deliberately novel experience can be called an experiment. The scientist's experiment, however, differs from mere haphazard trial in that it is a carefully planned program to investigate some aspect of nature in the hope of discovering new phenomena or, in the case of a phenomenon already known, to ferret out related phenomena and possibly quantitative relationships among the factors which contribute to the phenomenon.

Any occurrence in nature, usual or unusual, is called a *phenomenon*. Note that popular usage reserves this term for extraordinary or incomprehensible events. Occasionally the word is even used to characterize places or structures, so long as they are abnormal. Thus, the Mammoth Cave of Kentucky and the Natural Bridge of Virginia are called natural phenomena. In contrast, the scientist speaks of the falling of an object, the expansion of a heated gas, or the stretching of a spiral spring as a phenomenon.

Experimentation may be divided into two stages. In the preliminary stage the experimenter, after deciding what phenomenon he wishes to investigate, arranges for it to occur under conditions which he can vary, one by one. In controlling conditions, he is hopeful of relating any observed effects to the proper variables. In social "experiments" it is frequently impossible to control conditions with certainty or to vary them according to the will of the experimenter.

The second stage, usually quantitative, is an attempt to measure the influence of those factors which have been found in the first stage to be related to the phenomenon. The purpose here is to discover the pattern or law which seems to govern the natural occurrence. If the underlying law can be expressed as a mathematical relation among the factors which enter into the phenomenon, the investigator considers that he has made important progress, for his creed includes a faith that nature in all its seeming complexity conforms to a set of principles or laws whereby the same results always follow when the same conditions obtain.

As an illustration of the preliminary stage of experimenting, let us suppose that an investigation of magnetism is undertaken. Implicit in this statement is the element of selection. A particular property of certain materials, the magnetic property, has been chosen for study, and the experimenter proposes to confine his attention to that. He has already qualified his project as an experiment by giving it a purpose; this is different from merely hit or miss tinkering with things to see what will happen. Perhaps he selects a magnetized steel spike for the study. He tries its effect on a number of small metallic objects brought close to it. He suspends the spike by a thread and observes how it oscillates until aligned approximately with the north-south meridian. He dangles the spike by its thread near a wire through which electric current is flowing. He hits the spike with a hammer or holds it in a flame to find out whether the magnetism is weakened or enhanced. He places the spike at various distances from a similarly magnetized spike and sets the two in various orientations toward each other. These and numerous other experiences teach him certain characteristics of magnetized bodies and perhaps suggest a hypothesis which tentatively explains the magnetic behavior. This brings him to the second stage of experimentation, which is often a deliberately planned test of the experimenter's hypothesis.

A test of the inverse square feature of gravitational attraction is typical of the later stage of the experimental process. Preliminary observation or, in this example, a deduction from Kepler's third law, may have provided the tentative hypothesis that $F = K/d^2$. In preparation for the test one tries to make sure that no forces other than the gravitational one shall play a part, and so precautions are taken to eliminate air drafts, magnetic or electric effects among the test materials, and all other known factors which might complicate the observation. Experience warns that gravitational attraction is very small between bodies of moderate mass and so he is impelled to choose objects which are as massive as possible and to place them close together, so that they will exert as great a force on each other as possible. All such considerations are carefully contemplated by the experimenter while he plans the apparatus and the method of the experiment. He may conclude that the behavior of two large metal spheres suspended by cords in close proximity to each other offers the best means of testing the hypothesis expressed by $F = K/d^2$. The angle through which the suspending cords converge in consequence of the gravitational attraction exerted by each sphere on the other becomes the means of calculating the attractive force. Measurement of this angle when the spheres are hung at various short distances from each other supplies the data by which the inverse square relation is verified.

A well-conceived experiment should give an unambiguous answer to the question which the experimenter asks of nature. This demands that the effects be great enough and the instruments sensitive enough for reliable measurement. No experiment is conclusive unless it is reproducible by others as well as by its originator, and so the record must be meticulously correct, especially as regards the extent of deviations between successive measurements of the same factor. All recorded data should therefore include the experimental error, which is the combination of uncertainties in the observed magnitudes of the various factors. Such uncertainties inevitably enter into the data through the sensory shortcomings of the observer as well as through the limitations of the apparatus.

It need scarcely be pointed out that a great many important facts and phenomena have been discovered without the formal procedures which have just been described. Experimentation in the natural sciences, like all intellectual experience, is a complex combination of many factors that are planned and many that are accidental—or seem so. Nevertheless, it is helpful to examine those characteristics which are most evident in experiments, and perhaps this is best done by example.

We shall now propose an experiment which embraces both the preliminary investigating phase and the quantitative verification of a hypothesis. This experiment may be entitled "A Study of the Simple Pendulum."

A STUDY OF THE SIMPLE PENDULUM

A compact body suspended at one end of a cord whose other end is fastened to a hook in the ceiling makes an approximation to a simple pendulum. Ideally the mass of the body or *bob* should be concentrated at a single point, but if it is a small homogeneous sphere its distributed mass is affected by gravity almost as if the mass were all located at the center of the sphere. When the pendulum is held a little to one side of its position of rest and then released, it begins to oscillate with what is called simple harmonic motion. Starting with the pendulum bob hanging vertically below the point of suspension, we displace it slightly so that the bob oscillates in a vertical plane and measure with a stopwatch the time it consumes in making, say, 25 complete trips backward and forward along the same arc. The maximum angular displacement of the bob is called the *amplitude* of the oscillation, and this should be noted.

The measurement of time should be repeated for several sets of 25 oscillations with the same amplitude and the times recorded separately.

The same observations may now be made with a change of amplitude and again with a third and fourth amplitude in order to discover whether or not this factor affects the time of oscillation.

Other factors may now be varied, one at a time. For example, the pendulum bob may be replaced by another sphere of the same material but of different mass and a set of observations obtained for the new bob using a cord of the old length and one of the amplitudes tested previously. Next the bob may be replaced by one of the same mass but of different material and the measurements repeated.

A set of observations made at some place of considerably different altitude should be taken in order to learn whether a variation in g (the acceleration of gravity) affects the period of the pendulum.

The effect of varying the length of the pendulum should be investigated. Since the mass of the bob responds to gravity in the same way as if it were all located at the center of the sphere, the length should be measured from the point of suspension to the center of the sphere. This is conveniently done by measuring the length of the exposed cord with a meter stick and the diameter of the sphere with calipers. Half the diameter is then added to the length of the cord in order to get the length of the simple pendulum.

The observer is soon convinced from these preliminary observations that the only variable factor which affects the time of swing appreciably is the length of the pendulum, provided the amplitude is small and the measurements are all made at the same place. When this conclusion has been reached, he is ready for a more exhaustive study of the relation between time and length. This will consist merely of a repetition of the timing with the bob suspended by different lengths of cord, but the number of oscillations in each trial may be increased to 100 so as to diminish the error in timing. Division of the observed time by the number of complete swings gives the observed *period* for each length of cord used.

TABLE 5.   PERIOD OF A SIMPLE PENDULUM

Length of Cord, cm	Radius of Bob, To Be Added, cm	Length of Pendulum, L, cm	Time of 100 Full Swings, sec	Period, T, sec	Square of Period, T^2
15.4 ± 0.05	0.5 ± 0.005	15.9	80.6 ± 0.5	0.806 ± 0.005	0.650
24.3		24.8	100.4	1.004	1.01
41.5		42.0	131.0	1.310	1.72
55.4		55.9	149.8	1.498	2.24
80.3		80.8	180.7	1.807	3.27
98.7		99.2	200.2	2.002	4.01
119.6		120.1	224.0	2.240	5.02
155.1		155.6	251.7	2.517	6.34
195.2		195.7	283.0	2.830	8.01

Diameter of bob: 1.026 cm.
Radius of bob: 0.513 cm.

Table 5, on p. 115, shows possible data for the experiment. All entries in the actual record should include the uncertainty in the measurement. Thus, if the length can be measured only to the nearest millimeter (0.1 cm), a typical entry would be 55.4 ± 0.05 cm. When time permits, each measurement of length and the corresponding measurement of time should be repeated several times and the observed values averaged. The maximum deviation of each set from the average may be called the error for that set. The average error in length should be divided by the median of the length to obtain the fractional error in length. The fractional error multiplied by 100 is the per cent error in length; the per cent error in time should be obtained similarly.

Note that the values listed in the last column contain at most three figures, even though the square of any T value, say $T = 2.83$ (which is 8.0089), may contain more than three figures. The reason for the exclusion of the final digits is that we may not imply greater refinement in the values of T^2, which are derived, than we actually possess in the values of T, which are measured.[1] Also, if the exposed cord was found by the meter stick to measure 15.4 cm, whereas the radius of the bob as determined by the calipers was 0.513 cm, the length of the pendulum is reported, not as

$$15.4 + 0.513 = 15.913 \text{ cm}$$

but as

$$15.4 + 0.5 = 15.9 \text{ cm}$$

. . . .

[1] Actually, the per cent error in T^2 is twice as great as the per cent error in T.

If the cord length cannot be measured to greater reliability than the nearest 0.1 cm, the total length will not be reliable to more than the nearest 0.1 cm either.

INTERPRETATION OF TABLE

A convenient way of identifying an unknown relation is a graphic one. Having obtained a table of data showing corresponding values of two related factors, we may plot these values as points on cross-ruled paper and then draw a curve through or near these points. If a mathematical relation between the variables is anticipated, the curve should be drawn smoothly even if it fails to pass through every point. A sample graph of the pendulum data showing periods (T) plotted against lengths (L) is reproduced in Fig. 61. The curve appears to be of parabolic type and suggests that the relation sought may be expressible as $T^2 = kL$, where k is a proportionality constant. Acting on this hint, we might try next the plotting of T^2 against L and, if our surmise was correct, the points on this new graph should lie approximately along a straight line as in Fig. 62.

In plotting a graph it is always advantageous to choose those variables which have a linear relationship to each other, for a straightedge may then be used to draw the straight line that will best represent the observed points.

In the pendulum experiment we appear to have been groping blindly for a relationship not previously suspected of existing. The first operations were indeed conducted by trial and error as if to learn by chance what factors influence the

FIG. 61. Relation between T and L for a pendulum.

FIG. 62. Relation between T^2 and L for a pendulum.

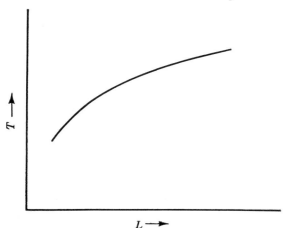

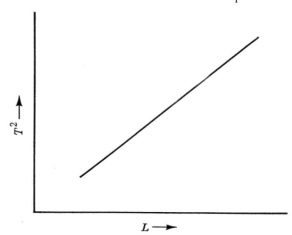

period of a pendulum. Actually in this case the pertinent factors can be identified in advance by mathematical derivation from fundamental principles, so that the experimenter merely verifies a relationship already suggested to him on theoretical grounds. This relationship shows that the period of a simple pendulum depends only on its length and on the acceleration of gravity at the place of trial.

DIMENSIONS

We shall omit the formal derivation as beyond our present purpose, but it will be instructive to see how the relationship between period, length, and acceleration of gravity must be consistent with the dimensions of the factors involved.

Suppose that we have convinced ourselves that the period is indeed determined by the gravitational acceleration g and the length of the pendulum. Then, provisionally, we may write

The period is a function of gravitational acceleration and length.

When this relation is ultimately developed into an equation, its components must be expressed in such units that the physical *dimensions* on both sides will be identical. Thus, if the period is expressed in seconds, the combination of acceleration and length must also be expressed in units of time, say, seconds. Since we do not know to what powers the dimensions of acceleration and length occur, we represent these unknown powers by the symbols x and y. The relation

the period of a pendulum is a function of the gravitational acceleration and the length of the pendulum

may then be translated into the dimensional identity

$$\text{Seconds} \equiv \left[\frac{\text{Centimeters}}{(\text{Seconds})^2} \right]^x \times [\text{Centimeters}]^y$$

Considering first the dimension of time, it appears to the first power on the left side of the dimensional equation and to the $-2x$ power on the right side. In the final result both must be the same. Therefore,

$$\sec^1 \equiv \sec^{-2x}$$

or

$$1 = -2x$$

and

$$x = -\tfrac{1}{2}$$

Considering next the dimension of distance, we see that this does not appear at all on the left side of the dimensional equation whereas it appears to the power $x + y$ on the right side. Therefore,

$$\text{cm}^0 \equiv \text{cm}^{x+y}$$

or

$$0 = x + y$$

and

$$y = -x = +\tfrac{1}{2}$$

The *units* in the ultimate equation must therefore be

$$\sec \equiv \left(\frac{\text{cm}}{\sec^2} \right)^{-\frac{1}{2}} \times (\text{cm})^{\frac{1}{2}}$$

Symbols for the period, the acceleration of gravity, and the length of the pendulum can now be introduced, each qualified by the exponents just discovered. Thus

$$T \equiv g^{-\frac{1}{2}} L^{\frac{1}{2}}$$

or

$$T \equiv \sqrt{L/g} \qquad \text{in dimensions}$$

In writing this symbolic relation, we have remembered that, even though the *units* of T, L, and g must be identical on both sides of the proportionality symbol, the relation itself is not necessarily an *equation*. It is more likely to be a *proportionality*, with the constant of proportionality undetermined by the dimensional analysis. Also, it is important to note that, in more complicated cases, several combinations of the various units may yield the correct resultant dimension even though only one of these combinations is consistent with experimental facts.

Theory and experiment indicate that the *complete* relation for a simple pendulum is

$$T = 2\pi \sqrt{L/g}$$

where 2π is the constant needed to convert the proportionality into an equation.

PROBLEMS

1. Plot on graph paper the curves suggested by Figs. 61 and 62, using the actual experimental data given in Table 5. If you had to estimate the value of the period for a pendulum 5 cm long, which curve would you choose? Such guessing, outside the region where actual data exists, is called *extrapolation*. Do you foresee any dangers in such extrapolation? Explain.

2. The straight-line relation represented in Fig. 62 can be written

$$T^2 = kL$$

where k is the slope of the line. Assuming the true relation to be

$$T = 2\pi\sqrt{L/g}$$

k should be equal to $4\pi^2/g$. Obtain the value of k from your graph, and from it calculate g.

3. Suppose that in the laboratory two separate phenomena have been investigated and that the data have been recorded as follows:

Phenomenon I		Phenomenon II	
t, sec	d, ft	F, dynes	d. cm
1.5	36.0	0.0167	20
2.1	70.6	0.0107	25
3.4	185.0	0.00741	30
4.3	295.8	0.00545	35
5.1	416.2	0.00417	40
6.2	615.0	0.00330	45
		0.00266	50

Plot on graph paper the values of t against d for phenomenon I, and from the appearance of the curve make reasonable guesses as to the equation which represents the true relation between the variables t and d. Plot these guesses until, as in Fig. 62, a straight line results. Determine the numerical value and the dimensions of the slope of this line. From this analysis, can you tell what phenomenon was being investigated? Repeat this procedure for phenomenon II.

Heat and Kinetic Energy

INTRODUCTION

In Part Two we began an inquiry into the nature of the physical universe of which our earth is a tiny part. Beginning with objects close at hand, whose dimensions were easily calculated by elementary geometry, we reasoned our way outward to objects remote and immense beyond imagination.

Now we shall attempt the reverse. Beginning with objects large enough to observe directly, we shall reason our way to smaller and smaller objects, microscopic and submicroscopic, until we feel that we have arrived at the ultimate particles of which all matter is composed.

Although these tiny particles cannot be seen with the unaided eye, or even with the most powerful microscope, the evidence for their existence will not be less conclusive on that account. On the contrary, the highly specialized measuring devices we are going to describe must be thought of as extensions of our senses, yielding information far beyond the range and sensitivity of direct sensory perception. Only a small region of colors or wave lengths can be seen with our eyes; a much larger range can be photographed, and with other devices our knowledge of the electromagnetic spectrum is enormously extended. There was a time when people doubted what they saw through Galileo's telescope or Leeuwenhoek's microscope, but now we accept with confidence the important information which such instruments reveal.

There are many ways of starting an inquiry of this kind, but perhaps the simplest is through a discussion of heat phenomena. When Francis Bacon described heat as "a mode of motion," he could not have foreseen how fruitful a study of this motion would be.

HEAT AND THE KINETIC THEORY

HEAT AS A FORM OF ENERGY

That which primarily distinguishes the earth from the barren and static condition of the moon is its wealth of energy resources, and man's unending struggle to dominate his environment depends for its success on his utilization of this energy. When all labor had to be done by the expenditure of human energy or that of beasts of burden, progress was extremely slow. It is our present control over immense stores of energy that has liberated the slave and accelerated manufacture, agriculture, transportation, and communication.

No form of energy is so obviously connected with life, growth, and daily comfort as the form which we know as heat. We shall find that an introductory study of heat will point the way to an extension of our knowledge regarding matter itself.

When water is boiled in a covered pot, the steam which arises tends to expand and in doing so may lift the cover of the pot. This mechanical effect is clearly an example of work, and, since the performance of work requires the expenditure of energy, it must be concluded that steam possesses energy. Indeed, it is the spontaneous expansion of steam that causes a steam turbine to rotate and, by suitable adaptation of its rotary motion, to perform work on a large scale. Similarly, the expansion of hot gases in the cylinders of an automobile engine drives the pistons back and forth, thereby enabling the engine to do work. But expanded steam condenses into water, and, in order to be converted into steam again, the water is exposed to a source of heat such as a fire. It is evident, therefore, that, when steam is produced by supplying heat to water, the abundant energy displayed by the steam must be derived from the heat which generated the steam. In short, heat conforms to our definition of energy since it can be made to do work.

HEAT AND TEMPERATURE

Although heat is associated with hotness or temperature, it is important to remember that heat and temperature are not synonymous terms. A burning match, a burning log, and a burning building may all have the same temperature, but the amounts of heat which they emit are very different because the *amounts of burning matter* in them differ so widely. Heat energy thus depends upon the *mass* as well as the temperature of the body which emits the heat. If a red-hot poker is immersed in a pailful of cold water, the water merely becomes a little warmer from the heat transferred to it by the poker. Because of the relatively small mass of the poker, it can deliver only a small amount of heat in spite of its high temperature.

These remarks are necessary because of the rather loose employment of the word heat in everyday speech. We speak of "heating up" a room when we mean raising its temperature. We read in a cooking recipe that this operation requires "a higher heat" than that one, and again it is temperature that is meant rather than heat.

The word *temperature* refers uniquely to the quality temporarily possessed by a body which is otherwise described as hotness or coldness. The word *heat,* on the other hand, refers to a particular kind of energy which can pass from one body to another if the bodies are at different levels of temperature. In this discussion, heat is a noun, not a verb, and it is misleading to speak of "heating a body" when we really mean "raising the temperature of the body." To be sure, it is usually by the addition of heat to a body that we raise its temperature, but temperature can be raised by other means such as mechanical or electrical ones; addition of heat is not imperative for the raising of temperature.

Heat, which is also called thermal energy, occurs in small or large *quantity;* there is no such thing as quantity of temperature. Quantity of heat depends quite as much on the mass of the body which supplies the heat as it does on the body's temperature. Thus a burning match is hardly a plentiful source of heat for, although the match flame is very hot, the mass of burning material is so small as to be soon exhausted.

DEFINITION OF HEAT

We shall define heat (thermal energy) as follows:

Heat is that form of energy which is exchanged between bodies because they are at different temperatures.

In the spontaneous transfer of heat it is always the hotter body that loses thermal energy and the cooler one that gains it. Hence, one characteristic of the quality which we call temperature is that it determines in which direction heat energy will pass of its own accord.

Note that the body at higher temperature need not necessarily be hot in the ordinary sense. It may even be very cold and yet act as a source of heat to bodies which are still colder. Thus, if ice is put in contact with solid carbon dioxide (Dry Ice), heat flows from the ice to the Dry Ice because the latter is at considerably lower temperature. Evidently the ice must contain some thermal energy in spite of its rather low temperature. For that matter, so does the Dry Ice, since it in turn will give up heat if its surroundings have a still lower temperature than its own.

MEASUREMENT OF TEMPERATURE

Although *quantity* of temperature is meaningless, *range* of temperature is something that can be expressed and measured on a numerical scale.

In a crude way our senses tell us that a body is hot, warm, tepid, cool, or cold, but such designations are neither definite nor reliable. It is easy to deceive the senses into deriving a sensation of hotness from a body that is relatively cold, and vice versa.

Bettmann Archive

PLATE XX. Early form of thermometer in which the change in volume of air at *A* was measured by the rise and fall of the liquid column *CB*. Copper engraving, 1707.

For the objective measurement of temperature it is necessary to utilize certain thermal properties of matter. One such property is change in length, and a related property is change in volume (Plate XX). With few exceptions solid bodies increase in their linear dimensions as they attain higher temperatures. Liquid substances, as a rule, increase in volume with increasing tem-

perature. If a small glass bulb, which communicates with a narrow capillary tube, is filled with the liquid metal mercury, any increase in the temperature of the bulb will cause the mercury to expand and occupy a larger volume (Fig. 63). The glass expands also, but to a very much smaller extent, and so the expanding mercury has to move upward through the capillary cylinder in order to find space for its increasing vol-

FIG. 63. Mercury thermometer.

ume. A scale engraved on the glass tube makes it easy to read the height at which the mercury surface stands at any particular temperature. When the instrument is suitably calibrated, it becomes a thermometer and, although not the best, it is one of the most convenient devices for measuring temperature. Fortunately, the thermal expansion of mercury is fairly uniform, so that equal increments of temperature result in approximately equal elongations of the mercury column.

TEMPERATURE SCALES

A temperature scale requires at least two definite temperatures which can be specified so precisely that these temperatures can be reproduced at will. Such a pair of "fixed points" are the temperature of melting ice and the temperature of boiling water when both transitions occur under normal atmospheric pressure. If a thermometer such as the one described is immersed in a mixture of ice and water, the mercury column will become stationary at some definite part of the tube, and the position of its surface can be marked on the glass as one of the fixed points. If now the instrument is suspended in steam arising from boiling water, the mercury column will again come to rest with its surface farther up the tube, and this position can also

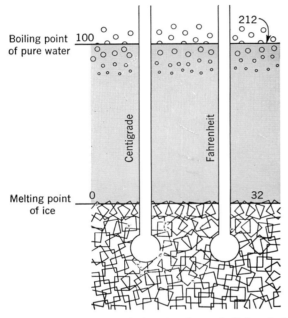

FIG. 64. Comparison of Centigrade and Fahrenheit scales.

be marked on the glass as designating the second fixed point.

The two most commonly used temperature scales are the Fahrenheit and the centigrade (Fig. 64). On the Fahrenheit scale, the temperature of melting ice (or freezing water) is chosen as 32° and the normal boiling point of water is chosen as 212°. On the centigrade scale, these same temperatures are called 0° and 100° respectively. Thus, 100 centigrade degrees represent the same temperature interval as 180 Fahrenheit degrees. It follows that one Fahrenheit degree equals $\frac{5}{9}$ of one centigrade degree. In converting any Fahrenheit temperature to the equivalent centigrade temperature it is necessary to subtract 32 from the Fahrenheit reading before applying the factor $\frac{5}{9}$, since 32°F and 0°C refer to the same temperature. For example, to express body

temperature (98.6°F) on the centigrade scale, we note first that $98.6 - 32 = 66.6$; i.e., body temperature is 66.6 Fahrenheit degrees above the temperature of melting ice. But $66.6 \times \frac{5}{9} = 37.0$; hence body temperature is 37.0 centigrade degrees above the melting point of ice. That is to say, normal body temperature is 37.0°C.

SOME IMPORTANT TEMPERATURES

Most of the stars have enormously high temperatures, some being as hot as 25,000°C in their outermost parts and undoubtedly very much hotter within. Such temperatures are not matters of guesswork; they are determined with precision by electrical thermometers actuated by the energy which the stars radiate through space. Our sun, which is merely an average star, has a surface temperature of about 6000°C. Some interesting temperatures are given in the following table.

Surface of the sun	6000°C
Melting point of tungsten	3400°C
Melting point of iron	1530°C
Melting point of lead	327°C
Boiling point of water	100°C (212°F)
Human body temperature	37°C (98.6°F)
Freezing point of water	0°C (32°F)
Freezing point of mercury	−39°C
Freezing point of CO_2	−78.5°C
Freezing point of alcohol	−130°C
Boiling point of liquid air	−195°C (approx.)
Absolute zero	−273.2°C

UNITS OF HEAT ENERGY

It would be difficult to discuss heat quantitatively without a unit in which to express this kind of energy. Of course we could use the joule (see p. 108), but at this point in our study we have no way of knowing just how much heat energy makes up 1 joule. It is more convenient to adopt a unit which has been invented specifically for the measurement of heat energy. This unit is the *calorie*. Like most physical units it is defined in terms of an experiment.

Suppose a hot object to be plunged into cold water. The object gives up heat to the water until both are at the same temperature. We assume that, with sufficient mixing, every gram of water must have acquired the same amount of heat; also that, if, for example, a certain amount of heat causes the water to rise in temperature from 25° to 26°, it will take just the same amount of heat to raise the temperature from 45° to 46°. The second assumption is not strictly true, although nearly enough so for practical purposes.

With these assumptions we now define the unit of heat.

The Calorie. One calorie is that amount of heat which will raise the temperature of 1 gram of water by 1° centigrade.

In the illustration cited above suppose that 300 grams of water, initially at 20°C, rise in temperature to 24°C when the hot object is immersed in it. By the foregoing definition the water must have gained 300×4 or 1200 calories of heat energy.

The Joule and the Kilocalorie. It will be shown subsequently that 1 cal is approximately the same as 4.2 joules. Owing to the small magnitude of the calorie, dieticians and others prefer to express thermal energy in the larger unit called a kilocalorie. This word is commonly abbreviated to kcal or Cal. As the prefix suggests, a kilocalorie equals 1000 ordinary or small calories.

HEAT CAPACITY

In general, the addition of heat to any substance causes the temperature of the substance to rise, unless the substance is undergoing a change of state, e.g., melting. It is a remarkable fact, however, that when two different substances of equal mass absorb the same amount of heat, the extent to which their temperatures rise is different. For example, if 1 gram of iron and 1 gram of aluminum absorb identical amounts of heat, the iron will undergo twice as great a rise in temperature as the aluminum does. The temperature effect of heat absorption is referred to as *heat capacity*—a misleading term, since it does not mean the total capacity of a body for heat but rather the amount of heat which will produce a given rise in temperature. Thus, aluminum has twice the heat capacity of iron, for it must absorb twice as much heat as iron does in order to undergo the same rise in temperature.

SPECIFIC HEAT

In place of relative heat-absorbing power it is customary to designate the heat-absorbing property of a substance specifically by the term *specific heat,* which is defined as follows:

The specific heat of a substance is the number of calories of heat energy which 1 gram of the substance must absorb in order to increase in temperature by 1° centigrade.

For illustrations let us begin with water. This substance evidently has a specific heat of 1 cal per gram per degree, for the calorie itself was defined as the quantity of heat needed to raise the temperature of 1 gram of water 1° centigrade.

Second, consider iron. Experiment shows that 1 gram of iron requires 0.11 cal to increase its temperature by 1°C. The specific heat of iron is therefore 0.11 cal per gram per degree. Third, consider aluminum which was just stated to have twice the heat capacity of iron. In other words, 1 gram of aluminum needs 0.22 cal to make its temperature rise 1°C. The specific heat of aluminum is therefore 0.22 cal per gram per degree.

The specific heats of practically all pure substances have been determined and tabulated. For any substance the specific heat differs somewhat with the temperature range over which it is determined, but often the variation is insignificant at the temperatures ordinarily encountered. A measurement of specific heat is very simple, at least in principle. It is usual to effect a transfer of heat between the substance under investigation and a known mass of water. This method can best be illustrated by a numerical example.

MEASUREMENT OF THE SPECIFIC HEAT OF SILVER

A 500-gram specimen of silver is heated to 100°C and then quickly immersed in 972 grams of water, initially at 25°C. The temperature of the water rises to 27.1°C, which we take to be the final temperature of the silver also. Assuming that all the heat absorbed by the water must have been lost by the silver, we write the equation

$$M_s S(100 - 27.1) = M_w(27.1 - 25)$$

where M_s represents the mass of silver, S the specific heat of silver, and M_w the mass of water. Substituting the data given,

$$500S(72.9) = 972(2.1)$$

whence,

$$S = 0.056 \text{ cal per gram per degree C}$$

HEAT AND COLD

Since the animal body recognizes not only the sensation of hotness but also the sensation of coldness, one might assume that heat and cold were different entities. In early times this assumption was widespread; indeed, we hear even today such admonitions as: "Shut the door; you're letting in the cold!" Actually, all evidence indicates that coldness is a negative quality due solely to the absence of heat, and this view has been held for several hundred years. It is now believed that heat energy is nothing but motion or kinetic energy on a very minute scale. Tiny particles, which supposedly make up all specimens of matter, are thought to be in perpetual rapid motion, and, when this motion is communicated from the particles of one body to the particles of some other body, the first is said to have lost heat and the latter to have gained heat. Coldness, by this view, is merely a state in which the component particles are moving relatively slowly; hotness is a state in which the particles move swiftly.

THE CALORIC THEORY OF HEAT

All experimental evidence now confirms the hypothesis that heat is nothing but kinetic energy possessed by the horde of material particles which make up any specimen of matter. This hypothesis is comparatively new. It was first published in 1857 by the German physicist, Clausius (1822–1888), although the underlying idea had been advanced much earlier by a few astute thinkers. Most scientists of the eighteenth and early nineteenth centuries, however, explained heat phenomena by what was called the *caloric theory*. They supposed heat to be an actual substance, called caloric, which was capable of flowing into or out of matter according to the temperature of its surroundings. Caloric was assumed to have no weight, since bodies weigh the same when they are hot as they do when they are cold. Heating and cooling were explained by saying that caloric flowed out of a hot body, leaving it cooler, and into a cold body, making it warmer. A piece of coal was said to have caloric *combined* with the carbon of the coal; hence there was no manifestation of it until the coal was burned. Under the conditions of burning, this combined caloric was set free and the surroundings became actively heated. Similarly, when water was changed into steam, a definite amount of caloric combined with the water and remained a latent part of the steam until the steam condensed again.

The caloric theory of heat is untenable and was discarded long ago. Yet it served for a time one of the useful purposes of every scientific theory or hypothesis, namely, to stimulate experiment. It is important to realize that a theory may have imperfections and yet be valuable as a motive for further investigation. The first voyage of Columbus was suggested by the hypothesis that the earth was spherical and that the orient could be reached by traveling westward. The belief

proved to be correct, although it might just as well have been false as far as the success of his objective was concerned, since he had underestimated the sphere's circumference. The point to be noted is that the hypothesis prompted the journey. Many important ventures have been undertaken through the stimulus of false theories. It is well to remember, too, that the erroneous geocentric theory did not prevent Ptolemy from making correct predictions of eclipses and planetary positions.

The plausibility of the caloric theory first came into question with the problem of heat generated by friction. It seemed reasonable enough to suppose that coal and other fuels had caloric combined in them; but what of incombustible materials which become hot when they are pounded or rubbed vigorously? Benjamin Thompson (Count Rumford, 1753–1814) was one of the first to investigate this problem while director of a Bavarian ordnance factory in 1798. Thompson was puzzled by the large amount of frictional heat generated when brass cannon were bored with a blunt drill. If this heat were something already existent in the brass, the supply should have given out after prolonged drilling; yet the operation produced heat steadily no matter how many hours it was continued. Thompson refused to believe that the metal contained an inexhaustible amount of caloric. He reasoned instead that, since heat was evolved as long as motion of the drill continued, heat must be an alternative form of the mechanical work which was performed in turning the drill. The calorists suggested that brass shavings might have less capacity for heat (i.e., less specific heat) than the massive metal; therefore, when a block of brass was reduced to powder, it could no longer retain all its caloric and the excess would be liberated.

Count Rumford concluded that the amount of heat liberated did not depend on the amount of shavings produced but was, instead, roughly proportional to the amount of mechanical work needed to continue the drilling. It is easy to show, moreover, that a substance has the same heat capacity in the form of small particles as it has in bulk. Soon afterward (1799) Sir Humphry Davy (1778–1829) used the frictional method to melt ice. He rubbed pieces of ice together in surroundings which he kept well below the freezing point. The friction of rubbing melted the ice. This result could not be explained by saying that the water had less heat capacity than the ice, for it was well known that water has *more*—about twice as much as ice, in fact.

THE MECHANICAL EQUIVALENT OF HEAT

The quantitative connection between heat and work was finally established by James Joule (1818–1889) in the 1840's. He arranged a paddle wheel so that it could be rotated in a tank of water by means of descending weights (Fig. 65).

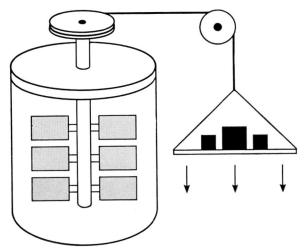

FIG. 65. Joule's apparatus for determining the mechanical equivalent of heat.

This enabled him to measure the work done in turning the wheel. Water is only moderately viscous, but it does take work to churn it, and the churned-up water becomes warm in consequence.

By noting the temperature rise as well as the quantity of water in the tank, Joule could determine how much heat had been generated. The experiment, many times repeated, showed conclusively that heat is always produced in amounts proportional to the work done and to nothing else; the more work, the more heat.

This correspondence between work and heat can be formulated very simply. If W represents the amount of mechanical energy used up as work and H the amount of heat liberated thereby,

$$W \propto H$$

or

$$W = \text{A constant} \times H$$

As a reminder of Joule's research let us choose J as symbolic of the proportionality constant.

Then

$$W = JH$$

The constant J is called the *mechanical equivalent of heat*. Joule's determinations led to its numerical evaluation, as the following fictitious example shows.

Suppose the quantity of work (W) is found to be 15,200 joules, and the heat (H) amounts to 3600 cal. Evidently

$$J = \frac{W}{H} = \frac{15,200}{3600} = 4.2 \text{ joules per cal (approx.)}$$

THE CONSERVATION OF ENERGY

It is obvious that the foregoing relation, $W = JH$, assumes that mechanical energy is indestructible, i.e., that all the work done is accounted for in the heat produced. It should be equally clear, however, that, if the ratio of work to heat is actually found to be constant in all determinations such as Joule's, the assumption is thereby confirmed as truth, and we may safely conclude that energy is indeed indestructible. A more conservative interpretation of the experiment would be:

Since mechanical energy is completely transformed into thermal energy in frictional operations, there is total conservation of energy when it is restricted to these two forms.

That energy appearing in other forms (electric, magnetic, etc.) is also totally conserved has been well established by other experimental determinations.

AN APPROXIMATE DETERMINATION OF THE MECHANICAL EQUIVALENT OF HEAT

The point raised in the last paragraphs is so fundamental as to warrant the description of another way in which J can be estimated. This method, although crude, is extremely simple to carry out with a minimum of apparatus and space.

A cardboard mailing tube about 1 meter long is tightly fitted with corks after being partially filled with copper or lead shot. When the tube is suddenly inverted, the shot will fall from top to bottom, thus losing whatever potential energy they had acquired by their elevation. If the potential energy thus lost is transformed into heat, the metal should then have a somewhat higher temperature than it had at the outset. This temperature rise is very slight, but, if the tube is reinverted many times in quick succession, the transformation of potential energy into heat is repeated over and over, and the temperature rise soon becomes appreciable.

For calculation of the potential energy used up, let m be the mass of metal and h the height through which it falls, whereas g stands for the familiar acceleration of gravity. At each descent there is consequently a loss of potential energy amounting to mgh. Let n be the number of inversions, whence

Loss in potential energy (or work done) $= nmgh$

For calculation of the thermal energy produced let s be the specific heat of the metal and t the rise in temperature which the metal sustains. Then

Gain in thermal energy $= mst$

If we assume no losses, the energy equation can be written as before but in greater detail. Thus,

$$W = JH$$

becomes

$$nmgh = Jmst$$

and

$$J = \frac{ngh}{st}$$

The assumption of no losses is fallacious, since the cardboard tube, the inclosed air, the corks, and the thermometer bulb all receive some of the heat which was assumed to remain in the shot. Some of this heat is lost to the surroundings. Nevertheless, a fair estimate of J can be made by this method. In the following example we shall assume that none of the losses mentioned has occurred. Let

$n = 100$ inversions.
$g = 980$ cm/sec^2.
$h = 100$ cm (1 meter).
$t = 7.8°$C.
$s = 0.03$ (the specific heat of lead shot).

Note that the mass (m) of the shot cancels out. That is, the more shot, the more work done but also the more metal through which the resultant heat must be distributed.

Using these figures,

$$J = \frac{ngh}{st} = \frac{(100)(980)(100)}{(0.03)(7.8)}$$

or

$$= 4.2 \times 10^7 \text{ ergs per calorie}$$

$$= 4.2 \text{ joules per calorie}$$

PROBLEMS

1. Make a list of instances in everyday experience where friction is significantly involved. Classify these into cases where (a) friction is a necessity, (b) friction is used to our advantage, (c) friction is a nuisance or causes only inefficiency.

2. At what temperature will a Fahrenheit and a centigrade thermometer have the same numerical reading?

3. In an experiment a 500-gram block of wood started out with an initial velocity of 30 cm/sec on a uniform horizontal board. Friction brought the block to rest in a distance of 45 cm. (a) How large was the frictional force? (b) How much work was done against the frictional force? (c) How many calories of heat were liberated? How many calories would have been liberated if the block had been on a rougher board so as to bring it to rest in 20 cm?
Ans. (a) 5000 dynes. (b) 225,000 ergs. (c) 0.00536 cal.

4. Should a car be brought to rest rapidly or slowly for minimum heating of the brakes? Assume that the stopping is due entirely to the application of the brakes, that no skidding occurs, and that heat does not escape very rapidly from the brakes.

5. The height of Niagara Falls is about 50 meters. How much warmer is the water at the bottom than at the top of the Falls?
Ans. 0.12°C.

6. A spiral clock spring is wound up and prevented from unwinding by packing it tightly into a glass beaker. The uncovered beaker and contents are then left outdoors exposed to the elements until the spring rusts and disintegrates. What do you think becomes of the potential energy originally stored in the wound-up spring?

7. On mixing 300 grams of alcohol at 70°C with 450 grams of benzene at 10°C the mixture attains a temperature of 40°C. Which has the larger specific heat, alcohol or benzene? What is the ratio of their specific heats?

Ans. $\dfrac{\text{Sp. ht. alcohol}}{\text{Sp. ht. benzene}} = 1.5.$

. . . .

REFERENCES

1. *A Source Book in Physics,* W. F. Magie, McGraw-Hill Book Co., 1935, pp. 125–173, 203–212.
2. *The Autobiography of Science,* Forest R. Moulton and Justus J. Schifferes, Doubleday & Co., 1950, pp. 241, 292–298.
3. *The Early Development of the Concepts of Temperature and Heat: The Rise and Decline of the Caloric Theory,* Duane Roller, Harvard Case Histories in Experimental Science, Case 3, Harvard University Press, 1950.

 *The Statistical Point of View*

The smoke from a burning match presents to the naked eye a smooth continuity, but if this smoke is strongly illuminated and examined under a microscope, each smoke particle in the visible field will seem like a tiny bright star moving about with great agitation in the gas. The first impression is one of complete chaos. Each little particle appears to be a law unto itself, darting about with frequent changes of direction and speed, behaving somewhat like an ant in an anthill which has been activated by poking a stick into the hole, or like a bee around a disturbed beehive, or like an agitated individual in an excited mob. This is the kind of motion first observed in 1827 by Robert Brown, a botanist, and since referred to as the *Brownian motion*. He observed it first for small particles of pollen suspended in water, and, when it became obvious that the motion could not be due to living organisms, he was unable to explain its real nature. In fact, it was fifty years before anyone else explained the phenomenon satisfactorily. By that time, the particle theory of matter had begun to seem attractive to many physicists and chemists, and in 1879 William Ramsay pointed out that the motion which Brown had observed must be due to the collision of the relatively large suspended particles with the far smaller particles of the liquid itself.

Even though the cause of the Brownian motion is understood, a mathematical analysis of the motion appears to be hopeless at first glance because it seems impossible to predict the position and velocity of any particle at any particular moment. Yet, at this very point mathematics comes to our assistance once more. When it is impossible to deal with a single individual or a single event, it is sometimes possible to deal with averages. The problem is like those encountered in life insurance, or in the whole field of actuarial statistics. Nothing could be more uncertain than the length of life of a single individual, and yet the average length of life for several thousand individuals is so accurately known that from this knowledge insurance rates can be successfully calculated. The particles observed in the Brownian motion can be treated in a similar manner. There is no telling what a single particle will be doing momentarily, but the average of its kinetic energies over a longer time is found to be constant as long as the temperature remains constant. Also, if one were to take snapshots of all the particles, it would be found that the average of the various kinetic energies at any instant is the same as the average over an extended period of time for a single particle. Furthermore, it has been substantiated that each particle moves, on the average, as much in one direction as in any other. That is, a particle seems to show no preference in the direction of its motion.

This, then, is an example of the statistical approach to problems; it involves many events and many individuals, and, when it has to concern itself with one event, it describes that event only in terms of the probability of its occurrence. For instance, in tossing a coin, tails will come up half of the time *provided* the coin is tossed many times. Similarly, if the sides of a uniform cube be identified by painting dots on them from one to six, any one side can be shown to turn up once out of six throws, *provided* that the cube is thrown a large number of times. If an event is certain to occur, we say that the probability of its occurrence is 1 (one). For the coin we say that the probability of tails coming up is one-half. For the uniform cube, the probability that any particular side will turn up on a single throw is one-sixth. But the fact remains that we cannot tell with certainty what the coin or the cube will do in a single trial.

Beginning at about the middle of the nineteenth century, this statistical approach was found to be particularly useful in describing the behavior of gases, for, in considering even a small specimen of gas, one deals not with one event involving one particle but with billions of events involving billions of particles. The manner in which statistical reasoning is applied to gases will be demonstrated in this chapter. Note that the conclusions which result from this kind of mathematical-physical reasoning always concern themselves with the aggregate externally measurable effects and never with the behavior of individual particles.

It is worth while considering to what extent the statistical method can be applied in fields outside the natural sciences. Its value in actuarial calculations has been amply demonstrated by insurance companies. The weakness of the method lies in its neglect of the individual. There may still be individual cases of starvation in a community whose average income is high. An enterprising chamber of commerce, pointing with pride to an average temperature of 70°, may be concealing the fact that it is bitterly cold in the winter and stifling in the summer. Once the

social scientist realizes this defect, the statistical method can be applied to a wide variety of problems where large numbers of people are concerned.

To illustrate further the limitations and weaknesses of the statistical method, consider the following example:

Let us suppose that there are inhabitants on Mars, vastly different from the humans on earth, and let us suppose that they have brought telescopes to such a state of usefulness that, focusing on the earth, they can just make out individuals as tiny dots but cannot distinguish any details of personal appearance. The Martian astronomer, wondering what these little dots may be, studies them carefully. Around many regions like New York City he observes an inward movement of dots in the morning and an outward dispersion in the evening. This rhythmic movement occurs for five consecutive days but fails on the sixth and seventh. The Martian, being a good mathematician, correlates this motion with sunrise and sunset, adding some corrections, perhaps in terms of lunar phases, for the anomaly of the sixth and seventh days. Also, he will note the strange attraction and repulsion that certain large structures have for the dots. Early in the morning there is an attraction and absorption of dots; around noon there is a repulsion and ejection of dots, followed very soon by another attraction. Finally, before sunset there is another repulsion. This motion is obviously a harmonic of the daily pulsation. He will observe interesting geometrical patterns repeated in the structures and in the appearance of the land; there will be an amazing preponderance of squares and rectangles. This must have significance because the movements of the dots seem to be influenced very much by this geometrical pattern. There will be seasonal effects to take into account; in the northern hemisphere some dots move southward in the winter and northward in the summer. The dots have a strange way of attaching themselves to larger moving objects. All these and many other details the Martian will observe and thoughtfully incorporate into a theory. This theory (remember the Martian is a clever mathematician) may be so refined that he can predict successfully what the density of dots will be at any point on the earth at any given time. He may be deceived into thinking that he understands a great deal about the dots, but we on earth know better. What does he know about the emotions that stir the human mind? What does he know about the motives that inspired the motions he has so carefully studied? He has observed and correlated only the trivial and the least interesting characteristics of the earthly native.

This illustrates not only the weakness of the statistical method but it points to a fundamental limitation in our understanding of the reality which lies behind the experimental observation. We must not be misled into thinking that a theory, even a good one, reveals the complete and ultimate truth about nature. Theories are based on experimental facts all of which may be true, but they are only parts of the truth and not the whole truth.

THE STRUCTURE OF MATTER

If one were to take a bit of seemingly uniform matter like iron or copper or silver and begin to break it down into smaller and smaller pieces, there are really only two ultimate possibilities which make any sense. Either it should be possible to subdivide the material infinitely, or, alternatively, a limit should be reached where further subdivision would be impossible. If the first of these possibilities were true, we should say that matter is continuous; if the latter, we should say that matter is discontinuous.

The belief that matter must be discontinuous is not new. Democritus and many others of the Greek philosophers took this point of view. In fact, they invented the word "atom" to designate the smallest particle into which matter might be subdivided. They attached so much significance to this idea that they built around it a whole philosophical school whose members were the so-called "atomists." Later on, Lucretius, the Roman poet, expressed a similar belief in a poem called *On the Nature of Things*. This remarkable poem contains many statements which seem strangely prophetic in the light of modern knowledge. When examined carefully, however, the ideas of Lucretius are little more than shrewd guesses because there was at that time no experimental evidence to substantiate them. Democritus and Lucretius guessed right; many others of equal ability guessed wrong.

It was not until the first few decades of the nineteenth century that experimental evidence began to accumulate in favor of a discontinuous theory of matter, and by the beginning of the twentieth century even its strongest opponents had yielded.

As a result of overwhelming evidence, we now believe that all bodies are aggregates of discrete particles. But what are the particles like? Are they smooth spheres like billiard balls, are they cubical, or do they have other complex shapes? Are these particles the ultimate limit of material simplicity, or are they, perhaps, constructed of still simpler constituents?

The discussion of gases which follows illustrates a common method of attack in the natural sciences. Certainly we do not know what the ultimate particles of matter are like from individual observation. But assuming that these particles have certain properties and that they obey the established laws of mechanics, let us see where logical reasoning leads us. If the conclusions reached with these assumptions are not in agreement with experiment, then the assumptions must be false and other assumptions must be tried. Perhaps they too fail. Finally, some set of assumptions yields results which do agree with experimental facts. These assumptions are then incorporated into a model which serves as a guide for further logical speculation. Such a model, to be successful, must not only be consistent with facts already known but, through its use, one should be able to predict hitherto unknown phenomena.

For example, let us suppose that the ultimate particles act like hard steel spheres which are so strongly built and so elastic that when they strike each other they rebound without breaking and without any loss of energy. Where will such an assumption lead us? We begin to reason mathematically about what should happen if we had a very large number of such elastic spheres confined in a vessel, and, in this case, the results agree with the known gas laws as observed in the laboratory. If such agreement had not been reached, we would have been forced to discard the original assumptions, make new ones, and start all over again. This is what we mean by a model, and when it is successful we say that a set of phenomena have been "explained." For many problems which concern gases, the model of the ultimate particle is like a tiny billiard ball—hard and elastic.

But no model derived from logic and experimental evidence can be complete and perfect; that is too much to expect. Only ultimate knowledge and insight could yield a flawless model. From time to time, the atomic model has had to be modified as more facts became known. For instance, the hard billiard ball had to be given an internal mechanism before it was possible to explain how the atom can emit and absorb light. That mechanism will be described later.

THE KINETIC THEORY OF MATTER

Joule's proof that mechanical energy and heat are interchangeable put an end to the caloric theory as an explanation of thermal phenomena. In place of it the idea that heat is the aggregate motion of material particles, which are the constituents of all bodies, grew rapidly into a comprehensive theory. This elaborate structure is sometimes called the *kinetic theory of heat,* but, inasmuch as it accounts successfully for many physical characteristics of matter other than thermal ones, it is more accurately named the *kinetic theory of matter.* This theory is extraordinarily useful, for not only does it reconcile many diverse phenomena and show their interrelationship but it has also predicted phenomena which might otherwise have remained undiscovered, unless by accident.

MOLECULES

We shall describe here only the rudimentary aspects of the kinetic theory. Much of the subject is exceedingly complex and not necessary to our present purpose. The underlying hypothesis is that every specimen of matter consists of small separate elastic particles which are perpetually moving and that it is the kinetic energy of these particles that reveals itself as heat. These hypothetical particles are known as *molecules.*

If one could somehow determine the number of such particles in a sample of matter, as well as the mass and velocity of each, one should be able to calculate their aggregate energy of motion, which would be the thermal energy of the sample. But the difficulty of accomplishing such a feat is indicated by the much more simple task one would face if he tried to calculate the energy of motion possessed by a crowd of people on a congested street. How could one hope to find the individual masses and velocities of thousands of persons at a given moment? Even if this could be done, how long would it last as correct information? Surely at a later moment the velocities would have changed significantly owing to inevitable collisions. Yet the kinetic theory assumes not thousands but billions upon billions of molecules in even a small specimen of matter. Moreover, the molecules are calculated to be so small that there is no prospect of making them

visible even with the finest optical microscope ever constructed. Accordingly, all information about molecules has to be inferred from their behavior as a crowd. Fortunately, there are well-developed statistical methods for studying crowd action, and the accuracy of such methods is greater the more individuals the crowd contains.

STATES OF MATTER

Although the solid, liquid, and gaseous states in which matter can exist are commonplace realities, it is useful to characterize these states systematically.

Solids. A solid occupies a definite volume and it has an enduring shape. Genuine solids are always crystalline in their make-up although the crystals may be so tiny as to be indistinguishable except under high magnification. Glass and some other materials which appear to be solid because they retain their shape are considered to be in reality very viscous liquids, since they lack the crystalline character of true solids.

In general, solids are denser than liquids (ice is a familiar exception), and even if a solid is subjected to pressure several thousand times as great as the pressure of the atmosphere it will shrink only slightly.

Liquids. Matter in the *liquid state* possesses definite volume, but no shape. Liquids flow, usually with ease, and the free surface at any point in a liquid is perpendicular to the resultant of all forces acting on the liquid at that point. Thus, if the liquid is at rest and subject only to the vertical force of gravity, its free surface will be horizontal. Liquids, like solids, are very slightly compressible.

Gases. Matter in the *gaseous state* is also devoid of shape. That is, gases flow if not confined, and, because of their flowing tendency, gases may be classed with liquids under the heading of *fluids.* More significant, however, is the lack of unique volume in a specimen of gas. To be sure, we shall refer again and again to the "volume" of a gas but what is meant by such a statement is the volume of the *container.* Suppose, for example, that a quantity of ammonia gas is confined in a small bottle. Then the space within the bottle is the temporary volume assigned to the ammonia gas. But, if the bottle is unstoppered, it will be only a few minutes before the familiar odor of ammonia is detectable throughout the room. There is no choice but to describe the new volume of the ammonia as the volume of the entire room, since the gas is evidently present in all parts of the room. But what of the air which was in the room all the time? Its volume also is described as the volume of the room. It is obvious that neither gas, ammonia or air, *completely* fills the room excepting in the sense that a herd of plunging steers in an inclosure fills the inclosure. Evidently a gas will occupy as much space as is allowed to it. This observation is extremely important to the hypothesis from which the kinetic theory is formulated.

It should be added that gases in general are far less dense than either liquids or solids. On the other hand, gases can be compressed enormously with corresponding increase in their density.

Finally, to emphasize the fact that the words solid, liquid, and gas refer merely to *states* in which matter occurs, let us remember that all substances can exist in each of these states according to the conditions of temperature and pressure imposed on them. Water is equally familiar as solid ice, liquid water, and gaseous steam. Air and ammonia, although ordinarily gaseous, can easily be liquefied or solidified by subjecting them to increased pressure and diminished temperature. "Dry Ice" is the ordinarily gaseous carbon dioxide, temporarily solidified. Metals, which usually occur in the solid state (with certain exceptions like the ordinarily liquid metal, mercury), will melt into liquids when their temperature has been raised sufficiently, and at still higher temperatures the molten metals enter the gaseous state. All such changes must be accounted for in a satisfactory theory of matter.

THE KINETIC THEORY OF GASES

THE SIMPLICITY OF GASEOUS MATTER

There is considerable uniformity in the behavior of all gases under changing external conditions; different gases obey, more or less faithfully, certain simple laws. The gaseous state is undoubtedly less complex than either the liquid or the solid states, and for this reason a consideration of gaseous properties affords the easiest approach to a theory which attempts to explain how matter is constructed.

Let us first ask ourselves what mechanism could account for the two properties which are most characteristic of any gas: (1) its lightness and (2) its ability to spread or *diffuse* spontaneously in all directions, never stopping until it has reached the barriers of its container.

GAS DIFFUSION FROM THE KINETIC VIEWPOINT

Let us begin with the hypothesis that any gas consists of many very small particles (molecules), all of them in rapid and continual but haphazard motion. Such particles could get through tiny apertures and, although frequently deflected by collision with one another, would eventually make themselves evident throughout all the available space. The diffusion of an odorous gas like ammonia or a colored one like bromine can be traced very easily. Suppose that a few drops of liquid bromine are placed at the bottom of an open vessel. Since the liquid is very volatile, it quickly evaporates to form bromine gas of a deep reddish-brown color. If we assume the gas to be a swarm of swiftly moving particles, these particles will dart off in many directions. But inasmuch as the vessel already contains air, that is to say, it is thickly congested with molecules of nitrogen and oxygen, the bromine molecules must be deflected almost immediately from their initial outward course. Their progress will be visibly delayed in consequence of frequent changes in direction resulting from collisions with the nitrogen and oxygen molecules. If the air were not present, the diffusion of the bromine would be unimpeded and very much faster. Here is a suggestion for an experiment. Actually, when liquid bromine is allowed to evaporate in an evacuated vessel the resulting gas diffuses throughout the vessel almost instantly as is apparent from the spread of the deep reddish-brown color of the bromine.

THE LIGHTNESS OF GASES

We have already referred to the extraordinary compressibility of gases. Any gas can be shrunk to a tiny fraction of its initial volume. To account for this high compressibility the kinetic theory assumes that the molecules of a gas under ordinary circumstances are relatively far apart, so that, in spite of their vast numbers, the molecules take up very little room of their own and can readily be forced into smaller and smaller volumes. In other words, a container which is "filled" with gas is, for the most part, empty of matter.

Here we have an explanation of the low density which characterizes all gases. Since density is the ratio of mass to volume, it is clear that the rather thinly distributed molecules of a gas must have an aggregate mass which is small in comparison with the ordinarily large volume available to them. And, if the molecular population in a gas is relatively thin, we can readily see why it is so easy to crowd more and more gas into a space which was originally considered to be filled with gas. Since an inflated automobile tire, for example, can have more and more air pumped into it, it must follow that the space within the tire, notwithstanding the inflation, is largely unoccupied.

GAS PRESSURE

That a gas such as air presses against all objects on the surface of the earth with considerable force is a familiar fact. This force in the case of air is merely the weight of the gases comprising the atmosphere. Inasmuch as the weight of any atmospheric column depends on its cross-sectional area as well as on its height, it is preferable to specify not the *force* exerted by the atmosphere but rather the *pressure* of the atmosphere. *Pressure* is defined as *force per unit cross-sectional area* ($P = F/A$). Normally the atmospheric pressure at sea level amounts to about 1 million dynes per square centimeter (a little less than 15 lb per square inch). For convenience this amount of pressure is taken as a standard unit called *1 atmosphere*.

The gravitational force exerted on a solid, and therefore its pressure as well, is directed downward. A gas, however, exerts pressure in all directions equally. Consider, for example, a newspaper with a superficial area of 2400 sq cm lying on a table. At 1 million dynes per square centimeter, the force of the atmosphere acting downward on the newspaper amounts to more than 2 billion dynes (nearly 4000 lb). If this force were not compensated by an equal force acting upward from beneath the paper, it would be impossible to lift it. Actually the air between the paper and the table does press upward with the same force, and hence the effort required to lift the newspaper is no greater than it would be if the paper were in a vacuum. Similarly a lateral pressure of 1 million dynes per square centimeter acts on the vertical sides of all objects standing in the air, and this in turn is balanced by an identical atmospheric pressure on the opposite faces of all such objects. In short, because of the equality of air pressure in all directions, the atmosphere scarcely interferes at all with attempts to move objects through it.

THE BAROMETER

Nowadays the measurement of gas pressure is so common that gages for measuring the pressure of gases are almost as familiar as clocks. We find a pressure gage on the steam boiler of a household furnace and on the lid of a pressure cooker. The prudent motorist carries a gage for testing the air pressure in his tires. Such gages usually contain a tube or surface of spring metal which is distorted by the pressure of the impinging gas, the distortion increasing with increasing pressure.

Gas pressure can also be measured, however, by its ability to elevate and support a liquid in a vertical tube. Here the height of the liquid column becomes a measure of the pressure exerted by the gas. This is the case with the liquid barometer invented by Torricelli in about 1643. For centuries before that time lift or suction pumps had been used to raise water from wells or mine shafts and it was familiar knowledge that such pumps would not function if the height of the water column exceeded 34 ft. (See Plate XXI.) Galileo himself remarked upon this limitation, but it was one of his students, Torricelli, who conceived the explanation for it. In order to comprehend the explanation, let us consider a series of demonstrations.

For the first, let us put any liquid into a U-shaped tube and observe that it comes to rest when the level is the same in both branches, even if the two branches differ in diameter (Fig. 66). Evidently the two liquid columns balance each other not in the *force* which they exert on the bottom but in the pressure which both exert on the bottom. The force in each case is the weight of the liquid column, and the right-hand column is depicted as larger and therefore heavier than the left-hand one. But if the right-hand column has a cross section which is, for example, twice that of the left, it will hold twice as much liquid as the left branch does, and, although the weight of this liquid column is double the weight of the narrower column, the *pressure* it exerts on the bottom will be the same, as the following comparison shows:

	Left Branch	Right Branch
Weight of liquid	W	$2W$
Cross-sectional area	A	$2A$
Pressure at the base of both	W/A	$2W/2A = W/A$

Having satisfied ourselves that liquid in a U tube will come to rest when both branches exert the same pressure on the communicating portion, let us examine next a U tube of uniform cross section in which *two* liquids are allowed to reach a state of balanced pressure (Fig. 67). For this let us choose liquids which do not mix, such as water and mercury.

No longer are the two surfaces at the same level, but we conclude that, as before, the pres-

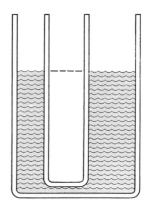

FIG. 66. Liquid stands equally high in both branches.

sure at the bottom of each branch must be the same. It must also be true that the pressure at the level of the dotted line is the same in both branches, since below the line the two branches

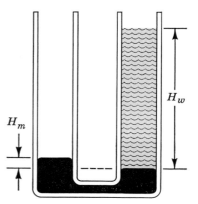

FIG. 67. A column of mercury H_m balances a column of water H_w 13.6 times as high.

are identically filled with mercury. In order to compute the pressure in either branch at this level, we simply divide the weight of liquid standing above the dotted line by the cross-sectional area of the tube.

PLATE XXI. Robert Boyle's experiment in which he determined the height to which water could be pumped. His vacuum pump was placed on the roof and attached to the end of a vertical pipe which

dipped into a water tank below. He found that water could not be pumped higher than about 33 ft on a day when the mercury barometer stood at about 29 in. From *The Complete Works of Robert Boyle,* second edition, 1772, Vol. III, Plate 5.

But the weight is expressible as height times cross-sectional area times the weight density, W/V, from which we obtain the pressure as

Pressure

$$= \frac{\text{Weight}}{\text{Cross-sectional area}}$$

$$= \frac{\text{Height} \times \text{Cross-sectional area} \times \text{Density}}{\text{Cross-sectional area}}$$

$$= \text{Height} \times \text{Density}$$

Where the density is taken to be weight per unit volume, or, in appropriate symbols,

$$P = HD$$

Now, since the pressure exerted by each liquid at the level of the dotted line is the same, we can state this fact in the form of an equation, using the subscripts w and m to denote water and mercury respectively.

$$H_w D_w = H_m D_m$$

Finally, since mercury is about 13.6 times as dense as water, we should expect the water column to be 13.6 times as high as the mercury column. Actual trial shows this to be true.

FIG. 68. A column of mercury balances a column of air H_a as high as the atmosphere.

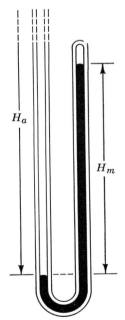

By a modest exercise of the imagination we can now picture a third demonstration in which the pressure of a liquid column balances the pressure exerted by a column of air. In this illustration (Fig. 68) we suppose the left branch to be open and very high—several hundred miles high, in fact, to reach to the top of the atmosphere. The right branch is closed with the space above the mercury entirely empty of air.

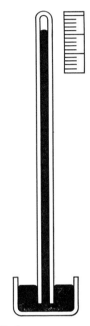

FIG. 69. Torricelli's barometer.

It should be clear that this imaginary experiment does not differ from the previous one in principle but only in details. One of the balancing fluids is a gas, and, because of its small density, a very long column will be necessary to give the same pressure that the short mercury column exerts. Furthermore, the gas, being compressible, will not possess uniform density. Otherwise we can still infer that the pressure of the atmosphere is the same as the pressure of a mercury column having a certain height. This height is normally about 30 in. or 76 cm if the experiment is conducted at sea level.

A few moments' thought should convince anyone that there is no need to inclose the atmospheric column in a tube. The air will exert the same pressure, whether or not it is confined by walls. That being so, we can convert our imaginary demonstration into a real one simply by omitting as much of the left-hand branch as we wish. This was what Torricelli did in his famous experiment (Fig. 69). (See also Plate XXII.) Filling a glass tube about 100 cm long with mercury, he covered the open end with his finger long enough to permit inverting the tube and plunging it into an open vessel containing more mercury. On removing his finger from the open end, he observed that the liquid metal flowed out of the tube until its level had reached a height of about 76 cm above the level of mer-

Bettmann Archive

PLATE XXII. In 1648 Périer, at the suggestion of Pascal, observed the height of a Torricellian mercury barometer at various levels while ascending the Puy de Dôme in Auvergne. As the altitude increased, the height of the mercury column decreased.

cury in the open dish. This simple device was the first barometer or instrument for measuring the pressure of the atmosphere in terms of the height at which a column of liquid must stand in order to exert the same pressure. The modern barometer is essentially the same except in having a linear scale mounted alongside the column for convenience in reading the height of the mercury. The space above the mercury is commonly called a Torricellian vacuum.

About the uses of the barometer we merely remark in passing that at elevations above sea level the atmospheric pressure diminishes, and, since it cannot then balance so tall a column of liquid, the column automatically decreases in height. Variations in the height of the mercury column can therefore be utilized to measure altitude. Furthermore, since storms are usually preceded by substantial changes in atmospheric pressure, the barometer is extremely useful in predicting weather.

The foregoing account of the barometer's evolution may seem to have no relation to our introductory statement about the limitation of the lift pump. The connection is quickly established, however, if we recall that mercury is 13.6 times as dense as water. A column of water capable of balancing the pressure of the atmosphere must therefore extend 30×13.6 or 408 in. above the open surface of the water. But 408 in. equal 34 ft. In short, the liquid column in a water barometer would be about 34 ft high at sea level. Inasmuch as this column of water exerts the same pressure as the atmosphere itself, we can now realize why a suction pump cannot lift water through any greater height than 34 ft. Only if the atmospheric pressure were increased could this height of water be exceeded.

COLLECTED ASSUMPTIONS REGARDING GAS MOLECULES

Before proceeding to investigate quantitative relations between various gas properties it is desirable to list the assumptions underlying the kinetic theory, insofar as it is applied to gases.

1. A substance in the gaseous state consists of individual molecules, all practically identical with one another and extremely minute in size. (From experimental data it is believed that the molecules of ordinary gases do not exceed a few hundred millionths of a centimeter in diameter.)

2. The number of molecules present in even a small specimen of gas is enormously great. [Experiments indicate that in 1 liter of gas (a liter is roughly equal to a quart) under ordinary conditions, there are 25×10^{21} molecules.]

3. A relatively large distance separates the average molecule from its neighbors. (Under ordinary conditions the average distance between a pair of molecules is calculated to be about 10 times the diameter of a molecule.)

4. The molecules are in continual rapid motion. Because of their vast numbers and the chaotic character of their movement, all directions in space will be equally pursued by them. That is, just as many molecules will be moving in one direction as in any other direction.

5. When heat energy is imparted to a gas, the molecules move faster and the increase in their average speeds is manifested by a rise in the temperature of the gas. It is to be expected that, even when the temperature of the gas is constant, not all the constituent molecules will be traveling at the same speed. Some may be moving very slowly or may even be at rest momen-

tarily, while others will be moving much faster than the average. The vast majority, however, will have speeds which fall within a comparatively narrow range. It is the average of the speeds within this narrow range that determines the temperature of the gas specimen as a whole. By this assumption absolute coldness corresponds to a cessation of molecular motion. The average molecular speed is very large even at 0°C; for hydrogen it is about 1 mile per second.

6. When gas molecules collide with one another or with the walls of the containing vessel, the collisions are assumed to be elastic. By this is meant that the total kinetic energy possessed by the molecules is conserved; no energy is lost in the impacts. If this were not so, if the molecules were to speed up or slow down after striking a stationary wall, we should detect a rise or a fall in the temperature of a gas which has been merely left standing in a container. No such change in temperature occurs unless the region outside the inclosure is colder or warmer than the gas. Hence we infer that molecules, on the average, rebound from the rigid walls of their container without loss in speed. On the other hand when gas molecules collide with one another, there is undoubtedly a transfer of energy from one to another. Taken as a whole, however, the entire specimen loses no energy in consequence of such impacts.

Beginning on p. 143 (Gas Pressure Derived from the Laws of Motion), these assumptions will be involved in a more rigorous mathematical derivation of the gas laws, but first it is worth while to see how far we can go in a more general kind of exploratory reasoning which appeals mostly to physical common sense, rather than to rigorous logic. Such arguments are frequently called *heuristic,* and in this case seem appropriate since, historically, they preceded the more rigorous statistical treatment.

THE MECHANISM OF GAS PRESSURE

A swinging door can be held open by the application of a single force. Alternatively the same effect could be produced by bombarding the door with a large number of rubber balls thrown at it in very rapid succession. Indeed, if the impacts occurred with great enough frequency, an observer could scarcely distinguish between the intermittent rain of blows and a steady push. It is just such a mechanism that is believed to explain the pressure which confined gases exert on their surrounding walls.

Let us imagine an assemblage of gas molecules being subjected to an experiment the purpose of which is to find out how the pressure resulting from molecular bombardment is affected by changes in the volume allotted to the gas. For diagrammatic purposes we must make the invisible molecules visible and exhibit just a few instead of the many molecules that must be present (Fig. 70). The velocity of each molecule is here represented by a short arrow. Furthermore, we assume the vessel to be kept at constant temperature so that there may be no change in the average speed of the molecules.

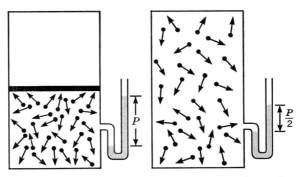

FIG. 70. Increasing the volume of a gas reduces the number of molecular impacts on the walls per unit area, provided the temperature remains constant.

The gas pressure, which is assumed to be caused by molecular impacts against the walls, can be read on a gage projecting from the container. The magnitude of this pressure must depend on the average force with which the molecules strike the walls and also on the frequency of their impacts. Thus, if a certain molecule were to strike one of the walls 20 times a second, it would evidently contribute twice as much average force as a molecule moving at the same speed which struck only 10 times a second.

After noting the pressure when the molecules are confined to half the box, we remove the sliding partition so as to allow the molecules to range through twice as large a volume. Since the average speeds are assumed to remain constant, the molecular blows will be no less forcible but they must occur on the average only half as frequently as before on a unit area of the walls. Consequently, the average pressure will be halved when the volume is doubled. Similar reasoning leads to the conclusion that, if the volume of the gas is *diminished* to ½, ⅓, or ¼ of its initial value, the gas pressure must *increase* to double, triple, or quadruple the initial pressure. In

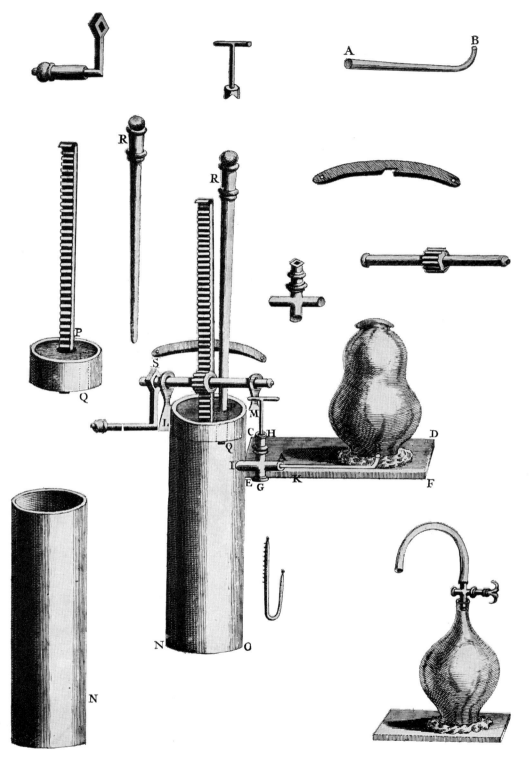

PLATE XXIII. Robert Boyle's vacuum pump. The crank *S* was turned, pulling the piston *PQ* up from the bottom of a cylinder. When the piston reached the top, the valve *HG* was opened, causing some of the air from *B* to be exhausted. The valve was then closed and the procedure repeated. As the piston descended, the compressed air in the cylinder was allowed to escape through *PQR*. Cylinder and piston were immersed in water to prevent leakage of air into the cylinder on the upstroke. From *The Complete Works of Robert Boyle,* second edition, 1772, Vol. III, Plate 2.

short, the volume and pressure of the gas are inversely proportional to each other—a relation which can be stated concisely by the equation

$$V = \text{A constant} \times 1/P$$

or

$$PV = \text{A constant}$$

BOYLE'S LAW

The relation here developed from molecular assumptions was actually discovered experimentally about three centuries ago by the eminent Irish chemist Robert Boyle (1627–1691). (See Plate XXIII.) This relation, commonly known as Boyle's law, may be stated as follows:

The volume of a gas is inversely proportional to the pressure, provided the temperature of the gas remains constant.

Many gases conform to Boyle's law with great fidelity; others obey it only approximately. The accuracy with which Boyle's law describes this aspect of gas behavior increases greatly when a gas is studied at high temperature and low pressure. Under such conditions the molecules may be thought of as practically independent of one another, and the space which they actually occupy is then an extremely small fraction of the total volume allowed to them.

We may therefore record as the first success of the initial assumptions an explanation of Boyle's experimental law connecting the volume and pressure of gases.

RELATION BETWEEN GAS PRESSURE AND THE SPEED OF MOLECULES

Next let us consider how a change in the average speed of gas molecules would affect other properties of a gas. We have already assumed that the average speed at which gas molecules move is somehow related to the temperature of the gas and that a rise in the temperature of a gas always signifies an increase in the average molecular speed. Let us suppose, therefore, that a specimen of any gas confined in a rigid vessel of constant volume is supplied with heat and consequently undergoes a rise in temperature.

From the laws of mechanics we can easily anticipate the mechanical effect of, say, *doubling* the average molecular speed. Assume for convenience that all molecules have the same speed, and suppose this speed to be doubled. Then the walls must receive twice as many molecular blows per second as they did before, and this alone would double the gas pressure. But every impact will also be twice as forceful, since the doubled momentum of the impinging molecules must result in a doubling of the momentum change which occurs when a molecule strikes one of the walls. We recall that force equals the rate of momentum change. It must be concluded, therefore, that a doubling of the molecular speed leads to a quadrupling of the gas pressure. By the same arguments tripling the speed would increase the pressure ninefold and so on. Hence, in a mixture of molecules of many speeds, the gas pressure is not proportional to the average speed of the molecules but to the average *square* of this speed ($P \propto \overline{v^2}$). When we also remember that the force (and of course the pressure) exerted by the bombarding molecules must likewise depend on their masses, it is plain that the factors of mass and squared velocity can be combined in the one property, kinetic energy, and that we may say more concisely:

The pressure of a gas is proportional to the average kinetic energy of its molecules.

KINETIC ENERGY AND TEMPERATURE

In the later part of the eighteenth century two French scientists, J. A. C. Charles and J. L. Gay-Lussac discovered that, if a gas is kept at constant

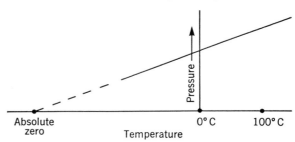

FIG. 71. Laws of Charles and Gay-Lussac.

volume and then varied in temperature, the pressures plotted graphically against the temperatures all lie on a straight line, even when the temperatures are very low (Fig. 71). One must only be careful that the gas under consideration does not liquefy at the low temperature. By extrapolation, this suggests that at some minimal low temperature the pressure becomes zero. Furthermore, since pressure is proportional to the average kinetic energy of the molecules, it must also be concluded that the kinetic energy becomes zero at this minimal low temperature; the molecules have lost all their motion and are lying quietly at the bottom of the container. It is this temperature which is called the *absolute zero,* and the temperature reckoned from this point is called the *absolute temperature.*

The temperature of a gas now takes on a new and significant meaning; it is a measure of the average kinetic energy of the molecules. We may say that the average kinetic energy is proportional to the absolute temperature, or, what amounts to the same thing, the pressure of a gas at constant volume is proportional to the absolute temperature.

$$P = KT$$

RELATION BETWEEN TEMPERATURE AND VOLUME

Suppose next that a gas confined in a rigid vessel is heated until the average kinetic energy of its molecules is doubled. The result will be a doubling of the absolute temperature and a doubling of the pressure, as we have just seen. When this condition has been reached, let us imagine the heated gas to be transferred from the first vessel to another vessel having twice its volume without any change in the kinetic energy of the molecules. In the larger vessel the gas will still have the higher temperature just imparted to it, but what will be its pressure? In the doubled volume the molecules can strike the new walls on the average only half as frequently as they did the old walls if their average speed is unchanged. In other words, the gas pressure, which was first doubled by doubling the kinetic energy, is now restored to its initial value by doubling the available volume. The result can be summarized in the following statement:

When the absolute temperature of a gas is doubled, the gas will take up twice as much room as before, provided the pressure is maintained constant.

CHARLES' LAW

The French scientist Charles also discovered this relation between volume and temperature in the later eighteenth century, and his experimental finding, commonly known as Charles' law, agrees with the inference just drawn from the kinetic theory. A general statement of Charles' law is:

At constant pressure the volume of a gas is directly proportional to its absolute temperature.

$$V = \text{A constant} \times T$$

An experimental proof of Charles' law can be conducted in the following way: Since the pressure of the gas is to be kept constant, a simple way of imposing that condition is to put the gas into a cylinder which is fitted with a light piston (Fig. 72). The constant pressure P of the atmosphere acts downward on the piston throughout the experiment. As heat is supplied to the gas and the temperature increases, the piston will rise but the gas will at all times be subjected to the same pressure. It will be found

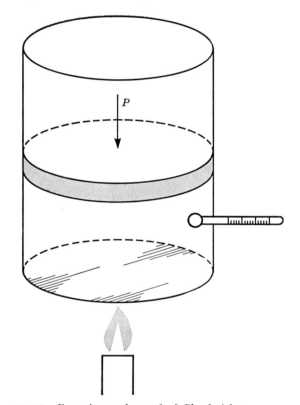

FIG. 72. Experimental proof of Charles' law.

that for equal increments of temperature the expanding gas will take on practically equal increments of volume.

THE COEFFICIENT OF EXPANSION OF A GAS

A graphic representation of either of the laws of Charles suggests a very interesting and significant consequence of the gas behavior just described. The fractional amount by which a gas expands when its temperature rises 1° is called the coefficient of expansion of the gas. This coefficient, which is practically the same for all gases, amounts to $\frac{1}{273}$ of the volume which the gas occupies at 0°C under a pressure of 1 atmosphere. Thus, if a specimen of gas is collected just sufficient to take up 273 cc at 0°C, and, if its pressure is 1 atmosphere, then at 1°C and the same pressure its volume will increase to 274 cc, at 2°C, its volume will become 275 cc, and so on. If it is cooled to −1°C, its volume will diminish to 272 cc, etc. Graphically, the relation between temperature and volume is represented in Fig. 73.

Now any gas will condense to the liquid state if its temperature is lowered sufficiently, and the laws we have been discussing have no application to liquids at all. Suppose, however, that we had a gas which did not condense to a liquid no matter how much it was cooled. Then, according to the graph, continuous cooling would cause

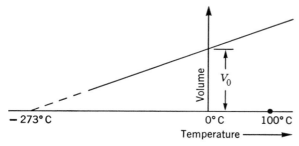

FIG. 73. Graphical representation of Charles' law.

its volume to shrink progressively until at −273°C the gas would vanish entirely. Although any such result is palpably impossible, the indication is of great theoretical importance, for it implies that −273°C (more exactly −273.2°C) is the absolute low limit of possible coldness. Temperatures within a few hundredths of a degree of this value have actually been reached during recent years but no one has ever succeeded in attaining the limit itself.

ABSOLUTE TEMPERATURE

Inasmuch as both theoretical and experimental lines of investigation support the probability that −273.2°C is the absolute minimum of temperature, it is logical to construct a temperature scale which starts at this point and thus eliminate negative temperatures, which are illogical in terms of the kinetic theory. The so-called absolute temperature scale is derived from the centigrade scale by merely adding 273.2° (for most purposes it is satisfactory to add 273°), to every centigrade reading. Referring to Fig. 73, this scheme has the advantage of simplifying the equation to which the graph corresponds

From $V = kt + V_0$
To $V = kT$

where V_0 and k are constants, t is centigrade temperature, and T is absolute temperature.

THE GENERAL GAS LAW

The dependence of gas volume on pressure when the temperature is unvarying is concisely expressed by Boyle's law (PV = Constant), and its dependence on temperature when the pressure is unvarying is equally concisely put by Charles' law (V/T = Constant). This brings us to the question: what can be predicted about the volume of a gas when both its temperature and its pressure are allowed to vary simultaneously? The answer is very simply obtained by applying the two laws stepwise. We shall assume that a sample of some gas is collected under an initial pressure P_i at an initial temperature (on the absolute scale) T_i. Let its initial volume under these conditions be V_i. We propose to change the pressure to a final value P_f while maintaining the temperature at T_i. This will cause the volume to expand or contract to some new value which will be specified by V' and can be calculated by applying Boyle's law. Thus,

$$P_f V' = P_i V_i \qquad \text{from which} \qquad V' = P_i V_i / P_f$$

Now suppose the pressure to be held constant at P_f while the absolute temperature of the sample is changed from T_i to some final temperature T_f. Again the volume will expand or contract, but this time in accordance with Charles' law. Calling the final volume V_f, we get its relation to V' from Charles' law as follows:

$$V'/V_f = T_i/T_f$$

All that remains is to substitute the equivalent of V' from the first equation into the second equation, getting

$$P_i V_i / P_f V_f = T_i/T_f$$

and this equation on rearrangement becomes

$$P_f V_f / T_f = P_i V_i / T_i = \text{A constant}$$

or, in general,

$$PV = CT$$

If we always select the amount of gas which occupies 22.4 liters at 0°C and 1 atmosphere pressure, for a reason to be discussed later, then C has been found from experiment to be *the same for all gases*. It is called the *universal gas constant* and is equal to 8.31×10^7 ergs per degree C per mole (the term used to designate the amount of gas used in this example).

PROBLEMS

1. When the volume of a gas is doubled, without changing the temperature, the pressure is reduced to ½ its original value. Explain this phenomenon in your own words in terms of molecular impacts upon a small surface on some wall. *Hint:* Choose a volume of such shape (perhaps a long tube with flat ends) that the argument becomes simple.

2. When a liquid evaporates, some molecules are breaking through the barrier of the liquid surface in spite of the attraction of the remaining molecules in the liquid. Why should such evaporation cool the liquid?

3. To cool ourselves in the summer we frequently stir up the air with a fan. Is not this contrary to the known fact that mechanical agitation heats the air? Explain.

4. Imagine a gas confined at high pressure in a cylinder which is so well insulated that no heat energy can enter or escape. A piston in this cylinder is then allowed to move outward, expanding the gas. Explain what happens to the pressure and temperature of the gas.

5. In a garage fire it was found that a metal tank, normally containing air at 30 lb/sq in., had exploded. Knowing that this type of tank could stand only 90 lb/sq in., the insurance inspector was able to calculate the temperature of the fire in the neighborhood of the tank. What was this temperature? Assume the normal temperature to have been 25°C (77°F).
Ans. 621°C.

6. Assuming a continuous structure (as opposed to molecular) for matter, try to explain the following: (*a*) the Brownian motion, (*b*) cooling by evaporation, (*c*) Boyle's and Charles' laws.

7. If an automobile tire is inflated to a pressure of 45 lb/sq in. on a cold winter day in your community, what would be the pressure in the tire on a hot summer day, assuming no appreciable leakage or change in volume?

. . . .

REFERENCE

1. *A Source Book in Physics*, W. F. Magie, McGraw-Hill Book Co., 1935, pp. 69–92 and 251–255.

15 *Formulation of the Kinetic Theory*

Having first explored the properties of gases empirically and more or less intuitively, we are now prepared for a more penetrating mathematical attack on the whole problem. The assumptions of the kinetic theory had such gratifying success in the preliminary trials of Chapter 14 that we are encouraged to attempt an analysis in terms of the exact Newtonian mechanics. This will be a more severe test and, if successful, will increase our confidence in the original assumptions.

GAS PRESSURE DERIVED FROM THE LAWS OF MOTION

If every gas is really a swarm of molecules in continual motion, it follows that any specimen of gas possesses what we might call *internal* kinetic energy. Moreover, each molecule also has *momentum,* and the force with which one molecule hits another or the force with which molecules hit the walls of their container should be deducible from Newton's second law of motion. If we hope to compute such forces, however, we must recognize one difficulty at the outset, namely, that molecules traveling at random will be moving at many different speeds and in many different directions, i.e., they will have a great variety of different momenta. On the other hand, their number, which is conceived to be very large even in a small specimen of gas, makes the application of statistical reasoning to their chance motions very reliable. For example, if billions of molecules are moving haphazardly within a box, we may assume that at any instant just as many must be going in one direction as in another. Since no one direction is favored over another in such random travel, we should expect the pressure exerted by the molecules against all sides of the box to be the same. This is indeed borne out by observation; in any container of gas (e.g., an auto tire or a balloon) the pressure is found to be uniform in all directions.

In deriving the law of gas pressure we shall take advantage of this statistical property in two ways: (1) by calculating the pressure of molecules on just one wall of the vessel in which they are confined, since all other walls must be subject to an equal pressure; (2) by assuming that among a great crowd of molecules roaming at random through the same inclosure, the statistical result is exactly as if $\frac{1}{3}$ of them at all times moved upward or downward, ⅓ forward or backward, and ⅓ to the left or to the right.

In order to understand this assumption, one must realize that a molecule traveling obliquely (velocity represented by vector **V**), as shown in Fig. 74, is in reality moving to the right as well as upward and toward the reader. That is to say, a component of its velocity points in the X direction and other components in the Y and Z directions. It is a great simplification to replace the actual velocities, which point in every

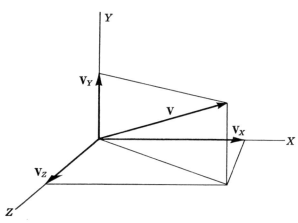

FIG. 74. The motion of a molecule in the **V** direction may be resolved into three motions in the X, Y, and Z directions.

direction of space, by their components in these three mutually perpendicular directions and to treat a large swarm of molecules as if their motions were equally divided among these three directions.

The real state of affairs is thus replaced by an artificial one in which the manifold directions of actual motion are reduced to just three mutually perpendicular directions.

Let us now treat a container of gas as if ⅓ of all its molecules were moving horizontally to the left or the right, ⅓ forward or backward, and ⅓ vertically upward or downward.

Suppose this gas to be confined in a large cubical box whose edges have the length, L, so that the area of any wall is L^2 and the volume of the box L^3. We wish to know the pressure exerted by the gas and this requires the average *force* with which the molecules strike the walls, since *pressure* is *force per unit area*.

When we recall Newton's definition of force as the *rate of change of momentum,* it is clear that, if we knew the change in momentum re-

sulting from each collision and also the number of collisions per second, the product of these two would express the force. That is,

$$\frac{\text{Change in momentum}}{\text{Collisions}} \times \frac{\text{Collisions}}{\text{Seconds}}$$

$$= \frac{\text{Change in momentum}}{\text{Seconds}}$$

In order to find the proper algebraic expression for the force, we start as simply as possible by considering just one molecule (Fig. 75). Let its mass be m, and let it be moving at a speed, v, toward the shaded wall, S. Since its motion before striking the wall is in the −X direction, the momentum of this molecule should be labeled −mv. But one of the fundamental assumptions of the kinetic theory is that every collision with a wall is elastic; hence, on hitting

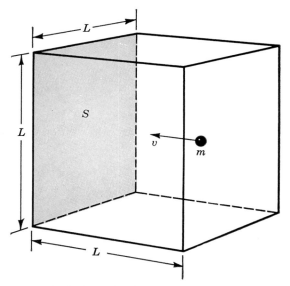

FIG. 75. A single molecule m will exert a pressure on the wall S when it collides with that wall.

the wall, the molecule must rebound to the right with momentum +mv. The *change* in momentum per collision is thus

$$(+mv) - (-mv) = 2mv$$

How many collisions will such a molecule make in 1 sec as it bounds back and forth between the left- and right-hand walls at constant speed? Since it must travel the distance 2L centimeters between successive collisions with the wall S, and since its speed is v centimeters per second, the time between collisions is evidently $2L/v$ seconds. This means that $v/2L$ expresses the number of collisions per second.

$$\frac{v \text{ cm/sec}}{2L \text{ cm/collision}} = \frac{v \text{ collisions}}{2L \text{ second}}$$

The average force f exerted by this one molecule is evidently its change in momentum per second, or

$$f = 2mv \times \frac{v}{2L} = \frac{mv^2}{L}$$

Having obtained a symbolic expression for the force of one molecule, we now apply it to the whole aggregation of molecules in the box. Assume the box to contain N molecules, which we take to be a very large number. From the simplifying assumption that $\frac{1}{3}$ of the N molecules, each with its own speed, v, are moving in the X direction and are therefore capable of hitting the wall, S, the force exerted by these molecules is consequently

$$F = \frac{N}{3} \frac{\overline{mv^2}}{L}$$

A word should be added about the meaning of the $\overline{v^2}$ which appears in the above result. For the horde of molecules present in the box there must be many different speeds. Let their values be $v_1, v_2, v_3, \cdots, v_N$. If we knew them all and were to square all their magnitudes and then add up the squares, the sum of these terms divided by the total number of molecules would give the average *squared* speed. Thus

$$\overline{v^2} = \frac{v_1{}^2 + v_2{}^2 + v_3{}^2 + \cdots v_N{}^2}{N}$$

It is the square root of this result which we call the root-mean-square (abbreviated rms) speed possessed by an average molecule.

Since pressure P is force per unit area,

$$P = \frac{F}{L^2} = \frac{N}{3} \cdot \frac{\overline{mv^2}}{L \cdot L^2} = \frac{N}{3} \frac{\overline{mv^2}}{L^3} = \frac{1}{3} \frac{N\overline{mv^2}}{V}$$

where V replaces L^3 as the volume of the box.

As already stated, there is no necessity for calculating the gas pressure against other sides of the box since gas pressure is known by observation to be equal in all directions.

The reader may be troubled by the thought that with the great congestion of gas molecules moving through the container there must be innumerable collisions between molecules and molecules, whereas our analysis seems to presume that molecules collide only with the walls. This complication turns out to have no effect on the result. When any molecule is turned back from its course by collision with another molecule, the particle which is struck receives momentum from the first molecule and the effect on the walls is the same as if no intermolecular collision had occurred.

The theoretical relationship here derived is important in two respects. One of these is the opportunity it affords for numerical verification. If one makes an actual determination of the pressure, volume, and mass of a gas, as well as the average molecular speed, and the values obtained are actually related in the way indicated by the pressure equation, such agreement confirms the soundness of our fundamental assumptions. In a second respect the relation is important because it is a means of deriving subsidiary gas laws which may be separately tested experimentally. Probably the most potent element in the scientific method is the evolution of just such relations as the foregoing, which are frequently confirmed by experiment. Presentday belief in the fundamental correctness of the kinetic theory of gases is based on the success with which actual gas behavior is described by the pressure law and other theoretical relations deduced from it.

KINETIC ENERGY OF GAS MOLECULES AND THE TEMPERATURE OF THE GAS

The form of the gas pressure law which we have derived from purely mechanical considerations can be recast slightly so as to signify kinetic energy. Writing the equation

$$PV = \tfrac{1}{3}N\overline{mv^2}$$

we note that the right-hand side is very nearly an expression for the average kinetic energy of the whole molecular aggregation. By merely introducing the factor 2/2,

$$\tfrac{1}{3}N\overline{mv^2}$$

becomes

$$\tfrac{2}{3}(\tfrac{1}{2}N\overline{mv^2})$$

or $\frac{2}{3}$ the total kinetic energy. If we now write

$$PV = \tfrac{2}{3}\text{K.E.}$$

(according to the kinetic theory) and remember (see p. 141) that $PV = CT$ where C is a proportionality constant (according to experiment), then a combination of the theoretical and experimental relations tells us finally that the kinetic energy of the gas is proportional to the absolute temperature of the gas.

$$\text{K.E.} = \tfrac{3}{2}CT$$

We are therefore justified in concluding that the absolute temperature of a gas is determined by the average energy of motion possessed by the molecules of the gas. This was just the conclusion to which our earlier qualitative study of molecular motion led us (see p. 139).

In short, when heat energy is supplied to a gas and the temperature of the gas is observed to rise, what takes place internally is a general increase in the speed of the molecules such that the average kinetic energy increases in proportion to the rise in temperature. This is effectually the same thing as saying that thermal energy or heat *is* energy of molecular motion.

DERIVATION OF BOYLE'S AND CHARLES' LAWS FROM THE PRESSURE EQUATION

Accepting the fact that $\tfrac{1}{2}Nm\overline{v^2}$ is proportional to the absolute temperature, the relation

$$PV = \tfrac{1}{3}Nm\overline{v^2}$$

obviously contains both Boyle's and Charles' laws. If T is constant, then $\tfrac{1}{3}Nm\overline{v^2}$ is also constant and

$$PV = \text{Constant} \qquad \text{(Boyle's law)}$$

If V is held constant, while T and P are allowed to vary,

$$P = \text{Constant} \times T \qquad \text{(Charles' law)}$$

THE BROWNIAN MOTION

An explanation of the Brownian motion, already referred to, is suggested at once by the kinetic theory of gases. If gas molecules are really in continual rapid and chaotic motion, then their impacts against any small, visible particles in their paths should jolt the visible particles and cause them to bob this way and that in response to the blows. Only particles of very small dimensions and inertia could be expected to show the effect of this molecular bombardment, hence the Brownian motion is not usually detectable excepting among particles of every minute size and mass. However, hot mercury vapor will produce similar agitation among fairly large sized chips of glass because the mercury molecules have comparatively great mass and high energy. The Brownian effect is comparable to what would be seen if a floating cask were the target of rifle bullets. A distant observer could only infer from the irregular bobbing of the cask in the water that its behavior was the consequence of a rain of blows; the probable agents (the bullets) would be assumed from their effect upon the object they struck.

The agitation of particles which exhibit the Brownian motion becomes more violent at high temperatures and rather sluggish at low temperatures, which is just the variation to be expected from the kinetic explanation of this phenomenon.

It is important to recall at this point that our derivation of the pressure law and other gas laws resulting from it was based on a statistical assumption, namely, that a great crowd of particles can be regarded as conforming to a uniform average pattern of behavior even though individuals among the crowd are known to vary considerably from this average. The basis for the assumption lies in the field of probability. It is probable that, in the absence of any directing influence, a crowd of molecules or, indeed, a crowd of people, will move in all possible directions. Imagine a thousand persons milling about on a football field, with no purpose other than to keep warm. For every person who is moving west, at random, it is likely that another person will be found moving east and likewise for any pair of opposing directions. For every person impelled to walk rapidly it is probable that another can be found who is moving slowly, and the majority of people may be expected to maintain a pace which is approximately average.

Now the Brownian motion is explainable only by abandoning the statistical argument of compensated motions. A particle of dust under microscopic observation is undoubtedly the receiver of many compensated molecular blows, but each visible displacement from one position to another is evidently due to an uncompensated impulse by some molecule of accidentally high momentum which strikes it on one side with a force greater than the average. In short, the statistical point of view which serves so well in accounting for the behavior of a multitude must be set aside in explaining the idiosyncrasies of an individual in the multitude.

DIRECT MEASUREMENT OF THE SPEED OF VAPOR MOLECULES

In 1920 the German scientist Otto Stern devised and carried out an ingenious method for

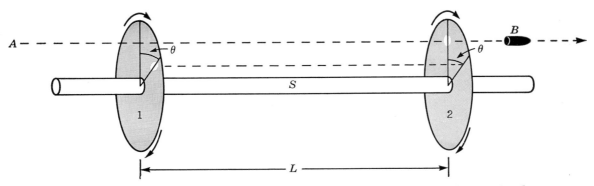

FIG. 76. Knowing the speed of rotation and angle θ, the velocity of the bullet may be calculated.

determining the speed of silver vapor molecules. The principle underlying the method is as follows: If a projectile is flying in a straight line toward a target while the target is moving at right angles to the line of flight, the projectile will strike the target a little to one side of the point toward which it was aimed. This will be the case even if the projectile moves very much faster than the target does. If, then, we know the speed at which the target is being displaced, we can easily compute the speed of the projectile.

As an exercise, introductory to Stern's experiment, consider the apparatus shown in Fig. 76. A bullet, fired originally from the source A, has made a hole in wheel 1 (a cardboard target) and later on makes a hole in wheel 2. Both of these wheels are firmly attached to the rotating shaft S whose speed of rotation, say n rps, is known. It is then possible to measure experimentally, from the relative angular displacement of the holes, the angle θ through which the targets and shaft have rotated while the bullet moved from one target to the other through the relatively long distance L. Since the time of one complete revolution of the wheels is $1/n$ seconds, the time t required to move through an angle θ will be

$$\frac{\theta}{360} \times \frac{1}{n} = t$$

and the speed v is given by

$$v = \frac{L}{t} = \frac{L360n}{\theta}$$

Although this experimental arrangement is quite satisfactory for measuring the speed of a single bullet, it could not be used in this form to determine simultaneously the many speeds among a swarm of molecules. However, the germ of the idea is carried over into the method of Stern.

A plan view of Stern's apparatus is depicted in Fig. 77. A rectangular box is arranged so that it can be rotated rapidly on a shaft perpendicular to the plane of the paper. Along the axis of rotation A there is a platinum wire coated with silver, and the passage of electric current

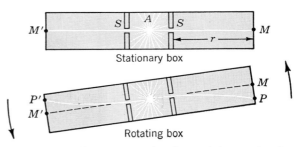

FIG. 77. Stern's apparatus for determining molecular speeds.

through the wire makes it glow like an ordinary lamp filament. Silver melts at 961°C, so that, by operating at 1200°C, Stern could be certain that silver would evaporate from the molten coating of the filament. In order that the vapor particles may have unobstructed motion in the desired directions, the entire chamber must be highly evacuated.

When the box is stationary, the silver molecules which fly off the filament in many directions are intercepted by the confining walls nearby with the exception of those molecules which happen to be moving toward the narrow slits, S, extending down the middle of each wall. Thus the only silver particles that escape from the central inclosure are the ones which are directed toward the middle, M and M', of the end plates. These molecules, having traveled the distance, r, strike the ends of the box at M, M' and deposit there to form a thin line of silver.

Consider now the destination of any silver molecules that pass through the slits *while the apparatus is rotating*. Since the particles take no part in the rotation, they will pursue straight paths just as if the machine were at rest. They will not arrive at M, M', however, since these points have moved through the distance MP ($= M'P'$) while the particles were moving through the distance, r. The same effect may be observed in a lawn sprinkler which rotates as it emits water. Though each water particle moves out radially, the path of the water stream is a spiral. Inasmuch as the distance MP and the distance r are traversed in the same time, we have here the data for a calculation of the speed.

If n represents the number of rotations per second made by the box, then $1/n$ represents the number of seconds required for one rotation. But MP is not one rotation. It is instead the fraction MP/C of one rotation, and it therefore corresponds to a time of

$$\frac{MP}{C} \times \frac{1}{n} \text{ second}$$

where C is the total circumference through which the ends move. Since the silver particles, on the other hand, move at the rate v over the distance r, the same time may be expressed by r/v. Hence,

$$r/v = MP/nC$$

and

$$v = nCr/MP$$

With such a device, Stern obtained speeds around 5.6×10^4 cm/sec, which is reasonably close to a value that we shall calculate from the kinetic theory below.

In the actual experiment it was found that a *sharp* line of silver particles deposited on the glass end plates only when the apparatus was stationary. The *displaced* line, produced during rotation, had considerably greater width and was in fact a narrow *band,* dark along its center and tapering off to extreme faintness at the edges. This observation was interpreted to mean that, although most of the silver molecules moved at a speed close to the value obtained in the last equation, some of the molecules traveled at higher or lower speeds and were accordingly displaced to lesser or greater degrees. Such a distribution

of speeds is entirely in keeping with the assumptions of the kinetic theory as already described.

CALCULATION OF THE SPEED OF GAS MOLECULES

The gas pressure law by itself enables us to *compare* molecular speeds, as we have seen. But the *actual* speeds of gas molecules can be calculated with the aid of the pressure law and the general gas law. That is, if for 1 mole of any gas

$$PV = \tfrac{1}{3}Nm\overline{v^2} \qquad \text{and also} \qquad PV = CT$$

it follows that

$$\overline{v^2} = \frac{3CT}{Nm}$$

As an example, let us estimate the rms speed with which molecules of silver in the vapor state move through space when the temperature is 1200°C. The quantities needed for substitution in the last equation are:

$C = 8.31 \times 10^7$ ergs per mole per degree C.
$T = 1200 + 273 = 1473°$ abs.
$Nm =$ The number of molecules (N) multiplied by the mass of each molecule (m) is obviously the total mass of silver vapor concerned. The mass to be used in the calculation is that of 1 *mole* of silver. This is the amount of silver vapor which would occupy a volume of 22.4 liters under standard conditions of temperature and pressure, and its mass is 108 grams, measured experimentally.

Substituting these values into the equation gives the rms speed of silver molecules at 1200°C as

$$\sqrt{\overline{v^2}} = \sqrt{\frac{3 \times 8.31 \times 10^7 \times 1473}{108}}$$

$$= 5.85 \times 10^4 \text{ cm/sec}$$

Taking into account the experimental difficulties of Stern's method, this calculated value of molecular speed is considered in good agreement with experimental fact.

RELATION BETWEEN SPEED AND MASS OF GAS MOLECULES

Since Stern's method is only one of many experimental procedures for determining molecular speeds, there are abundant data for gases other than silver vapor. Let us compare, for example, the rms molecular speeds for the two gases hydrogen and oxygen at the same temperature.

The result is that hydrogen molecules have four times as large an rms speed as those of oxygen at the same temperature. What can we conclude from this information? If we write

$$\frac{\sqrt{\overline{V_H^2}}}{\sqrt{\overline{V_O^2}}} = 4$$

where the subscripts O and H refer to oxygen and hydrogen respectively, then

$$\frac{\overline{V_H^2}}{\overline{V_O^2}} = 16$$

But it is now well known that the oxygen molecule has 16 times the mass of the hydrogen molecule, so that

$$\frac{\overline{V_H^2}}{\overline{V_O^2}} = \frac{m_O}{m_H}$$

This is a general fact, now established experimentally, so that for any two gases A and B at the same temperature,

$$\frac{\overline{V_A^2}}{\overline{V_B^2}} = \frac{m_B}{m_A}$$

Cross-multiplying,

$$m_A \overline{V_A^2} = m_B \overline{V_B^2}$$

This result has great importance because it proves that the molecules of all gases at the same temperature have *equal* average kinetic energies, independently of the pressure. Such a conclusion expresses far more than any of our previous statements relating temperature with kinetic energy. Statements like, "temperature *is proportional to* the average molecular kinetic energy," "temperature *is a measure of* the total kinetic energy of the gas molecules," etc., are far less useful than the statement that "the molecules of *all* gases have *equal* average kinetic energies, provided only that the temperature is the same." The strength of this knowledge is illustrated in the following section.

AVOGADRO'S LAW

We come now to a profound and important inference which can be drawn from our theoretical analysis and the experimental laws of gases. Suppose that two gases, say, oxygen and hydrogen, are kept in separate vessels at the same temperature. This means that the molecules of oxygen have the same average kinetic energy as the molecules of hydrogen. Symbolically,

$$\tfrac{1}{2} m_O \overline{v_O}^2 = \tfrac{1}{2} m_H \overline{v_H}^2$$

where the subscripts O and H designate oxygen and hydrogen respectively.

Suppose further that the two gases are confined at the same pressure in vessels of equal volume. We may then write

$$P_O V_O = P_H V_H$$

That is,

$$\tfrac{1}{3} N_O m_O \overline{v_O}^2 = \tfrac{1}{3} N_H m_H \overline{v_H}^2$$

But since the temperature is the same for oxygen and hydrogen,

$$m_O \overline{v_O}^2 = m_H \overline{v_H}^2$$

and therefore

$$N_O = N_H$$

Expressed in words, this equality means that all gases have the same number of molecules per unit volume if their temperatures and pressures are the same.

It follows, therefore, that if one gas has, for example, 3 times the volume of the other when it is at the same temperature and pressure as the other, it must contain 3 times as many molecules.

The conclusion just derived as a consequence of the kinetic theory was first advanced as a hypothesis in 1811 by the Italian physicist Amedeo Avogadro (1776–1856) in an attempt to explain certain facts of chemical combination. The pivotal character of Avogadro's assertion in the modern view of the structure of matter and the numerous experimental confirmations of his idea have elevated the above statement to the dignity of a scientific law. This law is highly useful in that it enables us to compare the masses of individual molecules. When we find, for example, that a given volume of oxygen weighs 16 times as much as an equal volume of hydrogen under the same conditions, we may conclude from Avogadro's law that a single oxygen molecule is 16 times as heavy as a single hydrogen molecule.

AVOGADRO'S NUMBER

From a realization that vessels of identical volume hold the same number of gaseous molecules to a determination of the number itself is a long stride forward in the application of scientific method, yet the actual count of molecules has been made by several different methods, all of which yield values which are in substantial agreement with one another. It has become cus-

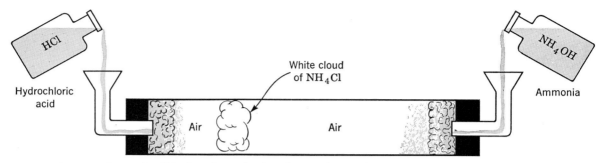

FIG. 78.   An experiment in diffusion through air.   Ammonia gas diffuses more rapidly than hydrochloric acid gas.

tomary to consider the number of molecules comprising 1 *mole* of a gas, i.e., the mass of any gas that takes up 22,400 cc of space when the pressure is 1 atmosphere and the temperature 0°C. This number of particles, called *Avogadro's number,* has been found to be 6.02×10^{23}.

GRAHAM'S LAW

For any two gases A and B we may now write with confidence

$$\frac{\text{Rms speed of molecules } A}{\text{Rms speed of molecules } B} = \sqrt{\frac{m_B}{m_A}}$$

In order to use this relation it is not necessary to know the individual masses of the molecules A and B, but merely their relative masses.

Such differences in molecular speeds manifest themselves in many phenomena. Perhaps the simplest and most easily demonstrated is that of diffusion. Light molecules, whose rms speeds are relatively high, should diffuse more rapidly than heavy molecules, whose rms speeds are relatively low. This phenomenon was observed some twenty-five years before the theoretical relation was worked out. The British scientist Thomas Graham discovered in 1830 that light gases leaked through small openings faster than do denser gases and that the relative rates of leakage were inversely proportional to the square roots of their relative densities. This is virtually the result obtained in the foregoing deduction.

DEMONSTRATION OF GASEOUS DIFFUSION

A striking demonstration of the swifter travel of lighter gas molecules compared with heavier ones gives us a rough confirmation of Graham's law. A long open-ended glass tube is mounted horizontally, and each end is plugged with absorbent cotton (Fig. 78). One plug is saturated with hydrogen chloride solution. At the same time the other plug is saturated with ammonia solution. The liquids begin evaporating immediately, and the gases hydrogen chloride and ammonia start diffusing toward each other through the air which otherwise fills the tube.

Hydrogen chloride gas is about twice as dense as ammonia gas; hence each of its molecules has about twice the mass of an ammonia molecule. Consequently, the swarm of ammonia molecules should diffuse faster than the hydrogen chloride molecules and it may be expected that the place of meeting between the bulk of the molecules of both kinds should be much closer to the source of hydrogen chloride than to that of ammonia.

The selection of hydrogen chloride and ammonia for this experiment is due to the conspicuous interaction which these substances undergo with each other. On coming into contact they form ammonium chloride, an easily discernible white cloud. The formation of a white band within the tube marks, therefore, the region of contact between the two gases. This band is actually observed well toward the hydrogen chloride end of the tube.

THE LAW OF ATMOSPHERES

In deriving the gas pressure law ($PV = \frac{1}{3}Nm\overline{v^2}$), we neglected entirely the influence of gravity on the gas molecules. This was because the very small mass of a molecule makes the earth's gravitational force on the molecule negligible compared with the large forces induced by molecular collisions. Nevertheless, gas molecules do respond weakly to the pull of gravity, and in a very tall column of gas this response is noticeable by the greater concentration of gas particles at the lower levels than at the higher ones. In other words, gases do tend to settle in spite of their perpetual thermal motion.

In the earth's atmosphere, for example, the air is densest at sea level, and it becomes progressively less dense with increasing altitude. The relation between concentration of molecules and height is called the *law of atmospheres,* and a formulation of this law contains Avogadro's number as one of the factors. Unfortunately we cannot make a direct count of gas molecules in the air, but if small, visible particles are suspended in a liquid a similar gradation of density from bottom to top may be anticipated. The particles tend to settle downward in response to the pull of gravity while the Brownian motion imparted to them by the impulses they receive from the molecules of the solvent makes them tend to spread out. In this way a miniature "atmosphere" is formed with the largest proportion of suspended particles near the bottom of the liquid.

PERRIN'S DETERMINATION OF AVOGADRO'S NUMBER

In 1908 the French scientist Jean Perrin devised an experiment (Fig. 79) to determine the distribution of suspended particles in an emul-

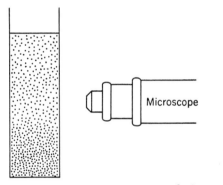

FIG. 79. Perrin's determination of Avogadro's number.

sion of gamboge particles in water, thus obtaining a value for the Avogadro number. Gamboge is a finely divided, resinous pigment which does not really dissolve in water but instead forms an emulsion of tiny clusters of molecules. The gamboge particles in the emulsion are a few ten-thousandths of a millimeter in diameter. Using a microscope, Perrin counted directly the number of gamboge particles visible in the same amount of space at slightly different levels. In the atmosphere it would take more than a hundred miles of ascent to get the same relative thinning out of particles as occurred in the gamboge emulsion with a change in depth of

less than 1 mm. The difference is merely one of degree, however, and an emulsion offers the double advantage that the particles are visible and that the range of observations is conveniently short.

From many repetitions of the determination Perrin calculated a value for Avogadro's number equal to 6.5×10^{23} molecules per mole. Other methods give nearly the same value for this important constant. The figure currently accepted as the most accurate measurement of Avogadro's number is 6.0247×10^{23}.[1]

It is unlikely that a figure so large can convey much meaning to the human mind beyond the idea that even small specimens of matter are made up of incredibly many particles. For example, a cube of gas only $\frac{1}{100}$ mm on a side would contain more than 10 times as many molecules as there are people in the entire world.

MOLECULAR SIZE

There are several ways of determining the actual sizes of molecules. One of these, a method devised by the American chemist, Irving Langmuir (1881–), is beautiful in its simplicity. An oil is dissolved in some volatile compound such as benzene and dropped upon the surface of water which has previously been covered with powdered talc. The solution spreads rapidly over the water surface, revealing its boundary by the talc which it pushes ahead of it. The benzene quickly evaporates, and when the spreading of the oil ceases it is presumably because the film has been reduced to a thickness of only one molecule throughout. Otherwise there is no reason why it should not continue to spread. A known mass of oil is used, and its density is determined beforehand. The volume of the oil is evidently its mass divided by its density, for

$$\frac{m \text{ grams}}{D \text{ grams/cubic centimeter}} = V \text{ cubic centimeters}$$

But the volume of the oil is also equal to the area of the patch times the thickness of the patch, so the volume just obtained is merely divided by the measured area to obtain the thickness of the oil film, which is the length of a single molecule. Vegetable oils like palmitic acid have molecules which are a few ten-millionths of a centimeter long. Molecules of the elements measure about a hundred-millionth of a centimeter in diameter.

· · · · · · · · · · · · · · · · · · ·

[1] J. W. M. Du Mond and E. R. Cohen, *Technical Report,* California Institute of Technology, November, 1952.

PROBLEMS

1. Describe in your own words the difficulties encountered in trying to explain diffusion phenomena in terms of a continuous theory of matter.

2. Recognizing that increased temperature means increased molecular activity, is it true that the rms molecular speed in our atmosphere is about twice as high in summer as it is in the winter?

3. In 22,400 cc of any gas at 0°C and 1 atmosphere pressure there are 6×10^{23} molecules (Avogadro's number). How many molecules are there in 1 cc of any gas at 30°C and 1 atmosphere pressure?
Ans. 2.4×10^{19}.

4. In Stern's experiment the stream of silver particles was not a straight line but a spiral. Prove this by plotting carefully the positions of several molecules on their way out to the end of the apparatus.

5. During World War II one of the most difficult problems encountered in producing the uranium bomb was the separation of two kinds of uranium particles from each other. The two particles had relative masses 235 and 238. They were finally separated by taking advantage of the difference in their rates of diffusion through porous materials. Would these two uranium particles be as easy to separate by diffusion as, for example, hydrogen and oxygen? Explain.

6. Using the calculation for silver particles on p. 148 as a guide, calculate the rms speed which hydrogen particles would have on the surface of the sun at a temperature of 6000°C. Assume that silver particles are 108 times as heavy as hydrogen particles.
Ans. 12.5×10^5 cm/sec.

. . . .

REFERENCE

1. *A Source Book in Physics,* W. F. Magie, McGraw-Hill Book Co., 1935, pp. 255–262.

Introduction to Chemistry

It is evident that, within the range of phenomena described thus far, the molecular hypothesis has had gratifying success. Gases do indeed behave as if they were made up of exceedingly tiny particles, all alike for any one gas, and so firmly constructed that they do not go to pieces when they collide with other particles of the same kind at ordinary temperatures. In a homogeneous gas like oxygen there appears to be little attraction of one molecule for another, but when molecules of different gases collide with each other, the result may be startlingly different. For example, when hydrogen and oxygen particles collide with sufficient velocity, so much energy is released that we think of it as an explosion; and when ammonia particles collide with particles of hydrochloric acid gas, a white solid is formed. Obviously, molecules are not just smooth hard particles which bounce harmlessly off every other molecule which they strike and which are devoid of any important internal structure. We are now about to study a wide range of phenomena which reveal significant details of that internal structure.

From his earliest groping awareness of the world around him, savage man must have observed that the environment is constantly changing. Growth and decay, fermentation and combustion, are just a few of the processes by which one kind of matter is changed into another. Knowledge of such changes and of the characteristics which differentiate one kind of matter from another makes up the science of chemistry.

Chemistry, with its present point of view, is less than two centuries old, but haphazard knowledge of a great many chemical properties and chemical changes was accumulated by some of the most ancient civilizations. Long before the Christian era, the Egyptians and others had gained considerable skill in tanning, dyeing, working of metals, and the preparation of alloys, salts, pigments, and medicines—all operations involving transformations of matter and, therefore, chemical processes.

As with other studies of nature, chemistry arose out of necessity. It was the uses to which the products of chemical change could be put that impelled men to study these processes and thereby acquire better tools, weapons, clothing, and other material advantages. The speculative and philosophical aspects, which are highly important to chemistry as a *science,* had little place in the chemical "arts" of the ancient Egyptians.

Theoretical speculation was, on the other hand, the chief concern of the eminent Greek philosophers who flourished during the centuries just preceding the Christian era; it was from these schools that we have the first serious hypotheses concerning the structure of matter.

Let us imagine ourselves starting out to subdivide a piece of ordinary matter, say, iron, which seems completely homogeneous to the naked eye. Suppose we continue the division and subdivision to an extreme degree of fineness. How far can we continue this division of matter into smaller and smaller particles? Only one of two possible assumptions can be valid; either the division may go on without limit (in imagination), or it may be continued only to the point where an indivisible particle, or *atom,* is reached. If the first possibility exists, we would say that matter is *continuous;* if the latter restriction exists, matter is *discontinuous.* Hypothetically, either of these assumptions might serve as a starting point for speculation, and the theories which resulted would have to be tested, in the usual way, against experimental facts.

Both points of view were represented in the Greek schools. The idea of a continuous structure for matter goes back at least as far as Empedocles (450 b.c.), and it was this view which Socrates, Plato, and Aristotle adopted. The opposite, or atomic point of view, was taken by Democritus (470–400 b.c.) and by Epicurus (342–270 b.c.). When the problem of reconciling secular knowledge with theology arose, it was the Aristotelian hypothesis which was approved, not because there was any objection to atoms but because there were other ideas taught by the Epicureans which the existing theology could not tolerate. For example, the Epicureans were *mechanists,* that is, they believed that all bodies in the universe, whether living or dead, terrestrial or celestial, were subject to the same natural laws. The Aristotelians, on the contrary, were *vitalists,* that is, they believed that living organisms contained some "principle" or "soul" which guided the organism toward perfection and which did not respond to the laws valid for inanimate objects. Thus it was that through the Middle Ages the accepted view was that matter was infinitely divisible, continuous, and completely homogeneous in structure.

The Aristotelians held that the universe consisted of a single kind of matter which, when endowed in various proportions with the characteristics of earth, water, air, and fire, yielded the immense variety of substances to be found throughout the world. The combinations were assumed to result from the influence of two all-pervading powers of attraction and repulsion comparable with the human emotions of love and hate.

The science of chemistry today is built on the concept of atoms. Like Democritus, we hold that a specimen of iron, for example, cannot be subdivided without limit. When the ultimate particle, or atom, of iron has been segregated, any further fracture would change its identity and the resulting fragments would no longer possess the properties familiar to iron. However, the atomistic doctrine of the Greeks was pure speculation, whereas the modern atomic theory is supported firmly by a strong chain of experimental evidence. It is the main purpose of this chapter to present some of the evidence for the reality of atoms.

ALCHEMY

Chemistry may be regarded as beginning in about the seventh century with the primitive investigations of the Arab alchemists. These men were not only theorists but experimentalists as well. They tried systematically to prepare new substances from ones already known and to expand specific knowledge of chemical change into generalizations which would apply to large classes of substances.

Alchemy was undoubtedly the immediate forerunner of chemistry, but its reputation has suffered because of numerous charlatans who debased its original purpose. Gradually the main object of alchemy became the search for a means of transmuting base metals into silver and gold. Now, considered as a problem of chemistry, there is certainly nothing disreputable about attempts to transmute metals. Transmutation is a project which is seriously and successfully pursued at the present time by scientists of the highest repute. What made transmutation a corrupting influence over the alchemy of the Middle Ages was the dishonesty of some alchemists who published false claims of success. The possibility of converting cheap metals into precious ones provoked such dreams of fabulous wealth and power that unscrupulous fortune hunters occasionally chose alchemy as the ready road to riches. Swindlers, promising potent elixirs or cheap gold, hoped to interest wealthy patrons who would subsidize the alchemical experiments until their confidence or their funds were exhausted. Secrecy and mystification became the alchemist's safeguards against exposure, and the records of his experimentation were often an intentionally confusing jumble of incantation and ambiguous writing. Supernatural influences were invoked, and the alchemist became an awesome creature, feared by the superstitious laymen.

Bettmann Archive

PLATE XXIV.   Francesco de' Medici (1541–1587) supervising work in his chemistry laboratory. Painting by Giovanni Stradano.

The contrast between this muddled and almost fruitless pseudoscience and the orderly, useful body of knowledge now classified as chemistry emphasizes several lessons which are applicable to any branch of learning. First, since cooperative effort yields the swiftest and surest advance, it is folly for scientists deliberately to conceal their achievements from one another. Especially is it necessary that they communicate their experiences in language of precise and simple meaning. Modern scientists try to avoid ambiguity in writing by the use of standardized terminology.

Second, investigation of the laws of nature demands sound experimental techniques. Experiments must be capable of duplication by others, and their results must be clear to all qualified observers without any implication of magic or occult influence. Supernatural factors have no place in the realm of natural science.

Third, if the seeker after new knowledge of the physical world is not objectively honest, he can easily fall into the error of self-deception. The experience of several centuries has shown that a habit of impartial observation is important to the research scientist. If he allows himself to be influenced by strong personal reasons for wishing that an experiment turn out one way rather than another, it ceases to be an experiment at all, for his bias will distort both his observation and his judgment.

The idea that base metals might be transmuted into noble metals probably arose, or at least gained plausibility, from a coincidence. Copper and gold are frequently found together in nature. So are the ores of lead and silver. Indeed, compounds of lead when prepared for commercial purposes are usually found to be contaminated with silver. The alchemists, having adopted Aristotle's postulate that nature seeks to perfect itself, inferred from the coexistence of copper and gold, lead and silver, in the earth that the baser metals were growing into the nobler metals by some process of natural refinement. It seemed to them entirely reasonable, therefore, that some means could be discovered to hasten the change. The agent, so long sought but never found, was referred to as the "philosopher's stone." It is scarcely necessary to point out that the very premise for the alchemistic reasoning lacks foundation. There is no evidence at all that nature is engaged in any self-perfecting operations or, indeed, that any one substance is more perfect than another.

It was not until the time of Robert Boyle (1627–1691) that the modern quantitative and atomic view of chemical change began to take shape. In 1661 Boyle wrote a remarkable treatise called *The Sceptical Chymist* in which he clearly broke away from the Greek idea of the four elements. In this book the concept of fundamental particles is discernible, and, what is most important, the evidence he submits is experimental and not metaphysical. Boyle made numerous important discoveries in chemistry and physics, especially in connection with the properties of gases.

DISTINCTION BETWEEN PHYSICAL AND CHEMICAL CHANGE

A description of matter includes some properties which are evidently due not to the specific substance under examination but to the state in which it happens to be. Thus, all kinds of matter in the gaseous state obey more or less faithfully the physical gas laws which have been described. Liquids, irrespective of kind, all share certain physical characteristics, and solids, in turn, have physical properties which belong only to matter in the solid form. Most kinds of matter can exist in any of these three states if suitable conditions are imposed on them. Hydrogen, air, and ammonia, although ordinarily gaseous, can be liquified and frozen. Ice, camphor, and iron, ordinarily solid, can be melted and vaporized. But if water is raised to sufficiently high temperature it changes into two kinds of matter which, although colorless gases like the steam from which they were derived, differ sharply in a great many other respects from steam and also from each other. Any process which changes the identity of matter is called a chemical change and the science of chemistry is concerned with such changes as well as with the properties which distinguish one kind of matter from another.

Inasmuch as there are many thousands of distinct substances, it is apparent that to catalog their numerous distinguishing characteristics and to describe the chemical changes which they undergo with one another is itself a stupendous task. But the science of chemistry is not merely a compendium of such factual data; it is also a record of generalized patterns of behavior which the different kinds of matter have been observed to follow in their interactions. It includes also the rationalizations by means of which such general behavior may be explained. It will be our concern to examine certain of these rationalizations or theories as illustrations of inference drawn from evidence.

THEORIES OF COMBUSTION

Burning is surely the most familiar chemical transformation in anyone's experience. It is spectacular; it is terrifying; it is useful. The combustible material catches fire, and the attendant flame is a source of heat, light, and, frequently, of sound. When the fire is extinguished, the burned material is found to be utterly changed in appearance, in individual properties, and in mass. Most notably, it is no longer combustible.

PHLOGISTON

Passing over the many fantastic and untested ideas by which primitive and medieval man sought to explain burning, let us examine a hypothesis which gained ascendancy among the most profound thinkers of the eighteenth century. This was the hypothesis proposed by two German physicians, J. J. Becher and G. E. Stahl, that all combustible materials contain a burning element or principle, which Stahl named *phlogiston,* and that it was the vigorous escape of this substance that constituted burning. Probably the idea was taken from Plato, who noted that burning was usually attended by the escape of something from the fuel. Superficially the proposition seems plausible, for during combustion something does appear to leave the burning substance. With many fuels, such as wood and coal, there is an actual loss of matter during burning, as proved by the diminished mass of the residue. But the reverse is true in other cases, and we shall see that proponents of the phlogiston hypothesis were, in the end, obliged to make quite unreasonable assumptions to account for burning in general.

We list first several pertinent facts which were generally accepted by eighteenth century scientists:

1. That burning and respiration are related, and that both operations require air.

2. That air in which burning has occurred undergoes some change which prevents further burning; moreover, this used-up air is also unfit for respiration.

3. That the rusting of iron is a phenomenon related to burning (if not the same thing occurring at a slower rate), for, again, air is required, and the rust is identical with the solid residue left after iron burns.

The student of today scarcely needs to be reminded that we now describe burning, rusting, and respiration as the union of a combustible substance with that ingredient of air which is called oxygen, the products of combustion being compounds of a class known as oxides. This explanation can be proved but we should notice that, as a preliminary hypothesis, it is no more plausible than the one proposed by Becher and Stahl—that a burning substance loses, rather than gains, something during the process.

Even a quantitative experiment, such as the

burning of a candle in a closed jar, is inconclusive. The candle flame soon goes out because, as we say, the oxygen of the confined air has united with the material of the candle; but, equally logically, the phlogistonists said that combustion ceased because the air had become saturated with as much phlogiston as it could hold and no further burning was possible unless fresh, unsaturated air were admitted. Such a closed system undergoes no change in weight in consequence of the burning, but this fact would be just as compatible with a loss by the candle to the confined air as by a gain of oxygen from the air.

Nevertheless, the phlogiston theory, which endured stubbornly for a century, might have been discredited much sooner than it was if proper attention had been paid to quantitative evidence. It was known, for example, that air in which a metal is burning shrinks in volume. Adherents of phlogiston did not conclude from this that some ingredient had been removed from the air. They preferred to believe that the liberated phlogiston made the air more compact.

Of greater significance was the evidence of weighing. The residue obtained by burning a solid metal is heavier than the metal specimen itself. This fact had been established repeatedly by experimenters of the seventeenth and eighteenth centuries. Today we may smile at the inference that a gain in weight could mean that something was lost by the body, but that was the very explanation offered by the phlogistonists. Phlogiston was assumed to have negative weight; hence, its escape from the burning metal must result in making the ash or rust heavier! One remembers, however, that in earlier times a principle of lightness or levitation shared equal dignity with the principle of heaviness or gravitation and that the idea of inherent lightness descended directly from Aristotle. Thus, in Aristotle's view, certain materials had a natural disposition to seek a higher elevation, and this upward urge could be conveniently described as negative weight.

It may have been the traditional respect for Aristotelian authority that misled Stahl and his followers in their original hypothesis, for most metals do not occur in the pure state in nature but, rather, as ores. In order to obtain the useful metals such as iron, tin, and lead, it is necessary to subject their ores to the process of smelting, a fact known since remote times. The ancient doctrine held that the materials stored up in nature were simple ones, whereas the products derived from them by man's ingenuity were necessarily complex. Hence the eighteenth century chemists regarded metals as combinations of the simple ores of nature with phlogiston, acquired during smelting.

THE DISCOVERY OF OXYGEN

The role of oxygen in burning, rusting, and respiration was not understood until this substance had been prepared in a relatively pure state or "discovered." This is to be expected, of course, but it is puzzling to reflect that the man usually credited with discovering oxygen—Joseph Priestley (1733–1804)—did not, at first, realize that he had found a unique substance. Instead, he regarded it as a remarkably pure air or, as he called it, dephlogisticated air. In present-day language this would mean air that is exceptionally fit for breathing or for burning as contrasted with ordinary air, which was considered to be partially phlogisticated.

Oxygen had actually been produced in 1669 by John Mayow (1643–1679) and possibly even earlier by Leonardo da Vinci, but the accounts of their experimentation seem to have escaped the eighteenth century investigators. Priestley obtained the element by heating an orange-red powder which we now call mercuric oxide, but which was then known as the *calx* or rust of mercury. Priestley's choice of this substance was most fortunate, since it is one of the few metallic oxides that readily gives up its oxygen when moderately heated. Oxygen had also been prepared a few years earlier by the Swedish chemist Scheele (1742–1786), but publication of his results was delayed and Priestley was unaware of them. Both men subscribed to the phlogiston theory of combustion, and Priestley persisted in upholding it even after the theory had been abandoned by many of his contemporaries.

It is not to be supposed that the phlogiston theory of burning was useless or even that it retarded the advance of knowledge. Quite the reverse. Like the erroneous caloric theory of heat, it formed a basis for experimentation and the results of experiment always augment man's knowledge. If we, in possession of better instruments and more complete factual information, should be inclined to decry the interpretations which the phlogistonists made of their experimental data, let us realize that, without some theory to stimulate experimentation, there would have been far less data to interpret.

THE MODERN THEORY OF COMBUSTION

Although Scheele and Priestley demonstrated that oxygen supports life and that materials burn in it with greater vigor than they do in ordinary air, both men missed the revolutionary significance of their experiments. It remained for Antoine Lavoisier (1743–1794), the brilliant Frenchman who is called the father of modern chemistry, to establish by conclusive proof the theory of combustion which is now accepted. His apparatus consisted of a retort whose neck reached into a closed container of air (Fig. 80). He placed a weighed amount of pure mercury in

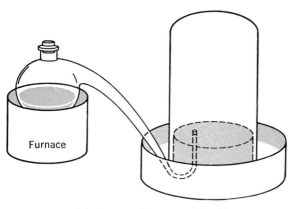

FIG. 80. Lavoisier's experiment to identify oxygen.

the retort and kept the mercury at a temperature just below its boiling point for a number of days. Gradually the mercury became covered with a red powder, which he recognized as the calx of mercury, while the confined air diminished to about ⅕ of its original volume. Lavoisier weighed the red calx and then heated it separately, whereupon it evolved the same bulk of gas as had been removed from the air and left a residue of mercury equal in weight to that which had been used up in the first stage.

Lavoisier confirmed the tests which had been made on the new gas by Priestley and extended them by burning various other substances in it. Finally he mixed the new gas with the residual gas from the air and found the product to be identical with common air. Inasmuch as no heat was evolved in the blending, he concluded that the two gases did not unite chemically, for he knew that chemical combination was attended by thermal effects. Instead, he reasoned, as we do today, that air is a mere mixture of a flame-supporting gas, which he named oxygen, and an inert gas, which he named azote (lifeless). This

latter is the element whose English name is nitrogen.

His grand conclusion was that combustion consisted only in the chemical combination of the combustible substance with oxygen; there was no need for phlogiston to explain burning. No such material had ever been isolated and examined. Moreover, since the mass of any fuel plus that of the oxygen involved in its burning is found to be equal to the mass of the products, phlogiston, if it existed, would be a material without mass and therefore not matter at all.

The doubly convincing character of Lavoisier's experiments depends on two features: (1) The chemical change was carried through a complete cycle in a closed system, leaving no doubt that the calx of mercury resulted from union of the mercury with some constituent of the air. This constituent was identical with the substance prepared by Priestley and Scheele, and, when liberated from the calx, it proved to be a gas which supported the combustion of many other things besides mercury. (2) The careful measurement of masses accounted quantitatively for all the substances involved, and demonstrated that oxygen was the only constituent of mercury calx besides the mercury itself. Incidentally, it showed that oxygen makes up about ⅕ of ordinary air.

Lavoisier also invented the symbols which we use today to represent chemical changes—a convenient shorthand and a great improvement over the astrological pictures theretofore employed. By means of symbols we can abbreviate the reactions in his celebrated experiment as follows:

$$Hg + O \rightleftharpoons HgO$$

where Hg stands for mercury (from the Latin name hydrargyrum) and the double arrow signifies that the reaction can proceed in either direction.

Regrettably, Lavoisier lost his life on the guillotine during the French Revolution while he was in the full flower of his genius. This man's talent was so remarkable that the progress of chemistry and the consequent advantages to all people might have been advanced by many years if he had lived for another decade.

Lavoisier's interpretation, which has been confirmed for every example of burning from 1774 to the present day, showed that this phenomenon is merely the rapid chemical union of an element (or in some cases of a compound) with oxygen. The change is accompanied by the evolution of

Bettmann Archive

PLATE XXV. Lavoisier conducting experiments on respiration.

heat and light, and the product is an oxide whose weight is the sum of the weights of the substance burned and that of the oxygen with which it combined. The oxides of metals are usually powdery solids; those of non-metals are frequently gaseous. Respiration, which is the oxidation by inhaled oxygen of carbonaceous waste products in the bloodstream, is attended by the liberation of heat, but the oxidizing temperature in this case is relatively low and there is no production of light. Finally, the ordinary rusting of metals in air is closely akin to, if not identical with, burning as regards the products formed. Thus, iron rust is an oxide or a hydrated oxide of iron, and a tarnished copper surface is darkened chiefly by the same black copper oxide which results when copper is burned in oxygen.

PROBLEMS

1. Summarize the arguments for and against the phlogiston theory. Arrange the arguments against the theory in the order of their effectiveness.

2. Acquaint yourself with some of the facts from the lives and times of Boyle, Priestley, and Lavoisier by looking up their names in the *Encyclopaedia Britannica*.

3. Design an experiment to demonstrate that the rusting of iron is really a slow burning process and therefore requires oxygen.

4. How would you prove experimentally that no mass is lost or gained in a burning process? Choose a convenient fuel, and describe the apparatus and procedure in sufficient detail to serve as laboratory directions.

. . . .

REFERENCES

1. *The Autobiography of Science*, F. R. Moulton and J. J. Schifferes, Doubleday & Co., 1950, pp. 218–232.
2. Harvard Case Histories, Case 2, James B. Conant, *The Overthrow of the Phlogiston Theory*, Harvard University Press, 1950.

17 Elementary Chemistry

PHYSICAL AND CHEMICAL PROPERTIES OF MATTER

The material composition of the world is exceedingly varied. Think of any ordinary setting, and the most casual survey will disclose such different kinds of matter as earth, water, air, wood, stone, metals, and vegetation. The bones, hair, blood, and flesh of animals represent additional varieties of matter. These and thousands of other materials all have recognizable characteristics, such as density, solubility, degree of hardness, color (or lack of color), which are properties of the material itself irrespective of the dimensions or shape of the specimen being examined. Such characteristics are known as *physical properties*.

When different kinds of matter are intimately mixed, either one of two possible results may be observed: (1) the mixture displays physical properties which are merely averages of the properties possessed by the ingredients; or (2) a distinctly different set of properties is obtained, not explainable by any averaging. This result implies that a different *kind* of matter has been produced. Such changes in the kind or identity of materials are chemical changes or *reactions*. They do not necessarily come about by mere mixing; a variation in external conditions such as temperature or pressure may be required. The reactions which any one kind of matter can undergo with other kinds determine its *chemical properties*.

Chemical changes or reactions are extremely numerous. Some examples of the commoner types are: burning, corrosion, digestion, fermentation, cooking, bleaching, and rotting.

MIXTURES AND SUBSTANCES

A handful of dry soil when closely examined is found to be variegated in its composition. With patience, granules of different kinds can be separated from one another. On the other hand, a sample of pure sand or of sugar or of table salt appears to be entirely uniform. Obviously the soil is a mixture, whereas the sand, sugar, and salt, being homogeneous, appear to represent in each case just one kind of matter. The term *substance* is applied to any specimen of matter that is all of one kind, meaning that the chemical and physical properties are the same throughout the specimen.

Homogeneity is evidently one criterion of a substance. There are, however, many apparently homogeneous materials which are not substances but intimate mixtures or solutions of two or more substances. Baking powder is a finely ground mixture of starch, salt, and certain solid substances designed to generate gas when the powder is wet. In spite of its seeming uniformity, baking powder does not have the same chemical and physical properties in all of its parts; a mechanical separation of its components, each one with unique properties, would be feasible although tedious. Sea water, although apparently homogeneous, comprises at least two substances, water and salt.

The ingredients of mixtures can always be separated without change of their identity by mechanical methods or by physical processes, such as dissolving, evaporating, freezing, or liquefying. Air is a homogeneous mixture or solution, principally of the two substances oxygen and nitrogen. If air is cooled sufficiently, it condenses to a liquid, but the nitrogen boils out of this liquid air more readily than does the oxygen. This is proof that air is not a single substance, for, in general, when a pure substance is subjected to physical operations like boiling, freezing, or melting, all parts respond identically.

Another criterion in identifying pure substances is the invariability of their properties. With certain reservations to be discussed later, it may be stated that all specimens of a true substance, wherever or however obtained, are alike. Water, cane sugar, and table salt have constant compositions and constant characteristics regardless of their origin. This is not true of a mixture. In air, for example, the proportions of nitrogen and oxygen vary somewhat from time to time and from place to place; a little more or less of either ingredient has scarcely any effect on the properties of the blend. We shall see that a far-reaching inference can be drawn from the constancy of composition which characterizes substances.

All specimens of matter are either substances or mixtures of substances, but, since mixtures are evidently unlimited in number, a systematic study requires that we begin by devoting our attention to substances.

COMPOUNDS AND ELEMENTS

The number of distinct substances now known is nearly a million. Out of this vast assortment it is found that scarcely a hundred are primary or fundamental substances. These are called *elements*. All the rest are composite substances in which two or more elements are intimately combined. These very numerous composite substances are called *compounds*. It is to be expected that compound substances should far outnumber the elemental ones, inasmuch as compounds are made up of elements. The situation is comparable to that of a language in which innumerable words can be formed from an alphabet of a few letters.

The proof that a given substance is a compound rests on our ability to decompose it into the elements of which it consists or, alternatively, to synthesize it from these elements. Thus water, the commonest of all substances on the surface of

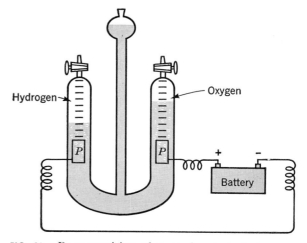

FIG. 81. Decomposition of water by electrolysis.

the earth, is established as a compound by the fact that it breaks down into hydrogen and oxygen under several methods of treatment, and that the weight of these products taken together add up to the weight of the water which was decomposed. The neatest way of decomposing water is by means of an electric current—a process which is called *electrolysis*, and which is most conveniently carried out in an apparatus like that pictured in Fig. 81. Two strips of platinum P are attached to the side tubes by wires which pass through the glass to the outside, and these wires are connected individually to the positive and negative terminals of an electric battery. If the water is slightly acidified to make it electrically conducting, an electric current will flow and bubbles of gas will be seen rising from the two strips of platinum (the electrodes).

The gas which collects above the positive electrode is recognizable by test as oxygen; that above the negative electrode is hydrogen. Hydrogen does not support combustion but is itself combustible; when mixed with oxygen and exposed to a spark, it combines explosively with the oxygen and the product of the explosion is water.

Quantitatively, we find that hydrogen collects twice as fast as the oxygen does. That is, the graduations along the tubes show twice as large a volume of hydrogen on the negative side as of oxygen on the positive side. If the two gases are collected separately and weighed, the double volume of hydrogen is found to weigh only $\frac{1}{8}$ as much as the oxygen does. These facts should be remembered:

Water composition: Hydrogen and oxygen
    By volume   H:O = 2:1
    By weight   H:O = 1:8

If water is decomposed by other means, say, by heating water vapor above 1000°C, the same products are always obtained and in the same ratios as given above.

Such experiments prove that water is a compound, but they do not prove that hydrogen and oxygen are elements. Innumerable attempts to decompose hydrogen or oxygen by comparable methods have failed, however, and we conclude, therefore, that these two substances are truly elemental. When any substance defies our efforts to break it down into simpler kinds of matter, the substance must be regarded, at least tentatively, as an element.

The classification of substances as elements by the criterion of failure to decompose them is not completely satisfying. There is always the possibility that a means not tried would prove successful. Certain very stable compounds, such as lime and silica, were once thought to be elements. Fortunately, other criteria are known and these will be introduced subsequently. There is, moreover, a very strong objection to complete reliance on stability as a criterion of the elemental character of a substance. There are numerous so-called radioactive substances, such as radium, uranium, and thorium, which possess great stability in one sense and yet are highly unstable in another sense. To illustrate, radium can easily be made to form a variety of compounds: radium oxide, radium chloride, radium bromide, radium nitride, radium sulfate, etc.—compounds which are interconvertible and which can be decomposed into radium by the standard procedures of chemistry. Yet all the while, and regardless of its state of combination, part of the radium is undergoing a steady, spontaneous decomposition into two lighter substances, radon and helium. This spontaneous change affects only a very small fraction of the radium, but it is a relentless change which progressively diminishes the amount of any radium specimen. In spite of this kind of instability, radioactive elements are still classed as elements, since in all other respects they participate in ordinary chemical changes in the normal manner of elements.

Evidently we cannot say that elements are substances impossible of reduction into simpler substances, since that would contradict the phenomenon of radioactive decay. But would the statement hold if we excepted these cases of spontaneous decomposition? Until recent years scientists believed the answer to be yes. Now, however, it has become possible to elevate the temperature of matter by millions of degrees and to accelerate small particles to such prodigious speeds that they can strike a specimen of matter with enormous force. Under such treatment many elemental substances can actually be *transmuted* into other elements. Nevertheless, we continue to regard the substances so treated as elements because they retain their identity through all ordinary chemical reactions where the energy involved is of moderate amount.

Another reason for caution in designating a substance as elemental can be illustrated by the decomposition of limestone or marble. This white, crystalline rock decomposes easily when it is made red hot. A gas is given off, identifiable as carbon dioxide, and the white, solid residue left behind is quicklime, the principal ingredient of mortar. It is not difficult to decompose the carbon dioxide into carbon and oxygen, and, inasmuch as these products cannot be further simplified by the usual chemical operations, they are classified as elements. The lime, however, is obstinately resistant to efforts to break it down. After the discovery of the element calcium early in the nineteenth century, it was soon found that lime could be prepared by allowing calcium to burn in oxygen, thus proving, by synthesis, that lime is a compound.

In spite of the foregoing illustrations and reservations, there is no disagreement about which substances are to be classed as elements, for extensive study has brought to light a natural and systematic scheme of classification (the *periodic arrangement*) into which all elements fit neatly. The existence of this natural arrangement gives to each element a provisional status as an irreducible entity. For some purposes we can regard the substances there listed as ultimate varieties of matter. Their ultimateness fails, however, when we extend our operations to include the transmutations which can now be accomplished by the cyclotron or the atomic pile.

THE DIFFICULTY OF DEFINING AN ELEMENT

Although the periodic arrangement of the elements, to be discussed in detail farther on, confirms the selection of these particular substances as elemental, there is still lacking a completely satisfactory definition of what an element is. The radioactive decomposition of heavier elements into lighter ones proves that elements are not ultimate or primary species of matter. Even hydrogen and helium, the two lightest known elements, are known to have constituents, although these constituents are not regarded as elements in the usual sense. One solution is to base our definition on theoretical premises. There is overwhelming evidence that matter of every kind consists of atoms, and one might define an element as a substance whose atoms are all of one kind. This sort of definition is unsatisfactory to many scientists, however, chiefly because it lacks the operational suggestion which experimentalists prefer in all definitions. By this we mean that a sound definition should state or imply the operations by which the definition can be tested. For example, acceleration is defined as the rate at which velocity changes. We can measure velocity directly as well as its rate of change; hence the definition of acceleration suggests the method of determining acceleration. Notwithstanding a wealth of evidence that atoms of matter exist, they cannot be observed directly, and our present knowledge of their construction is severely limited. To define an element in terms of these particles is to neglect the desirable indication of how an element could be identified experimentally.

It is probably better to fall back on the inadequate definition of an element as a substance which cannot be decomposed into simpler substances, and then to add the reservation that this stability holds for ordinary chemical or physical interactions but fails when the substance is exposed to conditions of extraordinarily high energy. This, although vague, is a useful working definition, for elements in general do preserve their identity unchanged through the very wide range of chemical reactions by which a scant one hundred simple substances yield ten thousand times that number of composite substances.

LAWS OF CHEMICAL COMBINATION

The most striking feature of compound substances as distinguished from mixtures is the constancy of their composition. For example, ordinary water is $\frac{1}{9}$ hydrogen and $\frac{8}{9}$ oxygen by weight. These proportions can be verified either by analysis or by synthesis. Thus, if 9 grams of water are decomposed and the products are separated, they are found to consist of 1 gram of hydrogen and 8 grams of oxygen. Or, if 1 gram of hydrogen and 8 grams of oxygen are mixed and a spark is applied to the mixture, 9 grams of water are produced. Moreover, the constancy of these combining proportions maintains itself automatically, for, if we spark a mixture of 2 grams of hydrogen and 8 grams of oxygen, the explosion again produces 9 grams of water. The excess 1 gram of hydrogen is found mixed with it. Alternatively, 1 gram of hydrogen, mixed with 9 grams of oxygen and sparked, yields 9 grams of water mixed with 1 gram excess of oxygen. Some inherent characteristic of the three substances involved controls the proportions so as to preserve the mass ratio $H:O = 1:8$ whether this ratio of masses has been selected by the experimenter or not.

DALTON'S ATOMIC THEORY

The single example cited is typical of all the multitude of compound substances known. Ignoring for the moment certain modifications which have arisen from recent research, it is possible to say that in all compounds the relative amounts of the constituent elements are definite and fixed by nature itself. This statement, which is known as the *law of definite proportions,* leads to an important theoretical inference, which was first put forward by the English scientist John Dalton (1766–1844) in about 1808.

Dalton suggested that every specimen of a pure element must be regarded as made up of identical particles, which he called *atoms;* these particles having the same characteristics as those displayed by the gross specimen. If this were so, the formation of compounds from elements would have to occur in fixed proportions, as it is known to do. By way of illustration, suppose the element oxygen consists of atoms having a mass of 1 unit each, whereas the element lead consists of atoms with a mass of 13 units each. Then the union of one oxygen atom with one lead atom would produce a compound particle having a mass of 14 units. Likewise, if a thousand oxygen atoms combined with a thousand lead atoms, the respective masses would be 1000 and 13,000 units, and the product would weigh 14,000 units. Moreover, if eleven hundred atoms of oxygen were brought into contact with a thousand atoms of lead, they would still yield a thousand particles of the compound, having a mass of 14,000 units as before, although one hundred atoms of oxygen would be left uncombined. This result could be observed without any need of counting the particles, since the mass ratios of the oxygen and lead which had combined and of the compound formed from them would be 1000:13,000:14,000 or 1:13:14 as before.

Now, if lead is heated in the presence of oxygen, a yellow compound known as lead oxide or litharge is produced, and the masses of the oxygen, lead, and lead oxide are indeed found to be in the ratios 1:13:14, using round numbers. Dalton's hypothesis that the elements combine atom by atom is to date the only simple and satisfactory way of accounting for this constancy of combining ratios.

In order to drive home the essential point, let us consider an analogy. Given two piles of hooks and eyes, we may shake them in a box so that many of the hooks will engage corresponding eyes. On separating the unattached members, we may verify the combination by counting, and thus find that there is just one hook engaged with each eye. But we could verify this result equally well by weighing. If it happened that every eye weighed 1 gram and every hook 13 grams, then the ratio by weight would have to be 1:13 in any collection of linked members, and the total weight of the combinations would necessarily be 14 times as much as that of the eyes alone.

To a person incapable of counting the hooks and eyes because of defective sight, or because the materials were excessively small, the weighing procedure would prove their existence as individuals besides establishing the mass of a single hook compared with the mass of a single eye. This is the case with atoms of elements. Their minute size precludes their recognition by direct observation. Yet we have convincing evidence of their existence from the law of definite proportions.

MULTIPLE COMBINATIONS

Pursuing this line of reasoning, it is necessary to admit the possibility of double-ended hooks and single eyes, as well as other variations, so that every hook could account for two eyes, and so on.

Then, no matter how large the number of both, we should always find by weighing that the mass ratio of double-ended hooks to eyes was 13:2, provided, of course, that all hooks were completely (not partially) engaged. Dalton was well aware of this variant in the mass ratios of those elements which could combine to give more than one product according to the prevailing conditions. Compounds of lead and oxygen furnish a good illustration. Besides the yellow litharge, in which the mass ratio of lead to oxygen is 13 to 1, there is a brown oxide of lead which forms on the plates of a storage battery during charging. In this substance the ratio of lead to oxygen is 13:2. By Dalton's reasoning these facts indicate that one atom of lead can unite with either one atom of oxygen to produce the yellow compound or with two atoms of oxygen to produce the brown compound. Indeed, there is a third compound of these elements which is called red lead, a substance extensively used in paint, especially for giving a rustproof priming coat to structural steel, and this compound consists of lead and oxygen in the ratio 39:4. Since the composition of the other two oxides suggests that an atom of lead is 13 times as massive as an atom of oxygen, we are led to conclude that the smallest particle of red lead consists of 3 atoms of lead and 4 atoms of oxygen.

SYMBOLS AND FORMULAS

Every chemical compound has a name which, in most cases, suggests its composition according to a standardized scheme of nomenclature. Of greater concern to the chemist, however, is the formula, which represents, by a system of internationally accepted symbols, the smallest unit (a molecule) of any compound in terms of the atoms of its constituent elements. In order to interpret such formulas it is necessary to use the following rules:

1. The symbol for an element is usually the first letter of its name, e.g.,

> A for argon
> B for boron
> C for carbon
> F for fluorine

or two prominent letters of its name, e.g.,

> Al for aluminum
> Br for bromine
> Cl for chlorine
> Mn for manganese

Those metallic elements which were known in ancient times take their symbols from the Latin names, e.g.,

Fe (ferrum) for iron
Na (natrium) for sodium
K (kalium) for potassium
Cu (cuprum) for copper
Hg (hydrargyrum) for mercury
Ag (argentum) for silver
Au (aurum) for gold
Pb (plumbum) for lead

2. When all evidence for the quantitative composition of a compound has been appraised and a decision reached as to the relative number of atoms of each element in one molecule of the compound, the symbols of the constituent elements are written down with subscript numerals after the symbols to show the relative number of atoms of each kind. For simplicity the subscript 1 is omitted after the symbol of any element which contributes just one of its atoms to each molecule of the compound. As examples:

The yellow compound, lead monoxide or litharge, in which every lead atom is believed to be combined with one atom of oxygen, is represented by the formula PbO.

The brown compound, lead dioxide, in which every lead atom is believed to be united with two atoms of oxygen, has the formula PbO_2.

The red compound known as red lead or minium, in which three atoms of lead are believed to be linked with four atoms of oxygen, reveals this composition by the formula Pb_3O_4.

Each formula thus represents not merely the compound in question but, specifically, a typical molecule of that compound. Sometimes formulas are written in such a way as to show not only the composition but also the probable structure of the compound molecule. Thus acetic acid, which occurs in vinegar, has the formula $C_2H_4O_2$, but the arrangement of its atoms is better revealed by the structural formula CH_3COOH. This substance, it may be noted, is made up of three different elements. There are a great many three-element compounds, and some consist of four or more, but we shall confine ourselves for the present to the simpler two-element compounds. The arrangement of the atoms in a compound molecule is determined in part by a characteristic called *valence*, which will be introduced shortly.

The existence of several compounds formed from the same elements, as exemplified by the oxides of lead, shows that atoms have a degree of versatility in their habits of combination. They are evidently not limited to unions in which single atoms of one kind join with single atoms of another kind. This versatility, however, complicates the problem of determining the relative masses of different kinds of atoms. For if in a compound of elements X and Y we find that the X constituent weighs 4 times as much as the Y constituent, does this mean that X has atoms which are 4 times as massive as those of Y? Or are they, perhaps, only twice as massive, so that the composition of the compound is not XY but X_2Y, a formula which would still account for the observed mass ratio of 4:1? Obviously there are many other possibilities.

In the series of lead oxides we assumed without proof that a molecule of litharge (PbO) consists of one atom each of lead and of oxygen. We know by experiment that the lead and oxygen needed to make litharge stand in the ratio by mass of 13:1, but this could mean on the one hand that the two kinds of atom have these same relative masses, so that possible molecules are representable by such formulas as PbO, Pb_2O_2, Pb_3O_3 or any other choice of equal numbers. On the other hand, we might assume that a lead atom is 26 times as massive as an oxygen atom, and the factual data would then be accounted for by the formula PbO_2, showing one lead atom of mass 26 combined with two oxygen atoms, each of mass 1, the combination giving a mass ratio of 26:2 or 13:1. Inasmuch as innumerable other combinations could be reconciled with the data, depending on the assumptions made, it is clear that some additional line of evidence is needed to resolve the questions of correct atomic masses and correct formulas.

GAY-LUSSAC'S LAW OF COMBINING VOLUMES

At about the same time that Dalton proposed his atomic theory, a momentous discovery was made by the French chemist Gay-Lussac (1778–1850) on the *volume* relationships between chemically interacting gases. Suppose that we take a number of gaseous elements which can, by combination, form gaseous compounds. For example, hydrogen and oxygen can yield steam; nitrogen and oxygen can combine in several proportions to give a series of gaseous nitrogen oxides; nitrogen and hydrogen form the gas called ammonia; hydrogen and chlorine combine to give hydrogen chloride, a gas whose solution in water is hydrochloric acid. Gay-Lussac observed that, if the gaseous elements and their gaseous compound products were all measured under identical conditions of pressure and temperature, the volume ratios were invariably almost exact whole numbers. This statement is a fully confirmed generalization known as the *law of combining volumes*.

To illustrate, let 1 liter of oxygen be mixed with 2 liters of hydrogen and the mixture exploded. If the resulting steam is brought to the original pressure and temperature, its volume is found to be almost exactly 2 liters. Similarly, 1 liter of nitrogen combined with 3 liters of hydrogen gives 2 liters of ammonia. Again, 1 liter of hydrogen combined with 1 liter of chlorine produces just 2 liters of hydrogen chloride gas. The numbers which express the relative volumes are always integers. Moreover, they are *small* integers.

The law discovered by Gay-Lussac might be expected to have important theoretical significance; simple quantitative regularities like this frequently do. Yet not until more than fifty years had elapsed was the law generally accepted, when Cannizzaro, a pupil of Avogadro's, showed how it could be used in conjunction with Avogadro's hypothesis to establish the atomic masses of elements.

If we recall Avogadro's assumption that gases which have equal volumes under like conditions contain equal numbers of molecules, even if the gases are different, it must follow that the relative weights of these equal volumes are the same as the relative weights of the individual molecules. Take, for example, the gases hydrogen and chlorine and the gaseous product of their chemical combination, hydrogen chloride. We list certain quantitative measurements made on these substances, each followed by a logical inference.

Observation 1. The densities of the three gases, determined under identical conditions, are found to be

	Density
Hydrogen	0.09 grams per liter
Chlorine	3.20 grams per liter
Hydrogen chloride	1.64 grams per liter

These densities are in the ratios 2:71:36.5.

Inference 1 (by Avogadro's law). The relative masses of a hydrogen, a chlorine, and a hydrogen chloride *molecule* are 2:71:36.5.

Inference 2. A molecule of hydrogen chloride cannot contain a whole molecule of chlorine, which is almost twice as heavy as the hydrogen chloride molecule. It appears to contain half a molecule.

Inference 3. A molecule of hydrogen chloride must contain at least one *atom* of chlorine and at least one *atom* of hydrogen. If a chlorine *atom* is just half a chlorine *molecule,* and a hydrogen *atom* is half a hydrogen *molecule,* then the relative masses of the atoms are

$$H:Cl = 1:35.5$$

and the relative mass of a hydrogen chloride molecule consisting of one atom of each element should be 36.5 as inference 1 shows it to be.

Observation 2. When 1 liter of hydrogen is allowed to combine with 1 liter of chlorine, the resulting hydrogen chloride is found to occupy 2 liters.

Inference 4 (by Avogadro's law). Every million molecules of hydrogen that unite with a million molecules of chlorine yield 2 million molecules of hydrogen chloride. This would be impossible unless each molecule of hydrogen comprised two hydrogen atoms and each molecule of chlorine comprised two chlorine atoms. This is clear from the diagram below in which every atom is represented by its symbol.

Such molecules are designated as *diatomic.*

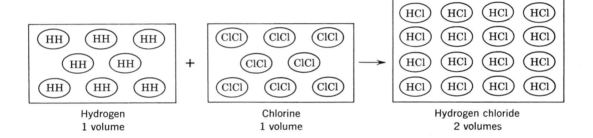

| Hydrogen 1 volume | Chlorine 1 volume | Hydrogen chloride 2 volumes |

Similar application of Gay-Lussac's and Avogadro's laws to various gas reactions shows that several other elemental gases (e.g., oxygen, nitrogen, fluorine, and chlorine) also exist normally as diatomic molecules. This is not a general rule, however. Evidence indicates that the gas helium consists of *monatomic* molecules which are symbolized by He; the gas ozone consists of *triatomic* molecules symbolized by O_3.

DETERMINATION OF ATOMIC MASSES

We are now prepared to understand how the law of Avogadro can be utilized to determine the relative mass of any kind of atom, provided gaseous compounds containing that species of atom can be made.

Before explaining the method, however, we might dispose of the questions "Why *relative?*" and "Relative to *what?*"

The first of these questions has two answers: (1) it is difficult to determine the absolute mass of atoms; (2) for some purposes it is unnecessary to know them, since, in actual practice, the relative values serve just as well.

So accustomed are we to judging sizes and amounts on a comparative basis that often we are unaware of doing so. We speak of a *large* insect if its total length is a few inches, whereas a *small* elephant may be one that weighs a ton. A large man is not large except by comparison with average men.

Again, what is the absolute value of a nickel, a dime, or a quarter? No one can say, for the value fluctuates continually. But to know that these coins have the *relative* values of $\frac{1}{20}$, $\frac{1}{10}$, and $\frac{1}{4}$ of a dollar is useful in daily transactions. Indeed, it is imperative knowledge.

There is, then, no obvious objection to the use of atomic masses if we know only their relative magnitudes.

As for the standard of reference, so that we may answer the question "Relative to what?" one might choose such a standard on several bases. One basis would be to select the commonest element and declare its atomic mass to be 1. Another would be to choose the element which occurs in the greatest variety of compounds or in many compounds which can readily be prepared in pure state. This latter is actually the reason for the present agreement to set the atomic mass of oxygen as a standard (at 16.0000). In earlier times, however, it was the practice to use hydrogen as a standard because it is the lightest known element. Then, by assigning to

hydrogen the atomic mass of unity, chemists were assured of avoiding values less than one. We shall adopt this older practice in our preliminary exposition, since there is no great difference between the old values and the new when round numbers are employed.

We begin, then, by calling the atomic mass of hydrogen 1, which is to say that a hydrogen atom is *defined* as having a mass of 1 unit.

For reference purposes the reader may need to know that all textbooks on chemistry call these figures atomic *weights,* a deeply entrenched, but erroneous, term.

The principle underlying atomic mass determination is very simple, although the experimental determinations are tedious and difficult. It consists of weighing a large number of gaseous compounds under identical conditions of temperature and pressure and thus obtaining their relative molecular masses. Each compound must contain the element whose atomic mass is desired. By analyzing all these compounds quantitatively, the investigator then finds how much of the element in question is present in the molecular mass of each of the compounds. The amounts he finds will, in many cases, be multiples of the atomic mass, but, if a sufficient number of compounds has been investigated, it is presumed that one of them, at least, must consist of molecules having only a single atom of the element under examination. The mass of the desired element present in the molecular mass of this compound is taken to be the required atomic mass.

MOLAR VOLUME

The procedure outlined can best be exemplified by tabulation of such analytical data for a typical element—say, bromine. For convenience we assume that the volume of each gas analyzed is 22.4 liters at a temperature of 0°C and under a pressure of 1 atmosphere. It is not necessary to do the actual weighing under these so-called standard conditions for, if the temperature and pressure are other than those specified, we can use the gas laws of Boyle and Charles to calculate what the observed volume would have been if standard conditions had prevailed.

The choice of 22.4 liters as a standard volume is due to the fact that this is (approximately) the volume occupied by 2 grams of hydrogen when the temperature is 0°C and the pressure 1 atmosphere. Having selected 1 as the atomic mass of hydrogen, and having the conviction that a molecule of hydrogen consists of two atoms, we conclude that the molecular mass of hydrogen is 2. Hence the volume of hydrogen that weighs 2 grams may be regarded as a standard or *molar* volume, and the same volume of any other gas when weighed gives the molar mass of that substance.

Strictly speaking, 22.4 liters of hydrogen at 0°C and 1 atmosphere has a mass not of 2 but of 2.016 grams. As already stated, atomic masses are now based on the value 16 for the element oxygen. On that basis the relative atomic mass of hydrogen, to four figures, is 1.008. Since both oxygen and hydrogen are diatomic, their molecular masses are respectively 32 and 2.016. The molar volume is strictly defined, therefore, as that volume which holds just 32 grams of oxygen under the standard conditions specified.

TABLE 6. ANALYTICAL COMPOSITION OF VARIOUS COMPOUNDS CONTAINING BROMINE*

Compound	C	H	O	Br	P	Na	Ca	Pb	Hg
Bromal hydrate	24	3	32	240					
Phenyl bromide	72	5		80					
Bromoform	12	1		240					
Phosphorus tribromide				240	31				
Phosphorus pentabromide				400	31				
Hydrogen bromide		1		80					
Bromine vapor				160					
Sodium bromide				80		23			
Calcium bromide				160			40		
Lead bromide				160				207	
Mercurous bromide				80					200

* Figures are the masses in grams of each element in 22.4 liters of the gaseous compound under standard conditions.

A much larger number of compounds than we have listed would have to be analyzed in order to fix the atomic mass of bromine with reasonable certainty, for conceivably, there might be some examples having 40 or even 20 parts of the element in a molar volume of the compound. Actually no compound has ever been found with less than 80 parts of bromine per molecule. The accepted atomic mass of this element is therefore taken to be 80.

In the case of an element that participates in so few volatile compounds as to make this method unreliable, there are other and indeed more accurate ways of getting the desired result, but an account of these alternatives is not warranted here.

LIST OF ELEMENTS

Table 7 lists alphabetically the most important or interesting elements with their symbols and approximate atomic masses for convenient reference.

CHEMICAL FORMULAS

Identification of the elements which go to make up any chemical compound is the subject of *qualitative analysis,* a branch of chemistry that has been brought to a high degree of perfection. In quantitative analysis the identifying technique is extended so as to concern itself with the relative amounts of the constituent elements in a molecule. Even the most accurate quantitative analysis needs interpretation, however, if it is to reveal the innate composition of the substance under consideration. For example, the noxious gas produced when sulfur burns proves on analysis to consist of just 50% sulfur and 50% oxygen. This information has a limited usefulness by itself if we wish to manufacture the compound, for it tells us that a half ton of sulfur would be required for every ton of the gas produced. The analytical figures do not give us, however, the relative count of sulfur and oxygen atoms in the compound, for the two species of atom do not have the same mass. Reference to Table 7 shows, in fact that the sulfur atom is twice as massive as the oxygen atom (atomic mass of sulfur = 32; atomic mass of oxygen = 16). Evidently then, the compound must contain twice as many oxygen atoms as it does sulfur atoms in order to contain 50% of each element, as it does. Accordingly we are justified in representing the formula of this compound as SO_2, from which the substance derives its name, sulfur dioxide.

A slightly more difficult example will suffice to show how all chemical formulas are obtained from quantitative analysis supplemented by a table of atomic masses. Lead chromate is a yellow pigment which is found on analysis to have the composition:

Pb   64.2%   Cr   16.1%   O   19.7%

The interpretation of these figures is as follows:

In every 100 parts by weight of the compound there are 64.2 parts of lead. Since the atomic mass of lead is 207, this amount represents 64.2/207 or 0.31 of a lead atom.

In the same weight of compound there are 16.1 parts of chromium. Since the atomic mass of chromium is 52, this amount represents 16.1/52 or 0.31 of a chromium atom.

Finally, in 100 parts of the compound there

are 19.7 parts of oxygen. Since the atomic mass of oxygen is 16, this amount represents 19.7/16 or 1.23 oxygen atoms.

Obviously a lead chromate molecule cannot consist of fractions of atoms, but, if we divide all three figures by 0.31, the ratios

$$Pb:Cr:O = 0.31:0.31:1.23$$

become

$$Pb:Cr:O = 1:1:4$$

That is to say, any amount of the compound lead chromate contains an equal number of lead and chromium atoms but four times as many oxygen atoms. Its simplest formula is therefore $PbCrO_4$,

and this is the formula used to represent a molecule of the compound.

This illustrates a general procedure which can be used whenever the atomic masses of all the constituent atoms are known. The problem resolves itself into an experimental determination of the percentage composition of the molecule.

CHEMICAL VALENCE

The formulas already exhibited illustrate a remarkable difference among elements in the capacity of their atoms for attaching atoms of other kinds to themselves. Whereas a stable molecule could be formed by the combination of

TABLE 7

Element	Symbol	Approximate Atomic Mass	Element	Symbol	Approximate Atomic Mass
Aluminum	Al	27.0	Magnesium	Mg	24.3
Americium	Am	243	Manganese	Mn	54.9
Antimony	Sb	122	Mercury	Hg	201
Argon	A	39.9	Molybdenum	Mo	96.0
Arsenic	As	74.9	Neon	Ne	20.2
Astatine	At	210	Neptunium	Np	237
Barium	Ba	137	Nickel	Ni	58.7
Berkelium	Bk	245	Nitrogen	N	14.0
Beryllium	Be	9.01	Osmium	Os	190
Bismuth	Bi	209	Oxygen	O	16.00
Boron	B	10.8	Phosphorus	P	31.0
Bromine	Br	79.9	Platinum	Pt	195
Cadmium	Cd	112	Plutonium	Pu	242
Calcium	Ca	40.1	Polonium	Po	210
Californium	Cf	246	Potassium	K	39.1
Carbon	C	12.0	Radium	Ra	226
Cerium	Ce	140	Radon	Rn	222
Cesium	Cs	133	Rubidium	Rb	85.5
Chlorine	Cl	35.5	Scandium	Sc	45.0
Chromium	Cr	52.0	Selenium	Se	79.0
Cobalt	Co	58.9	Silicon	Si	28.1
Copper	Cu	63.5	Silver	Ag	107.9
Curium	Cm	243	Sodium	Na	23.0
Fluorine	F	19.0	Strontium	Sr	87.6
Francium	Fr	223	Sulfur	S	32.1
Gallium	Ga	69.7	Tantalum	Ta	181
Germanium	Ge	72.6	Tellurium	Te	128
Gold	Au	197	Thorium	Th	232
Hafnium	Hf	179	Tin	Sn	119
Helium	He	4.003	Titanium	Ti	47.9
Hydrogen	H	1.008	Tungsten	W	184
Iodine	I	127	Uranium	U	238
Iridium	Ir	193	Vanadium	V	51.0
Iron	Fe	55.9	Xenon	Xe	131
Krypton	Kr	83.8	Zinc	Zn	65.4
Lead	Pb	207	Zirconium	Zr	91.2
Lithium	Li	6.94			

one hydrogen atom with one chlorine atom, or of one lead atom with one oxygen atom, the element sulfur requires two oxygen atoms to satisfy the combining capacity of the sulfur atom in SO_2. To borrow a sociological term, it appears as if some elements are monogamous, others bigamous, still others trigamous, and so on. Chemists refer to the *number* which denotes the capacity of an atom for combination with other kinds of atom as the *valence* of the atom, or the valence of the element which the atom represents. The word valence is a contraction of *equivalence*. Thus, an atom of sulfur is equivalent, chemically, to two atoms of oxygen.

As in the case of relative atomic masses, it is necessary to pick an element as a reference standard for expressing the valences of other elements. By general agreement the choice has fallen on hydrogen, to which we assign a valence number of 1. This means that an atom of hydrogen is capable of combining with just one atom of any other element whose valence number is also 1, or, put in reverse, any element X which can combine with hydrogen to produce a compound of the formula HX is, like hydrogen, univalent.

Returning to the electrolysis of water, which yielded twice as much hydrogen gas by volume as it did oxygen gas, we conclude that a water molecule must contain twice as many hydrogen atoms as it does oxygen atoms. Hence the familiar H_2O for water.

This formula is further confirmed by the quantitative analysis of water, which shows oxygen and hydrogen to be present in the mass ratio of 8:1. Since oxygen has the relative atomic mass 16, this ratio of 8:1 (or 16:2) indicates that the oxygen atom in a water molecule is linked to two hydrogen atoms.

At once we infer that oxygen must have the valence number 2. Proceeding, we conclude from the formula for sulfur dioxide, SO_2, that

the sulfur in that compound has the valence number 4.

It is convenient to represent valence pictorially by attaching short lines called *bonds* to the symbol of each element in a compound, making the number of bonds equal to the valence number. Thus

H—Cl   Hydrogen chloride   Water   Sulfur dioxide

If an element does not combine with hydrogen, we can analyze any compound that it may form with chlorine and thereby learn its valence, since an atom of chlorine is equivalent chemically to an atom of hydrogen. This leads us to a specific definition of valence:

The valence of an element is the number of atoms of hydrogen, or equivalent atom, needed to combine with one atom of the element in question.

Valence numbers run from 1 to 8; no valence greater than 8 has been discovered. An example of each is presented in Table 8, together with the analytical data from which the valence was obtained.

POSITIVE AND NEGATIVE VALENCE

Later we shall associate algebraic signs with valence numbers in accordance with their supposed electrical origin. In general the valences of metallic elements are taken as positive and those of non-metals as negative.

STRUCTURAL FORMULAS

The pictorial representation of formulas helps to explain the possible structures of alternative

TABLE 8

Element	Atomic Mass	Compound	Composition	Formula	Valence of Element
Sodium	23	Sodium chloride	23 parts Na; 35.5 parts Cl	NaCl	1
Magnesium	24	Magnesium chloride	24 parts Mg; 71 parts Cl	$MgCl_2$	2
Aluminum	27	Aluminum chloride	27 parts Al; 106.5 parts Cl	$AlCl_3$	3
Carbon	12	Carbon tetrachloride	12 parts C; 142 parts Cl	CCl_4	4
Phosphorus	31	Phosphorus pentachloride	31 parts P; 177.5 parts Cl	PCl_5	5
Sulfur	32	Sulfur trioxide	32 parts S; 48 parts O	SO_3	6
Manganese	55	Manganese heptoxide	110 parts Mn; 112 parts O	Mn_2O_7	7
Osmium	190	Osmium tetroxide	190 parts Os; 64 parts O	OsO_4	8

compound molecules. Frequently two or more compounds of the same elements exist, differing in the mass ratio of the constituent elements. Taking into account these mass ratios as well as the usual valences, we can postulate the probable structures of the compounds. For example, hydrogen and oxygen form the two distinct compounds *water* and *hydrogen peroxide*. In water the ratio by mass of oxygen to hydrogen is 16:2, and we have inferred from this that the water molecule consists of one oxygen and two hydrogen atoms. In hydrogen peroxide the mass ratio is

$$O:H = 16:1$$

This could mean that a molecule of hydrogen peroxide consists of one oxygen atom and one hydrogen atom, but with such a composition the oxygen could not exercise its customary valence of 2. If, on the other hand, we call this mass ratio 32:2 and regard a hydrogen peroxide molecule as made up of 2 oxygen and 2 hydrogen atoms, the structure can be accounted for in this way: H—O—O—H, which is the formula generally agreed upon for the compound. Independent methods beyond the scope of this book confirm the formula H_2O_2 rather than HO for hydrogen peroxide.

MULTIPLE VALENCE

Although some elements show a constant valence in all their chemical combinations, other elements exhibit different valences in different compounds. Nitrogen, for example, is remarkable for its multivalence, as is illustrated in Table 9 by the formulas of the several oxides of nitrogen.

TABLE 9

		Structure	Valence of N
Nitrous oxide	N_2O	N—O—N	1
Nitric oxide	NO	N=O	2
Nitrogen trioxide	N_2O_3	O=N—O—N=O	3
Nitrogen dioxide	NO_2	O=N=O	4
Nitrogen pentoxide	N_2O_5	O⫰ O⫰ N—O—N ⫰O ⫰O	5

In general, therefore, we cannot employ predetermined valences of elements as conclusive criteria for establishing the formulas of newly discovered compounds, since one or more of the elements in such compounds may be multivalent.

It cannot be too strongly emphasized that, notwithstanding man's success in fabricating a large number of useful materials and in mastering many of the rules which govern the behavior of inert matter, he is still very far from comprehending the fundamental causes of such behavior. A great deal of his useful knowledge is the result of trial and error methods which are tedious and wasteful. Nevertheless, the hypothetical picture which modern science has conceived of the fundamental character of matter is a helpful guide, for all its incompleteness and uncertainty.

CHAIN COMPOUNDS

The notion that a compound body is an aggregate of molecular units, each molecule consisting of a cluster of atoms held together by bonds of valence has proved especially fruitful in interpreting the structures of a huge variety of substances which chemists classify as *organic* compounds. The word organic was originally given to any compound that formed part of a living organism. It was believed in earlier times that such substances could not be made from the lifeless reagents of the laboratory, but in 1828 the German chemist Friedrich Woehler (1800–1882) succeeded in preparing an organic compound (urea) from inorganic sources, thereby disproving this long-standing belief. Today it is a routine procedure to synthesize artificially a great many of the substances which are otherwise formed in living processes, and so the term has lost its original significance. Nevertheless, the majority of materials present in living organisms, as well as thousands that are not, do share a common relationship which makes it convenient to treat them as a group apart from all other substances. This common link is the presence, in every so-called organic compound, of the element *carbon*. Some half-million compounds of this element are known, and the study of carbon compounds, under the heading of organic chemistry, is one of the major divisions of this science.

The reason for the disproportionately large number of compounds that carbon is able to form with other elements appears to stem from an almost unique characteristic of carbon atoms. Unlike the atoms of almost every other element, those of carbon are evidently able to link together to produce long chains or closed rings, and this versatility multiplies enormously the number of possible combinations. The interpretation of such possibilities calls for the application of the valence concept.

Elements other than carbon combine with one another to form, as a rule, relatively simple molecules. This simplicity is twofold: the number of elements in a molecule is small and the number of atoms per molecule is small. We offer at random the formulas of several common inorganic molecules to illustrate the point:

HgO	CaSO$_4$	HNO$_3$
Mercuric oxide	Calcium sulfate	Nitric acid
PbS	Na$_3$PO$_4$	KClO$_3$
Lead sulfide	Sodium phosphate	Potassium chlorate

Contrasted with the usual simplicity of inorganic compounds is the elaborate composition of many organic, or carbon, compounds. An organic substance having scores of atoms to the molecule is not uncommon, although it is again the rule that few elements are involved. Organic compounds group themselves into families whose formulas fit a general pattern, and the assumption that the carbon in such compounds almost invariably exhibits the same valence enables a chemist to predict the existence of compounds in advance of their discovery.

We begin by establishing the valence of carbon in the usual way. Consider the substance formed by the complete combustion of coal, charcoal, or other forms of carbon. It is a compound consisting of 27.25% carbon and 72.75% oxygen. Dividing these figures by the respective atomic masses of carbon and oxygen, we get

$$\frac{27.25}{12} = 2.27 \text{ parts of C}$$

to

$$\frac{72.75}{16} = 4.55 \text{ parts of O}$$

$$2.27 : 4.55 = 1 : 2$$

From this we deduce the formula of the compound to be CO$_2$, and we assign it the name carbon dioxide.

Taking account of the bivalence already discovered for oxygen, we conclude that the valence of C in this compound is 4 and that the CO$_2$ molecule is satisfactorily represented by O=C=O.

With few exceptions, carbon appears to be quadrivalent in all its hundreds of thousands of compounds. Many of these organic compounds are extremely complex, but our present purpose is served by exhibiting the structural formulas of a few simple ones.

HYDROCARBONS

The natural crude oil known as petroleum is possibly the most valuable item in the world's store of mineral wealth. It contains a great variety of compounds, but many of these are related to one another. For instance, there is a large family of substances called paraffin hydrocarbons, the simplest of which are found by analysis to have the formulas shown in Table 10.

TABLE 10

Compound	Formula	Structural Formula	State
Methane	CH$_4$	H—C—H (with H above and below)	Gas
Ethane	C$_2$H$_6$	H—C—C—H (with H above and below each C)	Gas
Propane	C$_3$H$_8$	H—C—C—C—H (with H above and below each C)	Gas
Butane	C$_4$H$_{10}$	H—C—C—C—C—H (with H above and below each C)	Gas
Pentane	C$_5$H$_{12}$	H—C—C—C—C—C—H (with H above and below each C)	Liquid

The limitation of these compounds to the constituents hydrogen and carbon accounts for the name hydrocarbons by which the class is known, and their chemical stability or inertness is responsible for the designation paraffin (from *parum affinis,* meaning scant affinity for reaction with other substances).

Chemical inertness always signifies stability or resistance to chemical change, and we might speculate about the cause of the high stability of the paraffins. A plausible reason for this is suggested by their structural formulas, as given in Table 10. The formulas indicate that the hydrocarbon molecules are symmetrical, and that each carbon atom has its quadrivalence fully satisfied by attachment to four other atoms. A compound in which the valence possibilities are fully satisfied is known as a *saturated* compound.

All hydrocarbons of the paraffin series are saturated compounds.

UNSATURATED HYDROCARBONS

Does saturation make for stability? This question may be answered by examination of another series of hydrocarbons known as the *olefines*. These are oily substances which readily undergo chemical reaction with other substances. Quantitative analysis shows that the first few members have formulas as follows:

Ethylene	C_2H_4
Propylene	C_3H_6
Butylene	C_4H_8

When we come to assign structural formulas to such compounds as these, it is clear that some further assumption must be made. Either (1) the valence of the carbon in this series is 3 instead of 4, so that the structure of ethylene, for example is representable by

$$
\begin{array}{cc}
\text{H} & \text{H} \\
| & | \\
\text{H--C--C--H}
\end{array}
$$

or (2) the carbon atoms still possess 4 valence bonds apiece, but two of these bonds are not utilized. The situation could be represented in the case of ethylene by

$$
\begin{array}{ccc}
\text{H} & \text{H} & \\
| & | & \\
\text{H--C--C--H} & \quad \text{or by} \quad & \text{H--C=C--H} \\
| & | &
\end{array}
$$

There are many reasons for supposing that the second alternative is the correct one and that compounds like the olefine hydrocarbons are simply not fully saturated. The most convincing bit of evidence for this view is derived from what happens when ethylene gas is allowed to bubble through bromine water. The red bromine solution is rapidly decolorized and the product is identified by analysis as ethylene dibromide, CH_2BrCH_2Br. Apparently the double bond has opened up in the presence of the bromine to

allow a pair of bromine atoms to attach themselves in accordance with the following pattern:

$$
\underset{\text{Ethylene}}{\text{H--C=C--H}} + Br_2 = \underset{\text{Ethylene dibromide}}{\text{H--C--C--H}}
$$

The same treatment applied to ethane gives rise to the same product but with the important difference that hydrogen bromide is formed at the same time. This shows that bromine cannot enter the ethane molecule without displacement of some of the hydrogen which originally formed part of the hydrocarbon. Exposure of ethane to bromine actually results in the stepwise formation of several derivatives whose formulas are confirmed as usual by chemical analysis. The first two steps may be represented by the equations:

$$
\text{H--C--C--H} + Br_2 \rightarrow \text{H--C--C--H} + HBr
$$

$$
\text{H--C--C--H} + Br_2 \rightarrow \text{H--C--C--H} + HBr
$$

It might be argued at this point that the reactions described have not shown the saturated ethane to be any more stable than the unsaturated ethylene. It can be demonstrated, however, that replacement of the hydrogen in hydrocarbons is more difficult than mere addition at the double bond would be. In fact, this difference is utilized in the purification of petroleum products. The oily fractions of the petroleum are washed with acids, which react with olefines and other impurities that may be present to form soluble byproducts, while leaving the saturated hydrocarbons unaffected. We conclude that the satisfaction of all valence possibilities in a compound leads to chemical stability.

As a final argument for the quadrivalence of carbon in the unsaturated olefines we note that no olefine is known having a composition simpler than that of ethylene, C_2H_4. If the carbon in this series were trivalent, there should be a member having the formula CH_3 to correspond with the simplest paraffin member, methane, CH_4. But, if carbon is quadrivalent in the olefinic series, the simplest possible member must have two carbon atoms in its molecule.

ISOMERS

The point of unsaturation in the olefine hydrocarbons, i.e., the location of the double bond, may be regarded as the weak spot in the structure of the hydrocarbon molecule. In propylene this double bond can occur in only one place, namely, between the central and one of the terminal carbon atoms. Evidently it should make no difference which terminal carbon is involved, since the structure exists in space and the left end viewed from one side would be the right end viewed from the opposite side. In the case of butylene, however, this is no longer true, for the double bond might join an end carbon with an adjacent one or it might equally well connect the two intermediate carbon atoms. These alternative structures are represented here together with the corresponding derivatives which ought to result from the addition of bromine.

The compounds formulated at the left should differ, even if only a little, from those at the right.

The question suggested by these possibilities is: Are both sets of compounds here depicted on paper actually capable of preparation? The implications of this question and its answer are exceedingly important, for, if the answer is yes, it signifies that our paper formulations based as they are on the assumption that every carbon atom has 4 bonds of valence available to it are correct for practical purposes and that these formulas take on the character of blueprints.

Not only is the answer to this question yes, but the same query directed to more complicated structures yields the same answer. It is always possible to make just as many compounds as the number of possible unique variations in structure allows. Just as many and no more. This fact becomes a powerful confirmation of fundamental theory.

Compounds which have the same atomic composition but different arrangements of the atoms are known as *isomers*.

It is clear that the number of possible isomeric compounds must increase rapidly as the number of atoms in a molecule increases. The variants occur among the saturated as well as unsaturated hydrocarbons, and are even greater among the derivatives because a third element besides carbon and hydrogen naturally provides more opportunity for variation.

Isomers of the saturated hydrocarbon pentane have the following structures:

BENZENE HYDROCARBONS

One of the important industries connected with the manufacture of steel is the distillation of soft (bituminous) coal to obtain coke. When soft coal is heated with exclusion of air, a substantial yield of fuel gas and ammonia distill from the retort, leaving behind the porous residue known as coke.

There is also a small distillate of oil and tar, which was once regarded by the coke makers solely as a nuisance. Actually it is the most interesting and valuable part of the coal, for this tar is the material from which thousands of important substances are made. The tarry liquid contains the raw material for the manufacture of drugs, dyes, explosives, photographic chemicals, and other organic compounds of great variety and usefulness.

First and most plentiful of the hydrocarbons obtained from coal tar is benzene. It is a limpid liquid of rather pleasant odor which is sometimes used directly as a motor fuel. Otherwise it is the principal source of a large assortment of useful organic substances.

Analysis of benzene proves that its composition is representable by the formula C_6H_6. In considering the paraffin hydrocarbons we might have encountered hexane, C_6H_{14}, or, among the olefines, hexylene, C_6H_{12}. The smaller proportion of hydrogen in the latter is accounted for by assuming that two of the six carbon atoms are joined by a double bond. No such assumption will account for the formula of benzene, however. The problem of benzene's structure has occupied chemists for many years, and it cannot be said to be fully settled yet. How can the carbon atoms have a valence of 4 and yet carry only one hydrogen atom apiece? Or course, we could assume that the valence of the carbon in this substance is not 4, but that is a view which the chemist is reluctant to take. On the one hand, carbon's quadrivalence is well confirmed by a great variety of evidence. We have already seen, for example, how it enables us to predict the existence of isomers. On the other hand, benzene can be prepared from, and also converted into, other compounds in which the carbon is clearly quadrivalent. There is no indication that the valence of the carbon changes during such transformations.

The conception of what is probably the true structure of the benzene molecule came as the result of long deliberation over the problem by the great German chemist Kekule. According to one account, he had been speculating about organic compound structures throughout a long period and was in the habit of daydreaming over the problem and imagining the molecules to be alive, weaving and wriggling like snakes before his mind's eye. It was during one of these spells of abstraction in 1865 that he imagined he saw the molecular snakes grasping their own tails, and the idea of a ringlike structure for benzene came upon him. Today the formula for benzene which was conjured up in Kekule's dream is practically unchallenged. It is a simple idea, yet one which had evaded scientists of the first rank for a long time, and we may well conclude

that imagination is a most important part of the creative scientist's equipment.

The benzene ring, so-called, is actually a hexagon and is represented as follows:

Note that 4 valence bonds are assigned to each carbon atom.

ACIDS

Further efforts to gain insight into the fundamental character of matter would be ineffectual without some knowledge of typical chemical reactions. It is unnecessary to go into great detail. Fortunately there are a few large and important classes of compounds whose members display pronounced similarities in their reactions and differ from other members of the same class chiefly in the vigor of their reactivity. Two of these classes of compounds are the acids and the bases.

The term acid occurs so frequently in ordinary speech as almost to dominate the lay notion of chemistry. Acids are commonly conceived to be potent, biting substances which destroy metals, wood, and fabrics. Actually they range in potency from the highly corrosive nitric and sulfuric acids to the mild, innocuous citric and malic acids occurring in fruits.

All acids have certain properties in common. Their solutions in water taste sour, and they give a distinctive color to certain dyestuffs known as indicators, of which *litmus* is perhaps the best known. When paper dyed with litmus is dipped into a solution of an acid, the litmus turns red. Constitutionally all acids are found to contain hydrogen, and this hydrogen can be displaced by various metals. The mere presence of hydrogen in a compound molecule does not make the compound an acid; the hydrogen must be replaceable. To illustrate, ethane, C_2H_6, is unaffected by the metal sodium, whereas acetic acid, $C_2H_4O_2$, reacts with sodium according to the equation

$$2C_2H_4O_2 + 2Na \rightarrow 2C_2H_3O_2Na + H_2$$
Acetic acid　　Sodium　　Sodium acetate　　Hydrogen

Note that only one of the four hydrogen atoms in the acetic acid molecule is replaceable by the metal.

The foregoing is a simple example of a "chemical equation." Each subscript numeral refers only to the element whose symbol precedes the subscript and gives the number of atoms of that element in one molecule of the compound. Thus, in acetic acid, $C_2H_4O_2$, there are two atoms of carbon, four atoms of hydrogen, and two atoms of oxygen per molecule.

A chemical equation must "balance," i.e., the number of atoms of each element must be the same on both sides of the arrow. In order to have the equation balanced, it may be necessary, as it was in the example, to include more than one molecule of certain substances. This is done by putting a numeral before the whole formula as a coefficient. Here $2C_2H_4O_2$ means two molecules of acetic acid, each containing two carbon, four hydrogen, and two oxygen atoms. Checking just one element, namely hydrogen, we find eight atoms of it in the $2C_2H_4O_2$ on the left. On the right there are six hydrogen atoms in two molecules of sodium acetate ($2C_2H_3O_2Na$) and the remaining two in one molecule of hydrogen (H_2).

The action of an acid on a metal affords the easiest way of obtaining hydrogen for laboratory use. The common hydrogen generator is no more than a bottle in which sulfuric acid is allowed to fall on granulated zinc. The reaction which occurs may be represented by the equation

$$Zn + H_2SO_4 \rightarrow ZnSO_4 + H_2$$

Many acids are obtained by the addition of water to oxides, particularly the oxides of non-metallic elements. Thus we have

$$CO_2 + H_2O \rightarrow H_2CO_3$$
Carbon　　　　　Carbonic
dioxide　　　　　acid

$$N_2O_5 + H_2O \rightarrow 2HNO_3$$
Nitrogen　　　　Nitric
pentoxide　　　　acid

$$P_2O_3 + 3H_2O \rightarrow 2H_3PO_3$$
Phosphorus　　　Phosphorous
trioxide　　　　　acid

$$P_2O_5 + 3H_2O \rightarrow 2H_3PO_4$$
Phosphorus　　　Phosphoric
pentoxide　　　　acid

$$SO_2 + H_2O \rightarrow H_2SO_3$$
Sulfur　　　　　Sulfurous
dioxide　　　　　acid

$$SO_3 + H_2O \rightarrow H_2SO_4$$
Sulfur　　　　　Sulfuric
trioxide　　　　acid

Because of their strong disposition to yield acids when combined with water, such oxides are called acid anhydrides (i.e., acids without water). Lavoisier believed that oxygen was an essential constituent of every acid; this was his reason for coining the name, oxygen, meaning acid former. It is hydrogen, however,—not oxygen—that is invariably present in acids. A few, such as HCl, HBr, and HI, do not contain any oxygen at all.

BASES

Another large class of compounds is that of bases. These compounds are also highly corrosive, especially to animal or vegetable tissue. Bases that can dissolve in water yield bitter-tasting solutions, and the indicator dyestuff litmus is colored blue by basic solutions. Bases react, often violently, with acids.

All base molecules contain doublets of oxygen and hydrogen atoms, constituting the so-called *hydroxyl radical*, and this two-element group seems to possess considerable stability. The commonest bases may be obtained from oxides of the lighter metals by union of these oxides with water. Thus

$$Na_2O + H_2O \rightarrow 2NaOH$$
Sodium　　　　　Sodium
oxide　　　　　　hydroxide
　　　　　　　　(also called
　　　　　　　　soda lye)

$$K_2O + H_2O \rightarrow 2KOH$$
Potassium　　　　Potassium
oxide　　　　　　hydroxide
　　　　　　　　(also called
　　　　　　　　potash lye)

$$CaO + H_2O \rightarrow Ca(OH)_2$$
Calcium　　　　　Calcium
oxide　　　　　　hydroxide
　　　　　　　　(slaked lime)

to which we add the formula of a base that is present in ammonia water:

$$NH_3 + H_2O \rightarrow NH_4OH$$
Ammonia　　　　Ammonium
　　　　　　　　hydroxide

SALTS

More numerous than either acids or bases are the members of a class of compounds called salts. These are the substances produced when acids and bases interact or when their anhydrides do so. A few such reactions are here illustrated by equations.

$$NH_4OH + HCl \rightarrow NH_4Cl + H_2O$$

Ammonium Hydrochloric Ammonium
hydroxide   acid   chloride
(sal ammoniac)

$$NaOH + HBr \rightarrow NaBr + H_2O$$

Sodium Hydrobromic Sodium
hydroxide   acid   bromide

$$KOH + HNO_3 \rightarrow KNO_3 + H_2O$$

Potassium Nitric Potassium
hydroxide acid   nitrate
(saltpeter)

$$3Ca(OH)_2 + 2H_3PO_4 \rightarrow Ca_3(PO_4)_2 + 6H_2O$$

Calcium Phosphoric Calcium
hydroxide acid   phosphate

$$CaO + CO_2 \rightarrow CaCO_3$$

Calcium   Calcium
oxide   carbonate

$$Na_2O + SO_3 \rightarrow Na_2SO_4$$

Sodium Sulfur Sodium
oxide   trioxide sulfate

One reason for the very great number of salts is that two or more different ones may sometimes be obtained from a single acid and base. Thus, from sodium hydroxide one can form with phosphoric acid:

Monosodium phosphate	NaH_2PO_4
Disodium phosphate	Na_2HPO_4
Trisodium phosphate	Na_3PO_4

or, again, with carbonic acid

Sodium bicarbonate	$NaHCO_3$ (popularly known as baking soda)
Sodium carbonate	Na_2CO_3 (popularly known as washing soda)

Another reason for the great abundance of salts is this: the oxides and hydroxides of many metals are insoluble in water and so they do not display the obvious characteristics of bases. Yet the same compounds may react readily with acids to yield salts. By way of illustration:

$$Mg(OH)_2 + H_2SO_4 \rightarrow MgSO_4 + 2H_2O$$

Magnesium   Magnesium
hydroxide   sulfate
(Epsom salt)

$$Cu(OH)_2 + H_2SO_4 \rightarrow CuSO_4 + 2H_2O$$

Cupric   Copper
hydroxide   sulfate
(blue vitriol)

$$2Fe(OH)_3 + 3H_2SO_4 \rightarrow Fe_2(SO_4)_3 + 6H_2O$$

Ferric   Ferric
hydroxide   sulfate

$$Al(OH)_3 + 3HCl \rightarrow AlCl_3 + 3H_2O$$

Aluminum   Aluminum
hydroxide   chloride

$$Zn(OH)_2 + 2HNO_3 \rightarrow Zn(NO_3)_2 + 2H_2O$$

Zinc   Zinc
hydroxide nitrate

$$HgO + 2HNO_3 \rightarrow Hg(NO_3)_2 + H_2O$$

Mercuric   Mercuric
oxide   nitrate

$$Ag_2O + 2HNO_3 \rightarrow 2AgNO_3 + H_2O$$

Silver   Silver
oxide   nitrate

CHEMICAL ARITHMETIC

To illustrate the quantitative character of chemical reasoning, consider the following example which has great practical value.

In a few scattered spots on the earth, there occur deposits of an iron ore called hematite. One of the most remarkable of these lies in northern Minnesota, where the rusty red ore is shoveled from huge open pits like sand. Chemically, hematite is found to be Fe_2O_3 with varying amounts of impurities. To obtain iron from this ore, Fe_2O_3 is mixed with coke (carbon) and heated strongly. The reaction which results is written compactly:

$$2Fe_2O_3 + 3C \rightarrow 4Fe + 3CO_2$$

(Note that this equation is balanced; there are as many atoms of each kind on one side of the arrow as there are on the other.) The molten iron is drawn off from the bottom of the furnace, and the CO_2 (carbon dioxide) escapes into the air.

There is no coke (coal) supply near the Minnesota iron mines. One of the important economic factors in the smelting of Minnesota iron ore is, therefore, the cost of transportation. Which will be cheaper, transporting the ore by specially designed boats over the Great Lakes to industrial centers in the east, or hauling coke up to northern Minnesota and smelting the ore there? To answer this question, the industrial chemist must be able to calculate the amounts of coke and iron ore needed to produce a specific mass, say 1 ton, of iron.

From the balanced equation above, we note that three atoms of carbon are needed to produce four atoms of iron. But each atom of carbon has an atomic mass of 12, and each atom of iron has an atomic mass of 55.8, so that 3×12 or 36 units (say, tons) of carbon are needed to produce 4×55.8 or 223.2 units (tons) of iron. Each ton of iron therefore requires $36/223.2 = 0.16$ tons of coke.

Again, we note that it requires two molecules of Fe_2O_3 or 319.2 units (tons) of iron ore to produce 223.2 tons of iron. Consequently, $319.2/223.2 = 1.43$ tons of ore yield one ton of iron.

This calculation shows that it will be cheaper to haul coke to Minnesota than to haul ore to the eastern industrial centers, and yet the present practice is to transport the iron ore to the east. This illustrates the complexity of industrial organization; there must be other economic reasons for the procedure which is now followed.

These are examples of a general procedure; atomic masses are inserted into the balanced equations which represent the chemical changes, and from these relations the ratios of all the masses involved may be calculated.

REPLACEMENT OF METALS IN SALTS

Suppose we have an aqueous solution of some salt whose formula is MX, where M represents any metal, and we introduce into the solution another metal, symbolized by N. It may happen that no chemical change occurs. Alternatively, M may be thrown out of combination, N taking its place, so that on evaporating the solution we find crystals of the salt NX. This behavior would seem to prove that N is more active chemically than M, at least in a competition for the element or radical represented by X.

Extensive repetition of this simple experiment, using many metals and many salts, enables us to list the metallic elements in the order of their avidity for the acidic group X of a salt. The nature of the acidic group is of little consequence; an active metal can displace a less active one from a chloride as easily as it can from a sulfate or from some other compound of the less active metal. It is not even imperative that the salt be in solution. A simple demonstration of this point consists of rubbing a dry crystal of the blue salt, copper sulfate, along the steel blade of a knife. A film of copper immediately appears on the knife blade, thus showing that iron, which is the predominant element in steel, is chemically more active than copper.

This replacement is adequately represented by the equation

$$Fe + CuSO_4 \rightarrow Cu + FeSO_4$$

$$\underset{\text{Copper sulfate}}{} \qquad \underset{\text{Ferrous sulfate}}{}$$

Whatever may be the mechanism which causes chemical combination between different elements to occur, it is clear enough from such experiments that no two metallic elements have precisely the same tendency toward combination. The same conclusion about non-metals is inferred from comparable evidence. In other words, there are inert elements and highly reactive elements and

there are elements intermediate between these extremes, each with its own degree of relative activity. Does not this gradation have some deep, innate relationship to the structure of matter, which is the subject of our principal concern? Let us apply a widely recognized principle. It has already been stated that all systems in the universe tend to achieve the greatest stability possible for them. Increased stability invariably results from a loss of energy. Hence, all systems tend to lose energy spontaneously. If we amplify this principle by assuming that the greater the potential energy possessed by a system, the stronger is the tendency for the system to lose some of it, we have a measure by which to compare the activities of the various elements. That the extension of the principle is reasonable may be demonstrated by the example of spontaneous cooling. Given two identical bodies at different temperatures, the hot one cools faster than the warm one. That is, the body whose energy state is higher loses energy at the greater rate.

Transferring the same idea to the problem of elemental activity, we should expect that when two metals form corresponding compounds, say iron oxide and copper oxide, the oxidation of the more active metal will be attended by the greater evolution of energy. This expectation is, in general, borne out. Very active metals, such as sodium and potassium, react spontaneously with other substances almost explosively, so great is the energy liberated.

THE ACTIVITY SERIES OF METALS

A partial list of metallic elements in descending order of their chemical activity is presented here. Such a list, familiar to all chemists, is sometimes called the *electromotive series of metals.*

Potassium
Sodium
Calcium
Magnesium
Aluminum
Zinc
Chromium
Iron
Cadmium
Cobalt
Nickel
Tin
Lead
Hydrogen

Copper
Mercury
Silver
Platinum
Gold

A striking illustration of relative chemical activity is observed when a rod of zinc is immersed in a solution of lead nitrate. Within a short time glistening crystals of metallic lead are found adorning the rod, and a test of the solution reveals the presence therein of dissolved zinc. The significant reaction may be expressed as follows:

$$Zn + Pb(NO_3)_2 \rightarrow Pb + Zn(NO_3)_2$$

Photographic prints are frequently "toned" by immersion in a solution of some gold compound, whereupon the relatively more active silver of the print dissolves, displacing the less active gold, which deposits on the paper in its place.

The reader may be surprised to find hydrogen listed here among the metals. Although this interesting element has none of the physical characteristics of metals, its chemical behavior is in many respects like that of a typical metal. As the active and essential constituent of all acids, hydrogen establishes its place in the activity series by the success or failure of metals in displacing it from acids. If a bit of some metal more active than hydrogen is dropped into a solution of any acid, the metal dissolves and hydrogen is set free.

Example: $Zn + 2HCl \rightarrow ZnCl_2 + H_2$

Observe that the acid behaves as if it were a salt of hydrogen.

If, however, a metal such as copper, which is less active than hydrogen, is exposed to the same acid, no reaction takes place at all.

Potassium and sodium at the top of this list are so active chemically that they can replace the hydrogen of cold water. When a small piece of either metal is dropped into water, a violent reaction begins and heat is evolved sufficient to melt the metal and ignite the liberated hydrogen. Fires in chemical laboratories are especially insidious because the inadvertent use of water as an extinguisher will only extend the conflagration if the water happens to come into contact with the sodium supply.

An interesting consequence of all this is that those metals which precede hydrogen in the activity series are never found free in nature, unless we except such recent arrivals on our planet as iron meteorites. The more active metals may have existed as free elements when the earth was newly formed, but they must soon have reacted with the naturally acidic waters which washed over them, replacing the hydrogen from these mildly acidic solutions. The metals which are less active than hydrogen, including gold and silver, could have withstood the corrosive action of such natural waters. That they did so is confirmed by the fact that these and all other metals which appear below hydrogen in the activity series do occur in the free state, although copper and silver are sometimes found also in compounds.

The ability or inability of metals to displace hydrogen accounts for a curious example of chemical nomenclature derived from the social structure of long ago. Those metals which we call precious metals, e.g., silver, platinum, and gold, appear near the bottom of the activity list, and this stamps them as relatively inert. They do not rust or react, even with such corrosive hydrogen compounds as hydrochloric acid. From earliest times they were esteemed for their resistance to corrosion—for their "incorruptible" character. Thus they came to be known as the "noble" metals. On the other hand, active metals like sodium, potassium, and calcium rust or corrode with great ease, and as corrodible or "corruptible" substances they have received the name of "base" metals. To such a fanciful origin do we owe the word "base" for such compounds as $NaOH$ or $Ca(OH)_2$. They are, after all, the products obtained on wetting the rust of a chemically active or base metal.

PROBLEMS

1. Powdered iron and sulfur, intimately mixed, can easily be separated by means of a magnet, which attracts the iron but not the sulfur. However, if the mixture of iron and sulfur is first heated strongly and then allowed to cool, the residue is not attracted by a magnet. What does this prove?

2. A glass bell jar is inverted in a tray of water as shown so that air is trapped inside the jar. On the water surface inside the jar a candle floats on a piece of cork. The candle is then lighted by means of a burning glass outside the jar. Describe what happens. Will the water level inside the jar rise or fall? Explain.

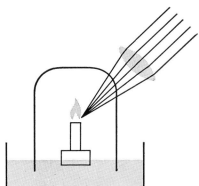

3. What is the valence of the several elements represented by X in the following formulas: XCl, X_2O_3, CX_2, Al_2X_3, Mn_2X_7, X_2O_5? Draw the structural formulas, indicating the valence bonds.

4. Of the two oxides of iron, Fe_2O_3 and Fe_3O_4, which contains the larger percentage of iron? Calculate the percentages.
Ans. 70% and 72.5%.

5. A compound of aluminum and oxygen is found by analysis to contain 53% aluminum. What is the formula for the compound?

6. When limestone ($CaCO_3$) is heated strongly it decomposes into lime (CaO) and carbon dioxide (CO_2). The reaction is written

$$CaCO_3 + Heat \rightarrow CaO + CO_2$$

How many tons of limestone must be used to produce 1 ton of lime? How many tons of gaseous CO_2 are liberated in this process?
Ans. 1.79 tons of $CaCO_3$ and 0.786 tons CO_2.

7. Balance the following equations: The burning of cane sugar:

$$C_{12}H_{22}O_{11} + O_2 \rightarrow CO_2 + H_2O$$

The preparation of ether from alcohol:

$$C_2H_5OH \rightarrow (C_2H_5)_2O + H_2O$$

The setting of slaked lime:

$$Ca(OH)_2 + CO_2 \rightarrow CaCO_3 + H_2O$$

The smelting of magnetite iron ore:

$$Fe_3O_4 + CO + Heat \rightarrow Fe + CO_2$$

The preparation of chlorine:

$$KMnO_4 + HCl \rightarrow KCl + MnCl_2 + H_2O + Cl_2$$

8. Draw the structural formulas for all possible isomers of hexane C_6H_{14}.

· ·

REFERENCES

1. *The Atomic-Molecular Theory*, L. K. Nash, Harvard Case Histories in Experimental Science, Case 4, Harvard University Press, 1950.

 *The Periodic Classification of the Elements*

At an early stage in the development of modern chemistry scientists began to realize that the chemical elements can be grouped into "families" on the basis of obvious similarities in chemical behavior. One such family, the halogens, comprises the elements fluorine, chlorine, bromine, iodine, and, now, astatine. Physically, these elements have little in common; the first two are yellowish gases, the third a red, volatile liquid, the fourth a gray, metallic-looking solid. Physiologically the halogens have very penetrating odors and are extremely irritating to the mucous membranes. Chlorine and bromine have both been used as irritant poisons in gas warfare. Iodine, also a strong irritant, is a potent antiseptic. It is familiar medical knowledge that iodine collects in the thyroid gland, and now astatine, the most recently discovered halogen, is found to do likewise. But it is in their chemical behavior that the halogens display the closest relationship. They react very energetically with most other elements, especially with metals. Each exhibits most commonly the valence number -1, although the halogen elements also show positive valence in various unstable compounds of which they form a part. Excepting astatine, all occur in nature as salts of common metals, these salts usually being present rather abundantly in sea water.

Halogen compounds of comparable composition likewise show remarkable similarity. The halogen salts of metals, for example, have much the same properties, both chemical and physical. Thus, sodium chloride, $NaCl$, sodium bromide, $NaBr$, and sodium iodide, NaI, are all white, crystalline solids, easily soluble in water, salty in taste, and capable of undergoing the same kinds of reactions with other compounds.

The recognition of numerous "families" of elements led to the suspicion, early in the nineteenth century, that *all* the elements are fundamentally related to one another. It was suggested that the atoms of different elements may be made up of the same constituents but in such different proportions and arrangements as to account for the differences in their properties. By analogy, all automobiles are built of practically the same materials but one make is easily distinguishable from another by familiar differences in design.

The idea of a primordial "stuff" serving as the

basic ingredient of matter in all its variations was held by many of the ancient Greek thinkers. They had no evidence to support such a view, but the notion was consistent with their belief in an essentially simple universe. In 1815 the English physician, William Prout, proposed that the element hydrogen was just such a universal element and that all other elements were built up out of hydrogen particles. Prout's suggestion came from the knowledge that a good many elements have atomic masses which are whole multiples of the atomic mass of hydrogen. His proposal lost favor, however, when it became certain that this relationship was in general not true.

THE PERIODIC TABLE OF MENDELEJEFF

In 1869 the Russian chemist Mendelejeff (1834–1907) pointed out the extraordinary family groupings which appear when the elements are arranged in the order of their atomic masses. Let us suppose that the symbols of the first seventeen elements are written in this sequence on a paper tape with their atomic masses indicated in round numbers. Let the tape then be torn after fluorine (F) and the pieces fitted together as follows:

H	He	Li	Be	B	C	N	O	F
1	4	7	9	11	12	14	16	19

	Ne	Na	Mg	Al	Si	P	S	Cl
	20	23	24	27	28	31	32	35.5

Then, reading downward, we find that each element in the second row strongly resembles the element above it in the first row. Thus, helium (He) and neon (Ne) are both inert gases, incapable of combining with other elements, and their valence number is zero.

Lithium (Li) and sodium (Na) are both soft, light metals which react readily with water, liberating hydrogen from the water and dissolving to give strongly alkaline solutions. Their valence number is $+1$.

Beryllium (Be) and magnesium (Mg) have chemical properties similar to those of lithium and sodium, but they are much milder in their chemical reactivity. Their valence number is $+2$.

Fluorine (F) and chlorine (Cl) have already been mentioned as part of an important chemical family. Their usual valence number is -1.

Oxygen (O) and sulfur (S) resemble each other in chemical behavior even though they are un-like physically. Commonly they display the valence number -2.

To a student of chemistry many other similarities in chemical behavior would be evident at once, but a further discussion at this point would scarcely benefit the general reader. Let us be content with the statement that, if all the known elements are arranged according to the system proposed by Mendelejeff, the elements appearing in each vertical column are, with a few exceptions, ones having similar chemical properties.

The arrangement becomes more complex as we go on to the heavier elements and the resemblances are often somewhat obscure, but the periodic recurrence of similar chemical properties is surely too definite to be accidental. It is a certain indication that the atoms of different elements contain some common constituent or structural feature which endows them with a degree of resemblance.

ATOMIC NUMBERS

Part of the periodic classification of Mendelejeff is reproduced in Table 11. The subscript to the left of each symbol is the ordinal number of that element in the series: 1 for H, 2 for He, 3 for Li, and so on, and is called the *atomic number* of the element. The superscripts to the right of the symbols are the relative atomic masses of the elements in round numbers. The staggering of symbols in any vertical column is done to separate the elements of a subgroup from those of another subgroup whose members they resemble to a smaller degree.

Our abbreviated table includes elements which were unknown to Mendelejeff. When he first published his classification, only 63 of the 100 or so elements now recognized had been discovered. He had enough confidence in the merit of his scheme, however, to predict the existence of at least three of them, together with their principal properties. When these three elements, now known as scandium (Sc, number 21), gallium (Ga, number 31), and germanium (Ge, number 32), were discovered a few years later, they were found to measure up almost exactly to the characteristics which Mendelejeff had prophesied for them. His argument was simple and rational. Noting, for example, that after calcium the next heavier element was titanium, which had no resemblance to aluminum but considerable likeness to silicon, Mendelejeff skipped a place in group III and put titanium into group IV. He then estimated the probable

TABLE 11. PART OF THE PERIODIC TABLE OF THE ELEMENTS *

I	II	III	IV	V	VI	VII	VIII			Zero
Hydrogen $_1\text{H}^1$										Helium $_2\text{He}^4$
Lithium $_3\text{Li}^7$	Beryllium $_4\text{Be}^9$	Boron $_5\text{B}^{11}$	Carbon $_6\text{C}^{12}$	Nitrogen $_7\text{N}^{14}$	Oxygen $_8\text{O}^{16}$	Fluorine $_9\text{F}^{19}$				Neon $_{10}\text{Ne}^{20}$
Sodium $_{11}\text{Na}^{23}$	Magnesium $_{12}\text{Mg}^{24}$	Aluminum $_{13}\text{Al}^{27}$	Silicon $_{14}\text{Si}^{28}$	Phosphorus $_{15}\text{P}^{31}$	Sulfur $_{16}\text{S}^{32}$	Chlorine $_{17}\text{Cl}^{35.5}$				Argon $_{18}\text{A}^{40}$
Potassium $_{19}\text{K}^{39}$	Calcium $_{20}\text{Ca}^{40}$	Scandium $_{21}\text{Sc}^{45}$	Titanium $_{22}\text{Ti}^{48}$	Vanadium $_{23}\text{V}^{51}$	Chromium $_{24}\text{Cr}^{52}$	Manganese $_{25}\text{Mn}^{55}$	Iron $_{26}\text{Fe}^{56}$	Cobalt $_{27}\text{Co}^{59}$	Nickel $_{28}\text{Ni}^{58.7}$	
Copper $_{29}\text{Cu}^{63.5}$	Zinc $_{30}\text{Zn}^{65}$	Gallium $_{31}\text{Ga}^{70}$	Germanium $_{32}\text{Ge}^{73}$	Arsenic $_{33}\text{As}^{75}$	Selenium $_{34}\text{Se}^{79}$	Bromine $_{35}\text{Br}^{80}$				Krypton $_{36}\text{Kr}^{84}$
Rubidium $_{37}\text{Rb}^{85}$	Strontium $_{38}\text{Sr}^{88}$		Zirconium $_{40}\text{Zr}^{91}$		Molybdenum $_{42}\text{Mo}^{96}$					
Silver $_{47}\text{Ag}^{108}$	Cadmium $_{48}\text{Cd}^{112}$		Tin $_{50}\text{Sn}^{119}$	Antimony $_{51}\text{Sb}^{122}$	Tellurium $_{52}\text{Te}^{128}$	Iodine $_{53}\text{I}^{127}$				Xenon $_{54}\text{Xe}^{131}$
Cesium $_{55}\text{Cs}^{133}$	Barium $_{56}\text{Ba}^{137}$	Elements 57 to 71	Hafnium $_{72}\text{Hf}^{179}$		Tungsten $_{74}\text{W}^{184}$		Osmium $_{76}\text{Os}^{190}$	Iridium $_{77}\text{Ir}^{193}$	Platinum $_{78}\text{Pt}^{195}$	
Gold $_{79}\text{Au}^{197}$	Mercury $_{80}\text{Hg}^{201}$		Lead $_{82}\text{Pb}^{207}$	Bismuth $_{83}\text{Bi}^{209}$						Radon $_{86}\text{Rn}^{222}$
	Radium $_{88}\text{Ra}^{226}$	Elements 89 to 101								

* A number of the less important elements have been omitted. Elements whose symbols appear directly below one another belong to the same family.

density, atomic weight, color, and chemical properties of the missing element by averaging the properties of the elements occupying the surrounding places.

With regard to the elements then known, Mendelejeff had to violate the order of increasing atomic masses in a few instances so as to fit elements into appropriate columns. For example, tellurium, of atomic mass 127.6, was made to precede iodine, of atomic mass 126.9, in spite of its greater mass, because this would put tellurium into the same column as sulfur and would put iodine into the same column as bromine. The properties of tellurium and iodine show clearly that they belong in these respective families.

It is now certain that family relationships among the chemical elements are attributable to similarities in the electrical constitution of their atoms. It is the electrical charge within an atom that determines the atomic number of the atom, and in a modern periodic table all elements are placed in the order of their atomic numbers without regard to their atomic masses. These matters will be dealt with in some detail in Chapter 26.

THE INERT ELEMENTS

It is not surprising that Mendelejeff failed to predict the existence of those elements now occupying group zero, since none of them had actually been discovered on earth by 1869. The absence of an entire group of elements could hardly be revealed by his system of recognition by default. In watching a parade of soldiers, we may notice that one man is missing from a particular squad if most other squads in the column are filled, whereas the absence of an entire squad goes undetected by the spectator.

The discovery of the elements of group zero makes a fascinating story. Helium, the lightest element of the group, first revealed itself to scientists as a constituent of the sun's atmosphere. This was in 1868, when a British expedition went to India to observe a solar eclipse, and here for the first time the newly invented spectroscope was used to examine the sun's light on a grand scale. The spectroscope, to be described farther on, is an instrument for analyzing the light from an incandescent source by separating it into a spectrum consisting of numerous colored lines. Every element has its own unique spectrum, thus enabling the observer to determine the elemental composition of very distant bodies provided they

emit light. Examining the sun's chromosphere during the eclipse of 1868, Frankland and Lockyer found a spectral line which had never before been noted for any terrestrial substance. Correctly attributing this line to a new element, they named the element *helium* (from *helios*, the sun). Not until about 1897 was helium found on earth, when Sir William Ramsay obtained it from a mineral. Traces of helium exist in the atmosphere, but considerable quantities of the element are now separated from natural gas with which it frequently occurs in oil wells.

The element, argon, although not identified until nearly the end of the nineteenth century, makes up about 1% of the earth's atmosphere and is therefore rather plentiful. It is, however, difficult to isolate except by evaporation of liquid air. Strange to say, argon was actually segregated for the first time in 1785 by the English scientist Henry Cavendish (1731–1810), the discoverer of hydrogen. He knew that a mixture of nitrogen and oxygen subjected to the action of electric sparks yields nitric acid, which can be completely absorbed by a solution of potassium hydroxide. Cavendish used this treatment on a confined volume of air fortified with additional oxygen, and found that, in spite of prolonged sparking, there remained a small bubble of gas which defied his persistent attempts to make it combine.

The report of this eminently careful experimenter escaped the attention of other scientists for more than a century, but in 1894 Rayleigh and Ramsay studied Cavendish's old memoir, repeated his experiment, and obtained the same gaseous residue, which they proved to consist of several new elements, principally the one which they named argon.

Within a short time Ramsay and his co-workers had succeeded in isolating three other inert elements, neon, krypton, and xenon.

The last member of this inert gas family, radon, was discovered in 1900 by Rutherford and Soddy. It is emitted during the spontaneous decay of radium in the form of a gaseous emanation. Like the parent element, it is itself radioactive.

PROPERTIES OF THE INERT ELEMENTS

Physically, all members of the group are colorless gases. Chemically, they may be said to have no properties at all. That is to say, none of these elements combines with anything, and this absence of reactivity sets them apart as representing the extreme of chemical stability. There is good evidence that an atom of any inert gas does not even combine with another of its own kind as atoms of hydrogen, oxygen, and other elemental gases do. By means of the kinetic theory one can make predictions about the specific heats of gaseous elements, according to which the molecules are presumptively monatomic or diatomic. The predictions agree very well with measurements of the specific heat in the cases of hydrogen and oxygen if these gases are assumed to be diatomic. Agreement between theoretical prediction and measured values is also excellent in the cases of the inert gases provided they are assumed to be monatomic. Consequently, when we find experimentally that helium is just about twice as dense as hydrogen, we do not infer that a helium atom is twice as massive as a hydrogen atom but rather that it is twice as massive as a hydrogen *molecule,* or 4 times as massive as a hydrogen *atom.*

USES OF THE PERIODIC CLASSIFICATION

That the periodic repetition of properties among the elements is due to some similarity in the structure of their atoms can hardly be questioned. A detailed explanation of this undoubted similarity will be postponed until we have described some of the outstanding experiments of recent times from which the present ideas of atomic architecture are inferred. But the utility of the periodic classification is immediately apparent. It has been used to correct erroneous atomic masses. It has served repeatedly to suggest how and among what materials to search for previously unknown elements. An empty space in the table not only indicated the existence of an element which should occupy that space but also provided valuable hints about the properties of such elements. Alternatively, the classification has helped in the location of new sources of useful but rare minerals among the ores of related common ones, since similar elements tend to form similar compounds and these compounds are more than likely to occur together in the same mineral deposits. For example, tungsten (W, group VI), the very serviceable metal from which lamp filaments are made, is found in the mineral wolframite, which accompanies the ores of chromium (Cr, group VI).

The resemblance in characteristics between elements which occupy the same column in the periodic classification also suggests uses for the less familiar ones. It is not surprising to learn, therefore, that tungsten, molybdenum, and chromium, all of the same group VI, have been found useful in making very hard steels.

HORIZONTAL SIMILARITIES

Although the most striking feature of the periodic table is the resemblance of elements in vertical columns, it is also true that in certain parts of the table the elements occupying successive places in the same horizontal row exhibit marked similarities. Particularly is this true of elements 57 to 71, which differ so little from one another that it is difficult to separate them by chemical means. For that reason these fifteen elements are commonly assigned to the same box in column III under their group name of "rare earth elements."

Again, beginning with element 89, actinium, a series of closely related elements is found.

Elements 26, 27, and 28 (iron, cobalt, and nickel), in spite of the difference in their atomic numbers, are so similar in both physical and chemical properties that they are placed together in column VIII. It is interesting to note that these elements are the only ones known to be strongly magnetic and, also, that they frequently occur together in meteorites.

To the student of chemistry the periodic classification is a great boon, inasmuch as he may infer a good deal about the behavior of elements and compounds which he has not studied from the properties of related substances which he has studied intimately. This is an important economy, for the number of elements and their compounds is so great that even a professional scientist can scarcely master all their known properties.

NEW ELEMENTS

Until very recent years it was believed that there were in all the universe only 92 different elements of which 90 had been discovered. The reason for supposing that element number 92, uranium, was the last of the series rested not only on the fact that no element of higher atomic number than uranium's had been discovered. In addition, it is familiar knowledge that uranium and several other of the heaviest elements are extremely unstable. Their atoms decompose spontaneously to yield lighter elements as well as electrical emanations and radiant energy. In the light of modern knowledge it was believed that the instability associated with elements of large atomic mass had reached its limit in uranium, so that heavier elements, if they ever existed at all, must have disintegrated long ago.

In the 1940's the preparation of elements still more massive than uranium was announced. Note that the word "preparation" rather than "discovery" is used, for these heavy elements are not found in nature but are prepared artificially. During the war years element 93, called neptunium (Np), and element 94, called plutonium (Pu), were produced in the United States in connection with the atomic bomb project. Plutonium especially was manufactured in amounts sufficient to realize the most formidable military operations ever attempted by man. More recently several additional elements of even larger atomic numbers have been prepared. These include:

Americium	$_{95}$Am
Curium	$_{96}$Cm
Berkelium	$_{97}$Bk
Californium	$_{98}$Cf
Einsteinium	$_{99}$E
Fermium	$_{100}$Fm
Mendelevium	$_{101}$Me

The subscript written before each symbol is the atomic number of the element. Four of the names were assigned in honor of great scientists; the others commemorate places of discovery.

PROBLEMS

1. Using the periodic table in conjunction with the activity series of metals (p. 179), list the following elements in order of decreasing chemical activity, explaining the reasons for the order you select: Barium, cesium, gallium, germanium, rubidium, strontium.

2. Niobium (also called columbium) is element 41 in the periodic table. Estimate its atomic mass, showing why this should be less than the mean of the atomic masses of arsenic and antimony. Would you expect niobium to be a less dense or a more dense element than molybdenum? Than vanadium? Give reason. Strontium, zirconium, and molydenum form compounds with the formulas SrO, ZrO_2, and MoO_3. Write the probable formula of an oxide of niobium.

3. The inert elements of group zero, although ordinarily gaseous, can be liquefied. In fact, a way of separating them from one another is by distilling liquid air, which contains several of these elements. Which one would you expect to be most easily liquefied and which one least easily? Which element in the liquid state should have the greatest density?

4. Cadmium is a metal which has become increasingly useful in modern times, especially as a protective plating on metallic articles. If you were seeking ores of this element in nature, with what commoner element would you be most likely to find cadmium occurring? In chemical characteristics would you consider cadmium to be more or less metallic than silver? Than tin? Give reason.

Electricity and the Electrical Nature of Matter

INTRODUCTION

There are many questions about the nature of matter to which our rudimentary concepts of molecule and atom thus far furnish no answer. What is an atom like? Is it an indivisible entity, as Dalton believed, or is it an aggregation of still simpler particles? How can we account for the partiality shown by atoms of one element toward those of another whereby these two elements enter into chemical combination with one another although either one may be incapable of chemical union with a third element? These are profound questions, and any attempt to answer them calls for extended investigation into the possible composition of atoms themselves—an investigation which has gone on for nearly a century with mounting intensity. Its results make up the main body of what is called *modern physics*. The record of this recent accumulation of knowledge demonstrates the extraordinary potency of the scientific method as no other inquiry has ever done.

In the development of the natural sciences there is a cumulative effect which speaks both for the consistency of nature and for the soundness of the methods used to investigate those consistencies. The facts surrounding a phenomenon, once established through careful observation, are respected through all subsequent time, and they remain as necessary checks on any new theories proposed. To be sure, the data of science are continually being sharpened by improved devices and techniques but they are rarely repudiated. The laws of the lever and the balance discovered by the Greeks are still valid. The law discovered by Archimedes describing the buoyancy of submerged bodies is still indisputable after more than two thousand years. Each new fact discovered about nature aids in the discovery of more facts. There are at least two reasons for this.

First, the terse statements of fact, or assemblies of facts, which we call laws frequently point in the direction of new phenomena. The Newtonian concept of force can be traced directly to the earlier experiments and speculations of Galileo, and there is little doubt that Newton found in Kepler's laws the germ of the idea of a gravitational force which acts between all masses everywhere in the universe. The theories which result from laws and data are perhaps even more helpful in guiding the experimenter toward new discoveries. It is, after all, one of the important functions of a successful theory that it must suggest new facts and new directions to which research should turn. Students must not be deceived by the occasional accidental and sometimes brilliant discoveries which appear as dramatic episodes in the history of science. Scientific research is not an aimless, hit or miss procedure; it is, for the most part, a carefully planned and directed activity guided by known facts, experiences, and theories. Automatically, these guides set the stage for the unexpected and spectacular discoveries which make scientific investigation so exciting.

Second, laboratory devices and techniques are continually being improved by new discoveries. Not only can more reliable measurements be made with less and less effort, but frequently it becomes possible to make measurements that previously could not be made at all. For example, the discovery of X rays by Roentgen in 1895 not only revealed a strange new radiation but it furnished man with a novel means of measuring extremely short distances, far smaller than anything that was possible before Roentgen's time. Discoveries in optics gave us the microscope and the telescope to overcome the limitations of size and distance. Our present knowledge of electricity has brought forth a multitude of instruments so sensitive and so versatile that we now have an enormous advantage over the experimenters of even a few decades ago. For just this reason the superficial student is likely to be unimpressed by early scientists and their contributions because much of their labor seems, offhand, like crude and aimless groping. That is an illusion, however, attributable to the severe handicaps imposed by a lack of sensitive measuring devices and by the absence of a stockpile of data or models to serve as guides. Indeed, the achievements of earlier investigators are all the more impressive for being accomplished without precision instruments. Students would do well to develop a sense of scientific history by reading generously from the classics which Galileo, Boyle, Priestley, Faraday, and many others have given us.

In order to illustrate these points and also to build up an experimental and logical foundation for the study of atomic phenomena, we shall use the material of electricity and magnetism.

FAMILIAR ELECTRICAL EFFECTS

If a comb is run through the hair on a dry day, one hears a crackling sound and the comb exhibits a momentary attraction for the hair and for other light objects. As early as 600 B.C. the Greek philosopher Thales recorded a similar effect for amber. Again, when a person shuffles across a carpet, especially on a dry winter day, he hears the sound of a spark and feels a slight shock on touching a metallic fixture. So common is this rather annoying phenomenon that cloth and carpet yarns are now treated in the mills with antistatic preparations to diminish it, and at every automobile tollgate a metal wand projects from the ground to discharge the electrification which has accumulated on the approaching cars. Countless people must have observed these familiar occurrences and thought them odd but unimportant. Yet such seemingly simple phenomena, when investigated systematically, have led to the impressive electrical age which we now enjoy. The useful development of electrical knowledge took centuries, however. For example, it was not clearly demonstrated that there are electrical repulsions as well as attractions until the time of Otto von Guericke (1602–1686), an interval of over two thousand years from the first recorded observations of Thales. One can scarcely believe that through all the centuries of Greek culture, with its esthetic and philosophical achievements, through the Roman civilization with its legal and political genius, through the Arabic domination of the cultural world, through all those centuries there was not enough experimentation to reveal the fact that two pieces of amber, similarly rubbed with silk, will repel each other. Even Gilbert (1540–1603), the Elizabethan physician, who was probably the foremost electrical experimenter of his day, failed to discover electrical repulsion.

The attitude toward experimentation during the Middle Ages was not merely one of indifference. Philosophers in general shunned nature study and consciously resisted any temptation to experiment. Man's chief concern was for safety, physical and spiritual, and abstract logic dominated whatever rational activity there was.

Now let us undertake to do what people of the Middle Ages did not do; let us yield to our curiosity about this strange property of amber and imagine ourselves in the role of experimenters.

ELECTRIFICATION

Suppose that we make a little ball out of cornstalk pith or balsa wood, and coat the outside with very thin metallic foil. This ball, suspended by a fine silk thread, will serve as a test object for the detection of electrical forces. The reasons for our choice of materials will become evident as the experiment proceeds. A glass rod, briskly rubbed with silk, attracts the pith ball strongly, but, on contact, the ball jumps away from the rod and stands off as if strongly repelled. On a very dry day this repulsion will persist for a long time, but as soon as the ball is touched by the hand, it reverts to its original, unexcited condition. We say that the glass rod has become electrified and that the pith ball, by contact with it, has acquired an electric charge. The word electrified comes from the Greek *elektron*, meaning amber.

The forces brought into play in this demonstration are not to be confused with the gravitational force which exists between all material bodies in the universe. Normally, a glass rod would have no visible effect on the suspended ball. When the rod is rubbed with silk, however, something exceptional happens to it and these spectacular forces come into being. It is as if invisible tentacles were attached to the glass rod, reaching out through space to act upon distant bodies. Unlike gravitational force, these electrical manifestations can be either attractive or repulsive and they may be far stronger.

Hard rubber, Lucite, sealing wax, and many other plastics and resins appear to behave in the same way as glass and amber. Metals, when held in the hand, do not exhibit electrical excitation.

Offhand, the electrification of various nonmetallic materials seems to be the same for all of them but a fresh experiment shows that this is not so.

POSITIVE AND NEGATIVE ELECTRIFICATION

Let us next rub a glass rod with silk and place it on an insulated stand which is free to rotate (Fig. 82). When another glass rod is rubbed with silk and held near the first one, the movable rod is seen to retreat as if repelled by the rod which was similarly electrified. But, if a rod of hard rubber which has been stroked with fur is held near the movable glass rod, the latter promptly advances toward it. Repeating the experiment with two rubber rods, each of which has been rubbed with fur, it is found that they repel each other as did the two glass rods.

Here is experimental proof that there are two kinds of electrification and that bodies having electrification of the same kind exert a repulsive force on each other, whereas, if they have unlike kinds, they exert an attractive force on each other. These two kinds of electrification were formerly called *vitreous,* for the kind acquired by glass or other vitreous materials, and *resinous* when acquired by amber, sealing wax, or other resinous materials. These terms have long been sup-

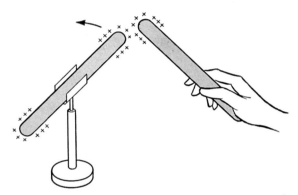

FIG. 82. Electrical repulsion between two similarly charged rods.

planted by the more abstract designations *positive* and *negative* which were first proposed by our own Benjamin Franklin, who was a very ingenious electrical experimenter in his day. We shall therefore use:

Positive for the kind of electrification acquired by *glass* or *Lucite* when rubbed with silk.

Negative for the kind of electrification acquired by *amber* or *hard rubber* when rubbed with fur.

A very suggestive accompaniment to the charging of a glass rod with positive electrification is this: the silk with which the glass is rubbed becomes negatively charged to an equal degree. Likewise, when a rubber rod becomes negatively charged by contact with fur, the fur acquires simultaneously a positive charge of the same magnitude.

QUANTITATIVE ASPECTS OF ELECTRIFICATION

Even in the crude experiment described it is apparent that the electrical forces, whether attractive or repulsive, decrease markedly as the distance between the charged bodies increases.

Quantitative investigation of electrical forces

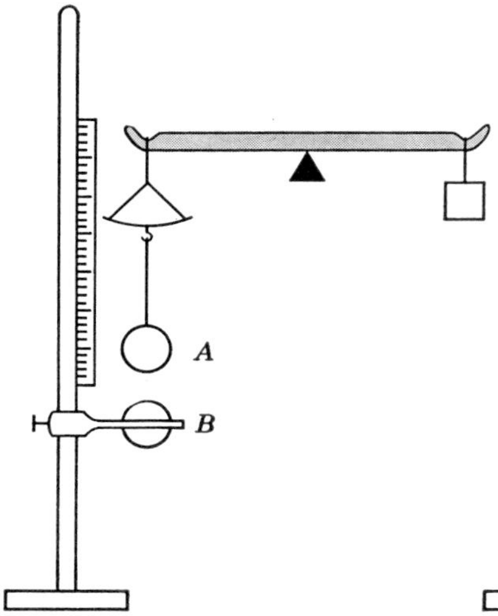

Balls uncharged	Balls charged	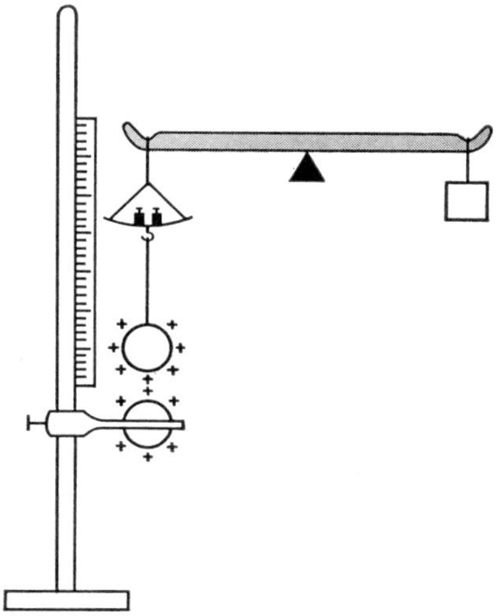 Balls charged and repulsive force balanced
FIG. 83	FIG. 84	FIG. 85

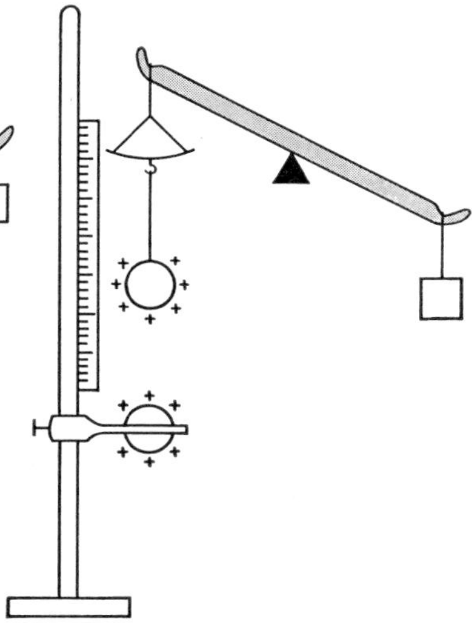

The relation between force and distance can easily be investigated with the aid of a balance.

From one end of the delicate balance beam a small metal ball *A* is suspended by a thread (Fig. 83). A counterpoise at the other end of the beam balances the ball and the weight pan. An identical ball *B* can be held fixed at various distances below the suspended one. Its supporting clamp must be of hard rubber or other non-conducting material to prevent charges from escaping through the support.

Let the stationary ball be touched with an electrified glass rod, which thereby imparts to it a certain amount of charge. The balance beam is now tipped so as to permit momentary contact between the two balls. Here we make the plausible assumption that the charge divides itself equally between the two identical spheres. On releasing the beam, the suspended ball is immediately repelled upward (Fig. 84) and we need only add weights to the pan on the left side until equilibrium is restored with the beam horizontal (Fig. 85).

The lower ball is now shifted to a new height and the weights altered to establish equilibrium again. The weights needed to balance the system in each case measure the forces between the spheres. Our data are shown in Table 12.

We note that, as the separation between the spheres increases, the force decreases in proportion to the square of the distance. This is quantitatively demonstrated by multiplying the distance squared by the repulsion for that distance. The product, in each case, is very nearly 10.

A second experiment is now conducted to discover the effect of varying the *amounts* of charge. The lower ball is held always in the same position—say, at 6 cm below the suspended one. A third identical ball is used to remove charges from one of the participants. We assume as before that when this third ball, held by rubber-covered tongs, is allowed to touch one of the charged balls, say *B*, it will take away half the charge that *B* carries. Also, if the third ball is discharged and again brought into contact with *B*, the charge of *B* will be further decreased from $\frac{1}{2}$ to $\frac{1}{4}$ of its original value. Repetition of this procedure leads to data like those in Table 13.

TABLE 12

Center to Center Distance between Spheres, cm	Distance Squared	Weights Added to Counteract Repulsion, grams
3	9	1.11
4	16	0.625
5	25	0.400
6	36	0.278
8	64	0.157
10	100	0.100

TABLE 13. TWO CHARGED SPHERES AT A FIXED DISTANCE OF 6 CENTIMETERS BETWEEN CENTERS

Charge on B	Weights Added to Counteract Repulsion, grams
Original	0.278
$\frac{1}{2}$	0.140
$\frac{1}{4}$	0.069
$\frac{1}{8}$	0.035

These specimen figures indicate that the force between charged bodies depends directly on the amounts of the charges.

COULOMB'S LAW

The inverse square relation between force and distance was discovered in 1784 by the French engineer Charles Coulomb (1736–1806), and the dependence of force upon distance and amount of charge is now known as Coulomb's law. The law is conveniently symbolized by

$$F \propto Q_1 Q_2 / r^2$$

where Q_1 and Q_2 represent the amounts of electric charge, and r is the distance separating them, it being assumed that the charges are concentrated at points r units apart. The law applies whether Q_1 and Q_2 have the same sign and repel each other, or opposite signs and attract each other.

Coulomb's law as written above has the same form as Newton's law of universal gravitation. In order to express the law by an equation, we need, as usual, a proportionality constant. It is the practice to put this constant into the denominator, whereby the formulation of Coulomb's law becomes

$$F = Q_1 Q_2 / K r^2$$

Although alike in form, the laws of gravitation and of electric force differ in certain important respects. One of these is that the electric law holds for either repulsion or attraction. Another concerns the region between the reacting bodies. Let a block of glass be inserted between the charged spheres in any of the foregoing experiments, and the electrical force is found to be greatly diminished. Tests of this sort show that the force is not only affected by the amounts of charge and the distances between the spheres but also by the kind of medium between them. This is not true of gravitational force, which is apparently uninfluenced by whatever lies between the gravitating bodies. Thus the pull of the sun on the earth is the same whether or not Mercury or Venus happens to stand between them.

Evidently the medium in which charged bodies are located must be taken into account in calculations utilizing Coulomb's law. Therefore K is not always the same constant but must be selected according to the environment. It is called the *dielectric constant* of the medium between the charges. Its minimum value is 1 for vacuous space. For gases such as air it is scarcely larger, but for many liquids and solids K is a great deal larger. Glass has a dielectric constant about 7 times as large as that of a vacuum. Pure water has a dielectric constant about 81 times that of empty space.

Again, let us note the idealized character of a mathematical equation which professes to describe a natural phenomenon. Coulomb's law really applies to charges so concentrated in space that r represents the distance between two points. Actually, we can never observe such a situation in the laboratory, although we can approximate it by using bodies which are very small compared with r. When the bodies are perfect spheres and the electric charge is distributed uniformly over their surfaces, the total force can be shown to be the same as if the charges had been concentrated at the centers of the spheres.

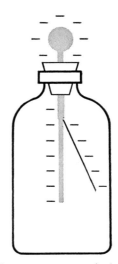

FIG. 86. The electroscope, negatively charged.

THE ELECTROSCOPE

A simple and convenient instrument for detecting the sign and the relative quantity of electrification is the electroscope, which is depicted in Fig. 86. This device is one of the most sensitive electrical instruments we have, and it is probably the oldest, having been invented in 1787. To a metal rod which is surmounted by a metal knob there are attached two small pieces of metal foil (or only one strip of foil and a rigid strip of metal adjacent to it). This arrangement is inclosed in a glass flask so as to shield the delicate foil from air currents.

When an electrified body touches the protruding knob, the metal leaves diverge, the amount of divergence being greater the greater the charge transferred. Since charges of the same sign exhibit mutual repulsion, it is reasonable to suppose that, as the charges enter the electroscope knob, they spread as far apart as possible throughout the rod and the leaves. Inasmuch as at least one of the leaves is movable, their mutual repulsion results in actual divergence between them.

Once the electroscope has acquired a positive or a negative charge, it may be used to identify the sign of charge on any other electrified body. Thus, if the charge which has been given to the instrument is negative, the approach of a positively charged object will cause the leaves to collapse owing, evidently, to a congregation of the negative charges on the knob of the electroscope in response to the attractive force exerted by the positive object. A negatively electrified object, on the other hand, causes greater divergence between the leaves when it is brought close to the electroscope and identifies the sign of its charge by this effect.

CONDUCTORS AND INSULATORS

On dry days a charged electroscope will retain its charge for several hours without appreciable convergence of the leaves but if the knob is touched by the hand of a person standing on the ground, the leaves suddenly come together, thus indicating that the charge has left the electroscope. If we repeat the test, touching the knob with pieces of various materials held in the hand, we find that some of them will cause the instrument to discharge suddenly whereas others will do so slowly. Still others are found to have, apparently, no effect at all. From these results we infer that electric charge can pass easily through some materials, whereas it flows with difficulty or seemingly not at all through others. Materials of the former class are appropriately called *conductors;* materials which do not permit the easy flow of charge through their structures are called non-conductors or *insulators.* All metals are found to be relatively good conductors. Glass,

amber, sulfur, sealing wax, mica, and non-metallic materials in general are insulators or at best poor conductors. Dry air must be classed as an insulator, since the charged leaves which are surrounded by air persist in their electrified state so long as the air is not very humid. Wood and cloth fabrics are poor conductors, but their conductivity varies with their kind, their compactness, and especially with their moisture content. There is, indeed, no sharp line of demarcation between conductors and insulators. Furthermore, there is no perfect insulator known; all materials conduct electricity in some degree, just as all materials conduct heat energy in some degree. It is interesting to note that the good electrical conductors are also the good heat conductors.

It is now apparent why we chose silk to support the pith ball in the experiments described earlier, for a dry silk fiber is an excellent insulator. Moreover, the metal parts of the electroscope have to be mounted in a non-metallic support to prevent the charges from being conducted away.

We can now consider the failure of metallic objects to retain electric charges when they are held in the hand. The human body is not an insulator, but its electrical conductivity is rather low. The body conducts well enough, however, to allow the escape of charges from an electroscope when the knob is touched by the fingers. For the same reason a metal bar held in the hand and rubbed with cloth will not retain any charges that it gets. That it does acquire charge by rubbing with the cloth can be demonstrated easily by holding the bar with rubber gloves while it is being rubbed. It then becomes charged as easily as glass or amber do.

Several references to the increased conductivity which moisture gives to poorly conducting materials call for additional comment. Everyone knows, or should know, that it is extremely dangerous to touch a live wire when the body is wet or even damp with perspiration. Fatal accidents by the thousand testify to this grim fact. Yet the body is a poor conductor and pure water an exceedingly bad conductor. The paradox clears up when we consider the word "pure." A small amount of salt, which is present in the moisture of the skin and in all natural waters, transforms water from a poor conductor into a good conductor.

A slight change in the design of the electroscope enables it to test the conductivity of liquids. Let the knob be replaced by a metal cup into which the liquid to be tested is poured. With the leaves charged, insert a finger into the liquid without touching the metal container. If the liquid is a salty solution, the instrument will be discharged; if it is an oil or other poorly conducting organic liquid, the leaves of the instrument remain charged.

ELECTRICAL FLUID THEORIES

Contemplating experiments like those described, we are not surprised to learn that electrification and conduction were formerly explained in terms of electrical fluids, which were believed to flow into and out of material bodies with varying facility. Since there were two kinds of electrification, what could be more natural than to suppose that there were two kinds of fluid—vitreous and resinous, or positive and negative? Neutral bodies were supposed to contain equal amounts of both fluids, producing equal and opposite external electric forces which canceled each other. A neutral body became positively charged when positive electric fluid flowed into it or negative fluid flowed out. An excess of negative over positive fluid made the body negative.

What was the nature of these fluids? A body did not seem to change its appearance or structure when it became electrified, and there was no measurable change in its weight. The fluids must therefore be invisible and weightless. We are reminded in all this of a similar primitive explanation of thermal phenomena in which a weightless *caloric* fluid was supposed to produce temperature changes by its flow into and out of bodies.

The two-fluid theory of electrification lasted until it was superseded by the theory of Benjamin Franklin (1706–1790), who, with characteristic insight, simplified these explanations by regarding electricity as a single fluid occurring in normal amount in any neutral body, whereas an excess of it made the body positive and a deficit made it negative. Modern research has indeed confirmed that only one kind of electricity passes through solids, but it has turned out to be the negative rather than the positive kind postulated by Franklin.

SINGLE FLUID THEORY

Let us assume that electricity is a single fluid having the negative characteristics displayed by an electrified piece of amber or hard rubber, and

let us use this hypothesis to explain some simple experiments.

Explanation of Charge by Rubbing. When a glass rod becomes positively electrified by being rubbed with silk, the positive manifestation is due to removal of electric fluid from the glass. If so, the silk must have become negatively electrified by an equal amount.

Verification. Place the glass and the silk inside an insulated metal pail which is joined to the knob of an electroscope by a wire. Rub the glass vigorously against the silk; the electroscope leaves show no divergence. This means either that the usual process has failed to electrify the glass or that equal positive and negative electrifications have developed on the glass and the silk. Remove the glass from the metal pail; the electroscope proves to be negatively charged. Replace the glass rod and remove the silk; the electroscope now proves to be positively charged. This verifies the guess about the equality of the opposite electrifications.

The previous demonstration makes it appear that electricity is neither created nor destroyed but that it exists in neutral matter together with an equal amount of positive electricity. Since the charging of two substances by intimate contact is characteristic of virtually all materials, we may infer also that different kinds of matter have different degrees of attraction for the electrical fluid; hence, when close contact occurs between two different substances, the negative electricity flows from the more weakly attracting one (e.g., glass) to the more strongly attracting one (e.g., silk). However, when amber is rubbed with silk, the amber becomes negatively charged and this time the silk acquires a positive charge.

Attraction of a Neutral Body by a Charged Body. From Coulomb's law we might, with mathematical justice, suppose that a charged body can exert no electrical force on a neutral body, since one of the charges Q in the equation is zero. But our very first experiment proved that a charged glass rod attracted a neutral pith ball. Whenever such apparent contradictions arise, we must have recourse to further experiments to settle the arguments. Here the reconciliation of Coulomb's law with further experimental facts gives us a good deal of insight into the whole process of electrification.

Consider once more the suspended pith ball with its coating of metallic foil (Fig. 87). When the positively electrified glass rod is brought into the vicinity, some of the negative electric fluid normally in the ball is displaced to the surface that is nearer the rod. Hence that side of the ball becomes temporarily negative, while the opposite side, diminished in electric fluid, becomes temporarily positive. The ball is now subject to a repulsion as well as an attraction by the rod, but the attraction must necessarily be the stronger force since the negative half of the ball is the one closer to the rod. Remember that Coulomb's law indicates a relatively large increase in force for a small decrease in distance. In response, then, to the larger attracting force, the

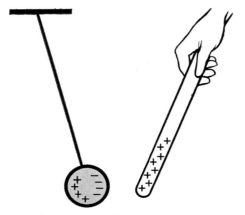

FIG. 87. A neutral body is attracted by another charged body.

ball approaches the rod and finally touches it. But, even before contact, the Coulomb force becomes so great in the space between that the air itself acquires conductivity. We hear a crackling sound and see a faint flash of light. This is an electric spark, proved by Benjamin Franklin to be of the same nature as lightning, with its attendant thunder on a small scale. In a dramatic experiment with a kite during a thunderstorm he showed conclusively that the electric fluid that accumulates on clouds and occasionally passes spectacularly to the earth in the form of lightning is no different excepting in magnitude from the electricity whose effects have been revealed in these experiments. (See Plate XXVI.)

After passage of the spark, the pith ball has become positive because negative fluid has jumped to the rod and the ball is then strongly repelled by the glass rod. Had a negatively charged rod of hard rubber been used, the explanation would have been the same except in the fact that negative electric fluid would have been transferred to the ball.

Charging by Contact. In similar manner we may charge an electroscope directly by touching the knob with an electrified rod of glass or hard rubber. As the positive glass rod approaches the knob, negative electric fluid rises into the knob and the leaves, temporarily deficient in fluid, are left positive. Hence, they repel each other and stand apart. On contact between knob and rod, or even before, some fluid escapes from the electroscope and leaves it positively charged.

When another electrified body with a charge of unknown sign is brought near the charged electroscope, the leaves will either come closer together or they will spring farther apart. It is easy to understand that a partial collapse of the electrified leaves must be due to partial **neutraliza-**

Bettmann Archive

PLATE XXVI. Benjamin Franklin's kite experiment, in which he proved that lightning was of the same nature as the sparks produced in electrostatic experiments in his laboratory. Woodcut, 1830.

tion of their charge. If that charge was positive, some negative fluid must have flowed down from the knob and this could happen only if the unknown body were itself negatively electrified. If the unknown body were positively electrified, it would attract negative fluid from the leaves into the knob, thereby making the leaves even more positive than they were before and causing them to repel each other with greater force. This

An electroscope charged positively by induction

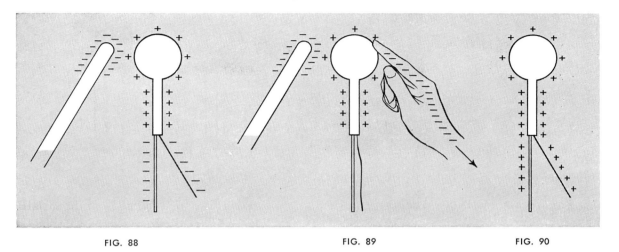

FIG. 88   FIG. 89   FIG. 90

ready response of a charged electroscope is useful as a convenient means of identifying unknown charges.

Charging by Induction.   Practically, it is undesirable to charge an electroscope by direct contact because the electrical force may easily be large enough to tear the delicate leaves from their support.   We describe now a more controllable process called charging by induction.

An electrified rod of hard rubber (negative charge) will cause temporary divergence of the leaves of an electroscope by its mere approach to the knob.   In terms of the hypothesis just proposed, this is due to the retreat of negative fluid, inherent in the metal, to the lower part of the system (Fig. 88).   In other words, the intrinsic electricity of the electroscope is temporarily redistributed.   When the rubber rod is removed, the leaves immediately collapse again.   But suppose that, *while the charged rod is held near the electroscope,* the operator touches his finger to the knob (Fig. 89).   This provides a fairly good conducting path through his body to the ground, and some negative electricity can escape from the apparatus under the repelling influence of the electrified rod.   When the finger is removed, further escape is cut off and the electroscope now bears an excess of positive charge which remains even after the exciting influence has been removed (Fig. 90).

Charging by induction, as this series of steps is called, results in electrification of opposite sign to that of the electrifying body.   If a charged glass rod had been used in place of the hard rub-

ber rod, the same procedure would have charged the electroscope negatively.

A convincing test of the foregoing hypothesis can be made by mounting two metal spheres on glass stands and allowing the spheres to touch while an electrified rubber rod is held close to one of them (Fig. 91).   Although the spheres are electrically neutral, some of the negative charge in them must be repelled from the nearer to the farther ball.   Let the spheres now be separated and the redistribution of charge becomes permanent, for the negative charge which flowed into the right-hand sphere can no longer return even after the rubber rod has been removed (Fig. 92).   A test of the state of the two spheres actually shows that the left one has acquired positive electrification and the right one an equal amount of negative electrification.

An Energy Problem.   The sparks which pass between bodies in these experiments may light a gas flame and kindle fires in other inflammable materials.   The combustible mixture in the cylinders of an automobile engine are fired by electric sparks.   In short, electric sparks are capable of doing work and are, therefore, a form of energy.   Since bodies can be charged by induction repeatedly without dissipation of the inducing charge, we may be tempted to believe that here is an inexhaustible energy source which might be made to run an engine of some kind perpetually.   Let us show precisely how such an idea can be proved fallacious.

Suppose a metal sphere *A* (Fig. 93) to be suspended by a fine, insulating fiber so that it may

Spheres charged by induction

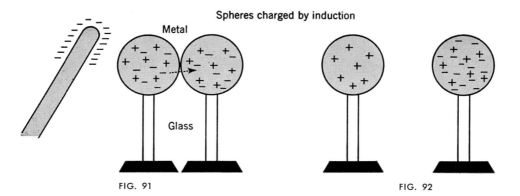

FIG. 91   FIG. 92

swing as a pendulum between another insulated sphere B and a metallic contact point at C. We give B a negative charge, and set A swinging toward it. When A gets close to B, without touching it, it is grounded by passing over a metallic brush D which is connected with the earth. This contact permits some of its inherent negative fluid to escape under the repelling influence of B. Sphere A has thus become positively charged by induction. The weight of A causes it to swing backwards with its induced positive charge. When A reaches C, it is neutral-ized by taking negative charge from the metallic circuit of which C is part. A is then free to oscillate again toward B and to repeat the first experience indefinitely. The only curbs on its continued motion would seem to be frictional ones, and these could be reduced almost to zero by making the contacts very delicate and mounting the apparatus in a vacuum. Conceivably the device might be built on a large scale and the amounts of energy obtainable at C in the form of sparks or charges would be considerable. There would be no shrinkage of the charge on

FIG. 93. Mechanical energy of a swinging pendulum being transformed into electrical energy.

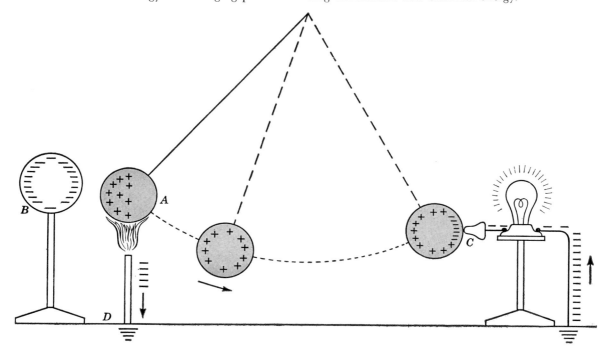

B, since *A* is prevented from touching it. Why would such an arrangement, once set going, not continue to operate and thus upset the law of conservation of energy?

The failure of this optimistic attempt is due to a circumstance not yet mentioned. Every time *A* separates from *B*, it must do so against the electrical force of attraction between their opposite charges. This requires work at the expense of the pendulum's mechanical energy, so that it decreases in amplitude with every oscillation, eventually coming to rest.

THE ELECTRIC FIELD

How is it possible for charged bodies to exert forces on one another even though the space surrounding them is completely empty of matter? Many great physicists have attacked this problem and brilliant theories have emerged from their endeavors, but the ultimate nature of electrical interactions is still a mystery. However, the force of gravitation is also still a mystery and yet Newton was able to "explain" the complicated motions of the whole solar system in terms of the inverse square law. The strength of the scientific structure lies in the wealth of its accumulated factual data and in the organization and rationalization of those facts. And so, even though the ultimate nature of electrical forces remains unknown to us, we may study them experimentally, describe them quantitatively by mathematical relations, relate them to other physical phenomena, and, finally, make practical use of them.

The region of influence surrounding an electric charge is called its *electric field*. Since a charged object placed in such a region experiences force, it is reasonable to describe the field in terms of the force associated with it. But the electric force experienced by a charged body depends in part on its own charge, as Coulomb's law shows. To avoid this complication we describe all electric fields in terms of the force which would act on a body carrying *unit* positive charge in that field.

This way of describing an electric field by its effect is similar to that by which we commonly describe the flow of a river. One could easily catalog the strength of a river at various points by casting into it a small float attached to a line, holding the other end of the line by means of a spring balance and reading off the force with which the river tugged on the line at every spot tested.

Although an electric field is not thought of as "flowing" and although it does not consist of fluid or anything else that we know of, the forces it exerts are very real and the scheme of designating its strength by these forces is very convenient. We need, however, to define the unit charge which is to be our "float" for imaginary tests of field strength. This is easily done by assigning the value 1 to all other factors in Coulomb's law. Imagine two tiny objects held 1 cm apart in a vacuum and each bearing identical electric charges. The charged bodies repel each other, and we measure the force of their mutual repulsion. Suppose it to be 1 dyne. Suppose, further, that the dielectric constant *K* for empty space be taken arbitrarily as 1. Then Coulomb's law

$$F = \frac{Q_1 Q_2}{Kr^2} \qquad \text{becomes} \qquad 1 = \frac{Q^2}{1 \times 1}$$

whence each of the *Q*'s must also be 1.

THE ELECTROSTATIC UNIT OF CHARGE

The unit charge defined in this way bears the name *1 electrostatic unit;* to scientists it is familiarly known as 1 esu.

THE COULOMB

The esu is inconveniently small, and in practical usage a unit of charge called a coulomb is employed.

$$1 \text{ coulomb} = 3 \text{ billion } (3 \times 10^9) \text{ esu}$$

ELECTRIC FIELD STRENGTH

We may now express the strength or intensity of an electric field either by reference to Coulomb's law or by reference to the effect of the field on the electrostatic unit of charge. Suppose, for example, there is a body situated in vacuum and having a charge of 100 esu. At any point 2 cm away a unit charge would experience a force of 25 dynes.

$$\frac{100 \times 1}{2^2} = 25 \text{ dynes}$$

At 5 cm distance the unit charge would experience only 4 dynes

$$\frac{100 \times 1}{5^2} = 4 \text{ dynes}$$

and so on. Alternatively, if a test body bearing 20 esu of charge experienced 60 dynes of force when placed in a certain electric field, this would show the field strength at that point to be $^{60}/_{20}$ or 3 dynes per unit charge.

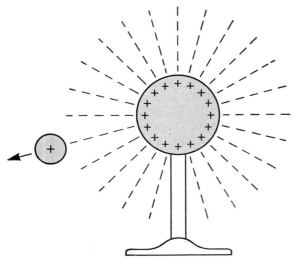

FIG. 94. Graphical representation of an electric field.

Formally, we define electric field strength or intensity as

the force in dynes which the field exerts on a unit positive charge placed in it.

The field strength varies from point to point as a rule. If the cause of the field is a positive charge, our convention defines the field direction as away from the originating charge and, if negative, toward it.

It is helpful to represent an electric field graphically by drawing lines whose directions and proximity to each other represent the field intensity in the neighborhood of the originating charges. A single charge all alone in space would therefore be represented as bristling with lines extending outward radially from the charge through infinite distance (Fig. 94). Practically, the influence of a charge decreases beyond measurement within a relatively short distance, but, to some small degree, the presence of any charge disturbs the whole universe!

The lines of force are a pure artificiality, but during the nineteenth century physicists began to look on them as realities in their efforts to visualize a mechanism in space which would explain electric force. The lines of force were thought of as if they were elastic bands stretched between positive and negative charges and pulling them together or, when like charges repelled, crowding one another apart laterally. If a charge was suddenly accelerated, kinks in the lines of force would travel outward into space, and this representation served as a model mechanism to account for the propagation of light and radio waves.

THE STRUCTURE OF THE ELECTRIC FLUID

The same question that perplexed man for centuries with regard to matter was raised more recently about what we have been calling the electric fluid. Is this fluid continuous and therefore infinitely divisible, or is it made up of ultimate corpuscles incapable of subdivision? In other words, does electricity exist in natural units as matter does?

MILLIKAN'S OIL-DROP EXPERIMENT

The problem of recognizing the particle nature of something that flows as if it were continuous is indeed a difficult one when the particles, if they exist, are too small for direct recognition by the senses. A brilliant technique for investigating the fundamental nature of electricity was worked out by the noted American physicist, Robert A. Millikan (1868–1955), beginning about 1909. Let us imagine ourselves performing this experiment much as Millikan first did it (Fig. 95). We set up two parallel metallic plates *P* and arrange to charge them to any degree we choose by connection to batteries. The lines of electric force between the plates will be all aligned in the central space so that *E*, the field intensity, will be nearly uniform. By means of an atomizer mounted in the upper chamber, a fine spray of

FIG. 95.   Millikan's oil-drop experiment.

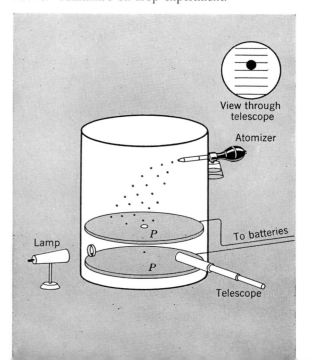

oil is squirted into the space above the plates. Drifting downward, some of these oil drops must eventually pass through a small hole in the upper plate. Since the drops are very small, they must be illuminated strongly from the side of the container in order to be visible to the observer at the telescope. In the process of formation, the oil drops become electrified by friction with the nozzle of the atomizer, so that when such a drop arrives in the region between the charged plates it is acted on by electric as well as gravitational forces.

We focus our telescope on one particular drop. Is its charge positive or negative? We make the upper plate positive and the lower one negative. Suppose the drop then increases in its velocity downward; we conclude that it is carrying a positive charge. When the charges on the plates are reversed, the drop slackens its speed and with careful adjustment of E the drop can be held stationary in space. The upward electric force QE is then exactly equal to the weight mg of the drop, where m is the mass of the oil drop and g the acceleration of gravity.

Then, for this first balance,

$$Q_1 E_1 = mg \quad \text{or} \quad Q_1 = mg/E_1$$

Suddenly, as we watch the drop, it begins to drift upward. We check the electric field. It has not changed, and the mass of the oil drop could hardly have altered. Its evaporation is negligible and, in any case, would be continuous rather than sudden. We are forced to conclude that the electric charge on the drop has suddenly changed, presumably by the gain of some additional positive charge. The source of such charge? It is a fact that air normally contains a small proportion of electrified particles which are called *ions*. These ions are believed to be fragmentary atoms resulting from the action of ultraviolet light, radioactivity, X rays, or other energetic agencies on the oxygen and nitrogen of the air. Violent collisions between molecules also break them up into these charge-bearing ions.

We have, then, a plausible explanation for the abrupt change in the charge of the oil drop. Of the numerous ions moving through the air of the chamber, one has crashed into the suspended drop. Whatever the sign of the additional charge, the drop is no longer balanced and, in order to arrest its motion, we must weaken or strengthen the electric field by changing the charges on the plates. Suppose the new value of the field intensity is E_2, and the new charge on the drop is Q_2. Then $Q_2 = mg/E_2$.

It is possible to observe many such changes of charge on the same droplet, each time readjusting the field for balance before the drop is finally lost to view. Before the various values of Q can be calculated, it is necessary to know the mass of the oil drop. This is by no means easy, for the drops produced in the experiment are exceedingly small (about 1/10,000 cm in diameter) and they appear in the telescope as tiny points of light like stars in a black sky. Fortunately there is an equation, derived by Sir Gabriel Stokes in 1850, which relates the size of any small sphere to its speed of descent through viscous material—air in this case.

We digress to remind the reader that the simple laws of falling bodies described earlier were strictly applicable only in a vacuum. Large dense objects, like metal balls, obey these laws fairly well when they fall through air, but this is not true of small bodies having low densities. Such objects quickly attain a steady speed and then continue downward without acceleration. Rain drops behave in this way, and particles of dust may commonly be seen slowly settling at constant speed through the air of a quiet room.

Applying Stokes' law to the descent of an oil drop when the plates were uncharged, Millikan was able to calculate its radius from the downward speed of the drop. This required timing the descent of the drop for a known distance, the latter being determined by means of a scale engraved in the eyepiece of his telescope.

Once the radius of the spherical oil drop under observation was known, a simple calculation involving the density of the oil provided the mass of the drop. For the volume of a sphere is $V = \frac{4}{3}\pi r^3$, and its density is $d = m/V$. Hence the desired mass was found from the equation $m = \frac{4}{3}\pi r^3 d$.

Having obtained the mass of the oil drop, Millikan was able to calculate all the charges Q_1, Q_2, Q_3, etc., which the drop had acquired in the course of the experiment. The differences between the various Q's was the clue to the solution of the whole problem. For if these differences were unrelated, the experiment had failed to reveal a uniform primary charge. If, on the contrary, these differences all had a common divisor, that divisor could be presumed to be the natural unit of electric charge. Suppose, for example, that the smallest difference ever noted between any two of the calculated values of Q was e, and that all others differed by $2e$, $3e$, $4e$, or some other whole multiple of e; there could then be little doubt that e represented the fundamental charge of which all the other amounts were merely aggregates.

Millikan achieved an impressive generality in his work by using drops of many different sizes and materials and by employing every known agency to produce ions in the air surrounding the drops. The principle underlying his method is like that of pouring small shot from a bucket. You cannot pour out less than one pellet, and any amount transferred from the bucket must be some whole number of pellets.

That this historic experiment and others like it did reveal the existence of a fundamental electric charge is one of the outstanding discoveries of experimental science. The magnitude of the fundamental charge, as now accepted, is 4.80×10^{-10} esu—a value which is the same numerically for either positive or negative electrification. In other words, electricity is discrete or discontinuous, and ordinary charges, such as those obtained by rubbing glass or amber, consist of large whole numbers of these elementary charges.

THE ELECTRON AND THE PROTON

It is convenient to have names for these elementary charges, since they play a large part in the description of many electrical and atomic phenomena. One of these names, the *electron*, was proposed by G. J. Stoney in 1880 long before the atomic nature of electricity had been proved, although even then it was strongly suspected.

The fundamental negative charge of -4.80×10^{-10} esu is now known internationally as *1 electron*.

In the Millikan oil-drop experiment it is quite certain that any change in charge occurred not because the drop itself lost any charge but because an ion from the surrounding air attached itself to the drop. Since the changes in charge were both positive and negative, there must exist in nature positive particles whose charges are equal but opposite to that of the electron. One such particle is called the *proton*.

Since the magnitudes of these charges are equal, it is evident that any body containing the same number of electrons as of protons will be electrically neutral.

Besides differing in sign, the two charges differ very greatly in mass, as we shall show in subsequent sections, the proton being nearly 2000 times as heavy as the electron.

PROBLEMS

1. Do you believe that Benjamin Franklin ran any great risk in performing his famous kite experiment? Explain.

2. Explain, in terms of the flow of negative electric fluid: (*a*) The attraction of a neutral pith ball by a hard rubber rod which has been rubbed with fur. (*b*) The charging of an electroscope inductively by means of a glass rod and silk. (*c*) The identification of an unknown charge by means of an electroscope. (*d*) The reaction of a positively charged electroscope when an insulated neutral metal ball is approached to its knob.

3. On p. 192 there is a numerical table in which electrostatic forces are related with distances between charges. Show by actual calculations that these data prove Coulomb's law.

4. In the experiment represented by Figs. 83, 84, and 85, would it not have been just as easy to measure the attractions between unlike charges? Explain.

5. Draw a design for the electroscope described on p. 194 to test the electrical conductivity of liquids. Repeat for an electroscope designed to test the conductivity of gases.

6. Approximately 1 coulomb of electric charge flows through the filament of a 100-watt lamp every second. How many electrons per second does this represent?

7. Suppose you were given the following information: (*a*) A sphere will fall with constant speed through a viscous medium if the viscous resistance is large enough to be equal to the weight of the sphere. (*b*) The viscous resistance is proportional to the radius of the sphere and proportional to the speed of fall.

Would you conclude from this that a sphere should be large or small in order to fall through a given medium with low constant speed? Why? Could Millikan have used spheres of metal in his experiment even if the densities of the metals were high? Explain.

. . . .

REFERENCES

1. *A Source Book in Physics,* W. F. Magie, McGraw-Hill Book Co., 1935, pp. 393–406.
2. *Development of the Concept of Electric Charge,* Harvard Case Histories in Experimental Science, Case 8, Duane Roller and Duane H. D. Roller, Harvard University Press, 1954.
3. *The Autobiography of Science,* Forest R. Moulton and Justus J. Schifferes, Doubleday & Co., 1950, pp. 234–235.

20 *Magnetism*

In order to understand some of the most interesting discoveries associated with electricity, we must now consider another phenomenon which, coincidentally, was first recorded by the same Thales who described the electrical attractions of amber.

There exists in nature a dark-brown iron ore called magnetite (Fe_3O_4), which was found by Thales to exhibit a strong attraction for pieces of iron. Samples of this ore were called *lodestones,* and accounts of their curious properties crept into the ancient folklore and even into the classical literature of early times. Some thought that lodestones had the power to heal wounds and to cure diseases. There were tales of magnetic mountains which could pull the iron nails out of ships that passed too close to them.

MAGNETIC POLES

A difference between electrification and magnetization should be emphasized at the outset. Any body may be electrically charged under proper conditions, whereas only iron, iron ore, and a few alloys seem to have very strong magnetic properties.

A little experimentation with a lodestone and small pieces of iron reveals that the magnetic force is not exerted uniformly by all parts of the stone but that this force reaches a maximum at certain points on the stone. There are usually two such points on opposite sides and we shall call them *poles.* The poles are most readily located by dipping the whole stone into iron filings and noting where the "whiskers" of iron particles clinging to the stone are most dense. We say that the lodestone is a *magnet* because it shows this polarity, which is not exhibited by an ordinary piece of iron. Iron is said to be *magnetic,* however, because it is attracted to the magnet, whereas silver, gold, lead, aluminum, wood, glass, and most other substances are non-magnetic because, in rough experiments, they are not measurably affected by a magnet. Nickel and cobalt do respond to magnetic attraction but so much more feebly that, by comparison, iron is practically in a class by itself.

Suppose now that we take a lodestone and, touching one of its poles to a strip of steel, draw the lodestone across the length of the strip from end to end and always in the same direction. After repeating this several times, we find that the steel has itself become a magnet, so that clusters of iron filings will adhere strongly to each end of it. If we magnetize several long steel knitting needles in this manner, each will be a magnet with its two poles so far apart that either end of such a needle can practically be regarded as an isolated pole. We can then make quantitative experiments on the forces of interaction between these isolated poles.

The experimental arrangement can be similar to the one used for investigating the forces between electric charges. Alternatively, we can suspend one magnet as shown in Fig. 96 and hold

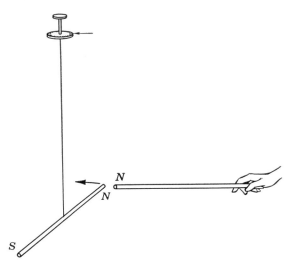

FIG. 96. Investigation of magnetic forces by a suspended magnetized steel needle.

another with one end near an end of the suspended magnet. The degree of twist of the suspending fiber becomes a measure of the magnetic force between the poles.

It is soon apparent that a pole of one magnet can either attract or repel a pole of another; also, that, if the effect of this pole on one end of a suspended magnet is to attract the magnet, its effect on the other end is to repel the magnet.

Although both ends of any magnetized needle appear to be identical and the poles at each end are equally strong, they are different *kinds* of poles nevertheless. The two kinds of poles can be distinguished by an application discovered by the Chinese long before the famous travels of Marco Polo (Plate XXVII). The Chinese found that a lodestone floated on mercury would turn itself until the line between its poles lay in an approximately north-south direction. A magnetized needle hung at its center by a very fine thread so that it can oscillate horizontally

will also come to rest parallel to a meridian of longitude. Such a needle is, in fact, a magnetic compass, and, by custom, we call the end which points north its north pole. The south-pointing end is, of course, its south pole. The north and south magnetic poles of any magnet are thus easily identified, and we learn that two north or two south poles repel each other, whereas the north pole of one magnet attracts the south pole of another magnet.

COULOMB'S LAW FOR MAGNETIC POLES

On quantitative measurement of the attraction or repulsion between magnet poles, we find that

Bettmann Archive

PLATE XXVII. Early Chinese compass attached to a cart. Within the right arm of the figure a magnet was concealed so that it always pointed south.

they conform to a relation similar to Coulomb's law for electric charges. The force diminishes as the distance between poles increases so that it is inversely proportional to the square of that distance. This relation was, in fact, discovered by Coulomb in 1784 along with his findings about electrostatic charges.

Coulomb's law of force between magnet poles reads like the electrostatic law:

$$F = \frac{M_1 M_2}{kr^2}$$ where F is in dynes

if M_1 and M_2 are the magnetic pole strengths, r is the distance in centimeters between poles (assumed to be points), and k is again a constant dependent on the medium between the interacting poles. It is called the *permeability* of the medium.

The similarity between the magnetic and the electrostatic Coulomb equations is very striking. Here is another natural force that varies inversely

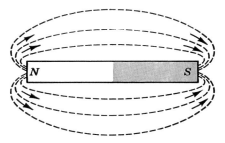

FIG. 97. Magnetic field near a bar magnet.

with the square of a distance. There are many such inverse square laws, and they lead us to believe that the inverse square feature is a property of the space in which the agencies act.

The fact that both magnetic and electric forces subscribe to the same form of mathematical equation encourages us to seek another similarity. Are there not elementary magnetic poles, north and south, which can be separated from each other and which correspond to the separable positive and negative charges? In the experiment represented in Fig. 96, the ends of the long steel needles did indeed seem to be isolated north and south poles, but if we were to chop off either end of the needle, in an effort to isolate that pole, we would find that both separated parts have become complete magnets, each with a north and south pole. Additional divisions of the needle produce the same effect. Here is a phenomenon for which there is no electrical parallel. North and south poles are not distinct and separate particles but merely directional characteristics of the same phenomenon.

Offhand, there seems to be no experimental connection between electric and magnetic phenomena and historically no such connection was known until 1820, when a discovery by the

Danish engineer Oersted showed that magnetic effects always occur in a region through which electric charges are moving. This fortunate observation could hardly have been made without a series of earlier discoveries that led to the inven-

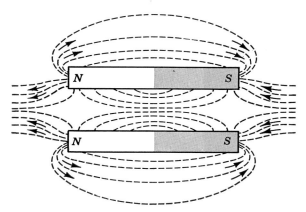

FIG. 98. Magnetic field near two bar magnets, similar poles adjacent.

tion of the electric battery. An account of these momentous discoveries will form the substance of a later topic.

MAGNETIC FIELDS

Just as every electrified body is thought of as surrounded by an *electric* field of force, so is

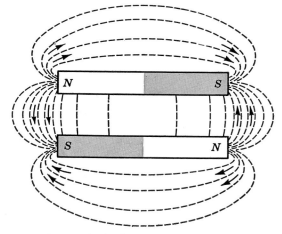

FIG. 99. Magnetic field near two bar magnets, opposite poles adjacent.

every magnetized body depicted as having a *magnetic* field of force associated with it. The magnetic differs from the electric field in that magnetic poles occur in local pairs and that the magnetic lines of force seem to connect the poles—at least, approximately. It is very easy to plot a section of the field around a simple bar magnet by placing the bar under a thin sheet of transparent plastic and sprinkling iron filings over the sheet. After gentle tapping of this platform, the filings will be seen to arrange themselves in a distinctive pattern of related loops embracing the magnet, most of them seeming to terminate at the poles as in Fig. 97. Tiny compasses placed near the magnet will become orientated along similar curved paths. Plotting magnetic lines with a compass is more tedious but more revealing than the iron filing method because the compass shows the direction as well as the shape of the magnetic field.

If two bar magnets are placed parallel and with their like poles next to each other, and the field is explored with iron filings or with little compasses, the space around the bars is found to have magnetic lines as shown in the sketch of Fig. 98.

Reverse the magnets, and the picture is like the sketch of Fig. 99, where lines from a pole of one magnet connect with the nearby pole of the other magnet, a consequence to be expected from the attraction between unlike poles.

Note that at every place the direction of the field is the direction in which a compass points when it comes to rest at that place. Thus, the magnetic lines are assumed to emerge from north poles and to enter at south poles.

It may be remarked in passing that the earth itself must be a large magnet surrounded by a magnetic field, since it causes magnetic compass needles to orientate themselves as they do. The earth's magnetic poles do not coincide with the geographic poles, being several hundred miles removed from them, yet their locations are close enough to make the magnetic compass a useful direction indicator. Also, it is evident that the south magnetic pole of the earth must be located near the north geographical pole in order to attract the north pole of a compass needle.

PROBLEMS

1. When Sir William Gilbert (1540–1603) wrote his famous treatise on the lodestone, it was supposed by many physicians that magnets exercised a physiological effect on human beings. What information from this chapter could you use to judge the correctness of this belief?

2. The earth's magnetic field is approximately as if there were buried inside the earth a huge bar magnet with its axis nearly coincident with that of the earth. On this assumption, draw the earth's magnetic field. If a compass needle were free to turn in three dimensional space, in what direction would it point at the equator? At the north pole? At a latitude approximately equal to that of New York?

3. It is possible to make magnets so strong that their forces of interaction are larger than their weights. What must be the pole strengths of two long identical magnets, each of mass 100 grams, so that when one is placed above the other, and like poles are adjacent, the upper magnet will "float" at a distance of $\frac{1}{2}$ cm above the other? In air, the permeability is nearly equal to 1.
Ans. 110.7 poles.

4. There is a theory that iron and other magnetic materials contain tiny internal magnets which can turn, though reluctantly, in the direction of an applied magnetic field. Hence, one can make a magnet out of a piece of steel by stroking it with a lodestone. Using this assumption, what would you expect to happen if: (*a*) A steel magnet were heated strongly? (*b*) A magnet were struck repeatedly with a hammer? (*c*) Various strengths of magnetic field were used to magnetize a piece of steel? (*d*) The temperature of a piece of steel were observed before and immediately after magnetization?

. . . .

REFERENCE

1. *A Source Book in Physics,* W. F. Magie, McGraw-Hill Book Co., 1935, pp. 387–393.

Electric Currents

When electric charges of either sign are in motion, their flow is called an electric current. Electric currents may be set up through solids, liquids, or gases—or even through a vacuum. Specifically, the number of electric charges passing through any given area per second is a measure of the current strength through that area.

Let us consider a few cases of electric currents in metallic conductors.

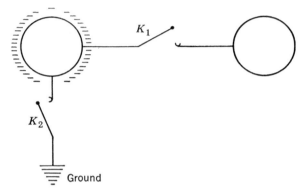

FIG. 100. A current flows from the charged body to an uncharged body, or to the ground, when the proper key is closed.

Suppose, for example, that a negatively charged body can be connected by wire to an uncharged body or to the ground. In Fig. 100, the connecting metallic paths are interrupted by switches K_1 and K_2 so that the paths may be closed at will. Now the negative charges must exert mutual repulsion on one another, and, if the switch K_1 in the horizontal line is closed, it is natural to expect that the charges should seize this opportunity to spread farther apart than they were when confined to the left-hand sphere. True to expectation, a current does flow from left to right until the two spheres, if they are identical, are charged to the same extent. The same reasoning explains why all the electric charge would flow into the ground if the left-hand switch K_2 were closed, for this connection enables the repelling charges to separate from one another by very large distances on the earth itself.

The situation is more obscure when the connected bodies are both electrified to different extents with charges of the same sign, especially if the bodies differ in dimensions or shape. Consider the arrangement depicted in Fig. 101 where two charged bodies communicate by means of a metallic wire which is interrupted by a switch K.

We show the bodies as negatively charged because evidence, to be presented subsequently, proves that, in solid materials, the only mobile charges are the electrons. This does not mean that an electric current cannot flow between positively charged bodies. They, too, contain many electrons, though not enough to neutralize the positive protons.

Returning to our problem, will electric current flow at all when both bodies bear the same kind of charge and, if so, in which direction will it flow? Offhand, it might be expected that negative charges must flow from the body with greater charge to the body with lesser charge, but that

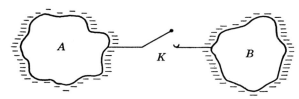

FIG. 101. When the key K is closed, current will flow from the body which has the higher potential.

will not necessarily be the case; it may happen that the actual flow will be in the opposite direction.

POTENTIAL DIFFERENCE

Let us suppose that, when the switch is closed, electrons flow spontaneously from A to B. This shows that electrons in body A have more potential energy than electrons in body B have. We allow a few electrons to pass before opening the switch again. If we had the means of driving these electrons back from B into A, the operation would require work in amount equal to the potential energy lost. Assume that we can determine the amount of work and also count the number of electrons that have been transferred. Then the work divided by the number of electrons is the difference in potential energy per electron between bodies A and B.

This ratio depends on the potential difference between A and B. The electrical *potential* at any point is the amount of potential energy which a unit positive charge would have if located at that point.

Potential difference equals the difference in potential energy per unit charge.

The potential difference between two bodies, or between two parts of the same body, turns out to be the sole criterion that determines whether

or not electric charges will tend to flow from one to the other. If both A and B are charged with electricity of the same sign and if the potential of unit charge on A is greater than the potential of those on B, then the tendency for spontaneous flow is always from A to B.

Note that potential is not the same as total potential energy, since the latter depends partly on the *number* of charges. Body B may actually contain more free electrons than body A does, and for that reason its total electrical potential energy may exceed that of A, but, so long as the energy per unit charge is more on A than it is on B, the tendency will be for A to discharge into B.

Note also that we repeat the word "tendency." Even though A has a greater electrical potential than B, current will not necessarily flow; there must be a suitably conducting path between the two. Thus, when the switch is open, there will probably be no current from A to B, for ordinary air is an exceedingly poor conductor of electric charge. Indeed, low electrical conductivity is characteristic of gases in general. For this reason the wire terminals in the common wall outlet can be safely fastened a fraction of an inch apart, since the air between them is too resistant to permit charges to flow through it from one terminal to the other. Nevertheless, the tendency of charges to flow is greater the greater the potential difference, and, if this is made large enough, they will leap the air gap and the current will manifest itself as a spark, accompanied by a crackling sound.

It should now be apparent that, if A can send current to B because B is at a lower potential, it can certainly send current to a neutral body, whose potential is even lower. If the other body is charged with electricity of the opposite sign, the potential difference is even greater and the tendency for current flow is stronger than in either of the previous cases.

All that has been said of two bodies applies, of course, to a single body when different parts of it are at different potentials.

It is instructive to examine analogous cases of energy transfer where the energy is in another form. What causes heat to flow from one body to another? A temperature difference. Only if one body is hotter than the other will heat transfer take place. And what is temperature but heat energy per unit mass (assuming bodies of the same material)? It is, in fact, the counterpart of electrical potential and is sometimes called thermal potential. Indeed, every form of energy consists of an *extensive* factor, which is dependent on quantity (of charge, of mass, etc.), and an *intensive* factor (electrical potential, temperature, etc.), which may be crudely paraphrased as the "level" of the energy.

SIGN CONVENTION

In the foregoing we have been describing electric current as a flow of negative charges or electrons. This is consistent with modern knowledge but is unfortunately at variance with the practice that prevails in engineering work, where, by long usage, the current direction is assumed to be that of a flow of positive charges from points of greater to points of smaller positive potential. This unfortunate difference can be confusing to the general reader, especially if he has some previous acquaintance with applied electricity. In view of this, it is perhaps wise to use the qualifications higher and lower *negative* potential for a source and receiver such as *A* and *B* in the aforementioned illustration.

THE VOLT

Regardless of sign, the unit of electrical potential difference in general use is called the volt. It was adopted to honor the great Italian scientist Volta and was originally taken as the approximate potential difference created by Daniell's cell—an electric battery cell which was in wide use as a standard during the nineteenth century. The common dry cell used to power flashlights is rated at about $1\frac{1}{2}$ volts and the lead storage battery, used in automobiles, at 6 or 12 volts (2 volts for each of its cells). Household electric mains usually differ in potential by 110 to 120 volts, whereas electric railroad lines commonly operate at 550 volts.

Since potential difference is defined as energy per unit charge, we may define unit potential difference as the ratio of any convenient unit of energy to any convenient unit of charge. In common practice, the unit of energy used is the joule and the unit of charge is the coulomb. Hence, if the difference of potential between two points in an electric circuit is 1 volt, this means that 1 joule of work would have to be done to drive 1 coulomb of electric charge from the point of lower to the point of higher potential. Alternatively, it means that at the higher point every coulomb of charge possesses 1 joule more of potential energy than it will have when it reaches the lower point. In flowing spontaneously from the higher to the lower point each coulomb

must therefore lose 1 joule of energy by conversion into some other form, such as heat.

$$1 \text{ volt} = \frac{1 \text{ joule}}{1 \text{ coulomb}}$$

THE ELECTRON VOLT

From the preceding equation, it is evident that 1 joule of energy may also be expressed as 1 coulomb volt. In research on problems of atomic energy, where calculations are based on the charge of individual electrons, it is customary to use a small but related unit of energy called the electron volt (ev). Its relation to the joule and the erg is easily shown, for

$$1 \text{ coulomb} = 3 \times 10^9 \text{ esu}$$

or

$$6.25 \times 10^{18} \text{ electronic charges}$$

Therefore 1 joule, which is 1 coulomb volt $=6.25 \times 10^{18}$ ev. Hence

$$1 \text{ ev} = 1.6 \times 10^{-19} \text{ joule}$$

or, since

$$1 \text{ joule} = 10^7 \text{ ergs}$$
$$1 \text{ ev} = 1.6 \times 10^{-12} \text{ erg of energy}$$

This is a very small amount of energy, and the output of modern atomic machines is more commonly expressed as so many million or billion electron volts (Mev or Bev).

ELECTRIC BATTERIES

Before 1799 there was no known way of producing sustained electric currents. Numerous ingenious machines had been devised for producing static charges on insulated bodies, but the discharges from such bodies were spasmodic and short-lived. Consequently a whole range of phenomena associated with the steady flow of charges could not be investigated.

About 1780 an Italian professor of anatomy, Galvani (1737–1798), while preparing frog's legs for dissection, noticed an occasional convulsive muscular reaction when a nerve was accidentally touched by a knife (Plate XXVIII). (For the complete story of the discovery, read reference 1 at the end of the chapter.) Galvani might have passed over this observation as a curious but unimportant fact and thus have unwittingly delayed progress in the understanding of electrical phenomena, but, instead, his curiosity drove him to a careful and extended investigation.

He found that there was always a muscular response when two different conductors, say, iron and copper, formed a complete circuit through each other and through the leg muscle, provided one of the conductors touched a nerve (Fig. 102). When an insulator was substituted for one of the conductors, there was no response. He also ob-

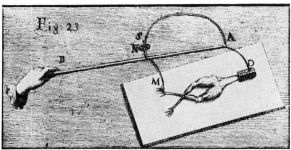

Bettmann Archive

PLATE XXVIII. Figure from Galvani's *De Viribus Electricitatis in Motu Musculari Commentarius*, 1791. This represents one of the experiments in which he thought he demonstrated the existence of animal electricity.

served that an electrical discharge nearby caused a muscular reaction under certain conditions, and from this he concluded wrongly that there was an animal electricity generated within the muscle that stimulated the nerve responses.

Galvani persisted in this erroneous view throughout his researches, but a contemporary, Alessandro Volta (1745–1827), concluded that the

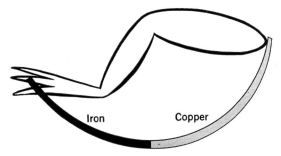

FIG. 102. Galvani's experiment with a frog's leg.

electricity was not animal but metallic in the sense that some agency at the junction between the two metals acted to make electric charges flow. This view turned out to be very fruitful, for it resulted in the construction of the first electric batteries. One of these, which came to be known as a *voltaic pile*, consisted of metallic

disks, usually of silver and zinc, stacked alternately in a pile with strips of cloth or paper or leather soaked in brine separating successive pairs (Fig. 103). He found that a substantial potential difference developed between the uppermost and the lowest plates and that it persisted, so that when these plates were connected through a wire circuit, steady current would flow for a considerable time. Volta tried various metal pairs and succeeded in arranging the metals

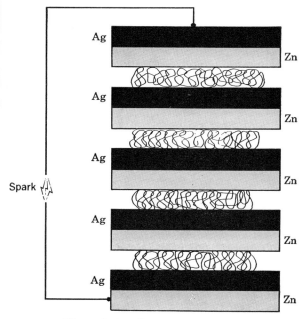

FIG. 103. The voltaic pile.

in a series of relative effectiveness, which agrees in the main with our modern activity series of metals.

Volta supposed that the electrification occurred only at the common surfaces of the metallic disks, and that the salt solution served merely as a conductor. To this day there is not complete agreement about the fundamental mechanism of the electric battery, but we are certain that the electrical potential is chiefly generated at the contact of metal with solution and not at the metallic junctions. Nevertheless, the successful development of the battery as a highly useful *portable* source of electric energy proves that it is not necessary to have complete or even correct understanding of a natural phenomenon in order to turn it to practical use. There are always baffling elements in every scientific discovery, and we cannot say that our comprehension is ever complete. Yet the structure of science grows steadily with every new fact learned, and eventually the seemingly unrelated and puzzling features lead to a rational and useful conception of nature, even though it may be an incomplete one.

Volta also designed a more effective battery which was fancifully known as the "crown of cups." This consisted of a row of glass tumblers containing brine with a metallic arch bridging the space between successive containers. The arches were made of two segments soldered together, one of copper and the other of zinc.

Modern battery cells, or voltaic cells, as they are usually called, vary widely in size, form, and choice of materials, but all have the same essential parts, namely, two dissimilar conductors, or *electrodes,* and a conducting solution, or *electrolyte.* The innate mechanism by which they function is still debatable after 150 years of controversy. What is certain, however, is that a spontaneous chemical reaction—one that liberates energy—always occurs within the cell. Take for example a voltaic cell having zinc and copper rods as electrodes with dilute sulfuric acid as the electrolyte. Zinc, an active metal, tends to dissolve in sulfuric acid—a chemical change in which hydrogen is set free and considerable energy is released. When a copper rod is immersed in the solution, the hydrogen collects as bubbles of gas on the copper. A simple test reveals that the zinc rod has acquired a negative charge and the copper rod a positive one. The zinc is found to have a potential about 0.6 volt more negative than that of the solution, whereas the copper has a potential about 0.5 volt more positive than that of the solution. Measured externally the two electrodes show a potential difference of about 1.1 volts, as might be expected, the zinc being electronegative with respect to the copper.

This potential difference of 1.1 volts, which decreases somewhat when the cell is operating, is called the electromotive force (emf) of the zinc-copper cell.

While such a cell is delivering electric current to a circuit, the zinc electrode gradually wastes away and zinc sulfate crystals are obtainable by evaporation of the electrolyte.

It is interesting to note that any pair of metals in the chemical activity series, hydrogen included, could serve as electrodes in a voltaic cell. The more active metal always becomes the negative electrode. The electromotive force is found to be large for elements which are far apart in the list and small for those whose positions in this list are near each other. This merely re-emphasizes what was mentioned before—that the degree of chemical activity is related to the amount of energy evolved when one element replaces another from chemical combination.

ELECTROLYSIS

The reverse of battery action is electrolysis, a process by which acids, bases, and salts can be decomposed by the immersion of oppositely charged electrodes of the same material into their solutions. We have already referred to the electrolysis of water, which seems to have been the first electrolysis recorded. In 1800 Nicholson and Carlisle found that water could be decomposed by attaching a platinum wire to each end of a voltaic pile and dipping the free ends of the wires into water. They collected the gases that were evolved and found that the hydrogen, which collected at the negative wire, occupied twice the volume of the oxygen, which collected at the positive wire. It was information of this kind that led to the adoption of H_2O as the formula for water.

Although all such electrochemical experiments furnish strong indications that electrified particles of matter (*ions*) must be very common natural units in the construction of compound substances, it was not until 1887 that a rational explanation of electrolysis was proposed. This came from Svante Arrhenius (1859–1927), a Swedish chemist, who postulated that all acids, bases, and salts must consist in part of positive and negative ions. These ions, acquiring mobility by the dissolving of a compound, especially in water, would be free to respond to the electrostatic attraction and repulsion of charged electrodes immersed in their solution. As an illustration, suppose that the salt zinc chloride is dissolved in water and a pair of oppositely electrified platinum wires is placed in the resulting solution (Fig. 104). The negative wire is rapidly coated with zinc, while chlorine gas collects at the positive wire. The masses of zinc and chlorine deposited are found to be in the ratio of 65.4 to 71. Since 65.4 is the atomic mass of zinc and 35.5 is the atomic mass of chlorine, this ratio indicates that two atoms of chlorine are being liberated for every single atom of zinc. Analysis has already shown that zinc chloride has the formula $ZnCl_2$, so we conclude that every zinc particle plated out during the experiment must have borne a positive charge just twice as great as the negative charge associated with each chlorine particle liberated. There is no reasonable mechanism to explain why the particles should acquire these charges *during* the electrolysis, but, if we assume with Arrhenius that they had them *beforehand,* the whole operation becomes more clear. Let us state it stepwise.

1. The zinc chloride crystals do not consist of molecules but of zinc and chloride *ions.* Thus

$$ZnCl_2 \rightarrow Zn^{++} + 2Cl^-$$

These ions are held together in the crystal by the electrostatic attraction between their opposite charges.

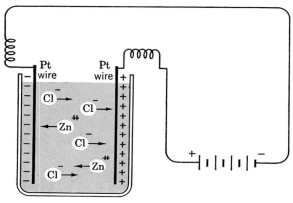

FIG. 104.   Electrolysis of zinc chloride.

2. On being dissolved in water, the ions become separated in consequence of thermal agitation and of their own mobility in the liquid state. It should be recalled that pure water is a dielectric or extremely poor conductor. Zn^+ and Cl^- ions having one or more water molecules between them find their mutual attraction greatly weakened, due to the extremely high dielectric constant of water.

3. When the electrified platinum wires enter the solution, those ions which are nearby must inevitably experience a strong attraction or repulsion according to their sign and, being free to move, they will do so, the positive zinc ions toward the negative wire and the negative chloride ions toward the positive wire. Once arrived, their charges will be neutralized, so that what remain on the platinum electrodes are neutral atoms of zinc and chlorine.

The electrolysis of acidified water is similarly explainable, except that a secondary reaction at the positive wire apparently has to occur before the oxygen is liberated.

It is important to realize the fundamental distinction between electrolysis and voltaic action. Both are electrochemical phenomena, but the energy changes are the reverse of each other. In the voltaic cell there occurs a spontaneous, *energy-producing* reaction, and this energy is liberated in electrical form. In the electrolytic cell energy must be *supplied,* also in electrical form, to promote a reaction which would not take place spontaneously. Thus, zinc chloride does not decompose into zinc and chlorine of its own accord but only when energy in some form is contributed to it. Zinc and chlorine, on the other hand, can unite spontaneously, and the union is attended by an *evolution* of energy.

FARADAY'S LAWS OF ELECTROLYSIS

Michael Faraday (1791–1867), who was the first to study electrolysis quantitatively, discovered two laws which describe this remarkable type of decomposition succinctly. The first law states that the amounts of substance set free during the electrolytic operation are directly proportional to the quantity of electric charge that flows between the electrodes. Note that the potential difference, the temperature, or the concentration of a solution do not determine the extent of the chemical decomposition but, rather, that this is dependent only on the quantity of charge transferred.

The second law states that, if the same quantity of electric charge is transported through several electrolyte solutions, the amount of substance that is liberated in each case is proportional to the *chemical equivalent* of the substance. The term chemical equivalent in the case of an element refers to the atomic mass of the element divided by the valence number of the element in the compound of which it forms a part.

An interpretation of these laws in the light of Arrhenius' hypothesis is gratifyingly simple. Suppose, for example, that we place two vessels side by side (Fig. 105), one containing a solution of zinc chloride ($ZnCl_2$) and the other a solution of hydrobromic acid (HBr). Our hypothesis presumes that the former is rich in ions of the types Zn^{++} and Cl^- and the latter well populated with ions of the types H^+ and Br^-.

Four stiff wires made of some inactive metal like platinum are inserted in the solutions and connected as shown to a battery. Electrons from the negative electrode of the battery immediately spread over the platinum wire at the extreme

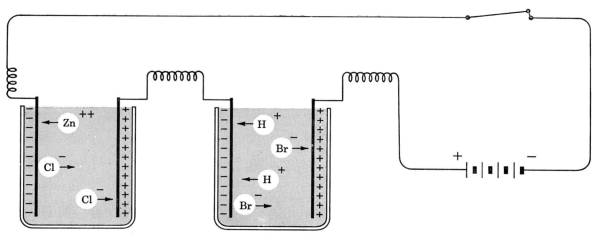

FIG. 105. Illustration of Faraday's laws of electrolysis.

left in obedience to their mutual repulsions. Electrons normally in the extreme right-hand platinum wire are drawn toward the positive electrode of the battery. This leaves the platinum wire positive and enables the submerged part of it to pull electrons from the more distant to the nearer of the two intermediate wires. These actions produce the charge distribution shown in the sketch.

When the switch is closed, the dissolved ions are attracted to the platinum wires according to their signs and a two-way migration of these ions begins. Every Zn^{++} ion must require two electrons to neutralize it, whereas an H^+ ion needs only one. The zinc liberated clings to its platinum wire as a plating, but the other three elements are gaseous and must be collected carefully for subsequent weighing.

After a time, the switch is opened again and the masses of the four products of the electrolysis are carefully determined by weighing. According to the foregoing explanation, for every Br^- ion discharged, an H^+ ion and a Cl^- ion must be discharged simultaneously, but two of each kind would have to deposit while one Zn^{++} ion was being discharged. Since a Br^- ion is 80 times as massive as an H^+ ion, the masses of an equal number of each would stand in the ratio of 80:1. Actually the four elements are found to be liberated in the mass ratios of

$Br : H : Cl : Zn : : 80 : 1 : 35.5 : 32.7 \ (= \frac{1}{2} \text{ of } 65.4)$

in complete agreement with Faraday's second law.

THE ELEMENTARY CHARGE

These quantitative results point strongly to the discrete character of electric charges, in agreement with Millikan's experiments. This problem is of such fundamental importance that a solution of it by alternative means is surely warranted. The calculation requires only two figures: (1) the quantity of charge needed to liberate one chemical equivalent of an element (e.g., 1 gram of hydrogen or 35.5 grams of chlorine) and (2) the number of atoms in this amount of the element (Avogadro's number). The calculation itself follows:

$$\frac{\left| \begin{array}{c} \text{Charge transferred} \\ \text{in liberating} \\ \text{1 gram of H} \end{array} \right|}{\text{Avogadro's number}} = \frac{29 \times 10^{13}}{6.02 \times 10^{23}}$$

$$= 4.8 \times 10^{-10} \text{ esu}$$

This method of reasoning, first used by Johnstone Stoney in 1874, long before Millikan's brilliant researches, did not give the excellent agreement shown here because Avogadro's number was not accurately known. Also, the calculated charge represented a statistical average and it could not, therefore, be concluded from this figure alone that all elementary charges were identical. Second, the argument lacked generality, since it applied only to ions in solution.

PROBLEMS

1. If you found yourself in desperate need of a small electric current, how would you make a battery from materials most easily available?   Which terminal of your battery would be positive?

2. What simple change in the design of the voltaic pile of Fig. 103 would you make, consistent with modern information which Volta did not have?   Explain.

3. Two spheres, A and B, are charged negatively with 10^{-9} coulomb.   To bring 100 additional electrons up to sphere A is found to require 10^{-14} joule of work, whereas it requires 10^{-13} joule to bring up 500 additional electrons to sphere B. (*a*) Which of the spheres is at the higher negative potential?   (*b*) If they were connected by a wire, in which direction would the electrons flow?   (*c*) What was the voltage of each sphere at the beginning of the experiment?
Ans.   (*a*) Sphere B.   (*c*) A, 625 volts. B, 1250 volts.

4. Which of the following metals:

Copper, silver, aluminum, zinc

will require the least current to electroplate 1 gram of it per hour?   What will be the ratios of the currents necessary?

. . . .

REFERENCE

1. *A Source Book in Physics.* W. F. Magie, McGraw-Hill Book Co., 1935, pp. 420–431

 **22** *Some Effects of*
Electric Currents

The invention of the electric battery set the stage for a whole series of experiments which could not have been performed before Volta's momentous discovery.

If a metallic wire is connected between the terminals of a battery, the steady electric current flowing through it causes a rise in the temperature of the wire. If the battery is a large one and the wire is of suitable size, this rise may be so spectacular as to make the wire red hot or even to melt it. With our present understanding of the structure of matter, we are not surprised that this is so. The metal, which appears to be smooth and impenetrable, is believed to be actually a porous material with enough open space between the atoms to allow free electrons to pass among them. The passage of these electrons through the porous structure must be a devious one, however, marked by many collisions with the atoms they encounter. The resulting atomic agitation must reveal itself by a rise in the temperature of the wire. The free electrons lose kinetic energy by such collisions, and energy must be supplied by the battery in order to drive them along the wire.

CURRENT STRENGTH; THE AMPERE

When charge flows through a wire, it is important to know the *rate of transfer,* for the more electrons passing a given point each second the stronger must be the electric current, and the power obtainable from flowing electricity must evidently depend on the strength of the current as well as the potential difference responsible for it. If we could count the number of electrons that flow past any cross section of a conductor in 1 second, this number would express the strength or intensity of the electric current. When the number of electrons that move past any point in a circuit every second amounts to 1 coulomb (i.e., 6.25×10^{18} electrons), the current strength is said to be *1 ampere* (amp). In general,

Current strength

$$= \text{Quantity of charge per unit time}$$

In symbols,

$$I = Q/t$$

or in practical units,

$$\text{Amperes} = \frac{\text{Coulombs}}{\text{Seconds}}$$

The symbol I stands for intensity (or strength) of an electric current, and the unit of intensity is named in honor of A. M. Ampère (1775–1836), an eminent French physicist.

The last equation enables us to express electrical energy in terms of current strength instead of electric charge; for, since

Energy (in joules)

= Potential difference (in volts)

× Charge (in coulombs)

it is also true that

Energy (in joules)

= Potential difference (in volts)

× Current strength (in amperes)

× Time (in seconds)

or

$$E = VIt$$

Recalling that energy expended per unit time represents power consumed, we obtain an expression for power from the last equation on simply dividing by time

$$E/t = VI = P$$

A practical unit of power has been named in honor of the British scientist James Watt:

1 watt of power $\approx$ 1 joule of energy per second

$\approx$ 1 volt of potential difference × 1 ampere of current strength

In general

$$P \text{ (watts)} = \frac{E \text{ (joules)}}{t \text{ (seconds)}}$$

$$= V \text{ (volts)} \times I \text{ (amperes)}$$

Since

$$P = E/t \qquad E = Pt$$

and a joule of energy may also be called a watt-second (wsec) of energy. Inasmuch as this unit is rather small for practical purposes, electrical energy is customarily measured in the larger units called kilowatthours (kwhr).

1 kw equals 1000 watts and 1 hr equals 3600 sec

Hence

1 kwhr = 3.6 million wsec or 3.6 million joules

ELECTRICAL RESISTANCE; OHM'S LAW

When the terminals of an electric battery are connected by a metallic wire, electrons flow through the wire because of the potential difference existing between the electrodes of the battery. One would expect this current to be stronger the greater the potential difference, and this proves to be true. Indeed, provided the temperature of the wire conductor is kept constant, the current strength is directly proportional to the potential difference.

$$I \text{ (amperes)} \propto V \text{ (volts)}$$

On the other hand, wires of different materials or of different dimensions resist the flow of electrons to different extents, and we should naturally expect that the greater the resistance of the conductor the weaker would be the current that could be set up in it by a given potential difference.

So we may write:

$$\text{Strength of current} \propto \frac{\text{Potential difference}}{\text{Resistance}}$$

If a unit of resistance is so chosen that a potential difference of 1 volt across this resistance produces a current of 1 amp, the above relation can be written as an equation. The unit of resistance defined in this way is called the *ohm*, after G. S. Ohm (1789–1854), the German scientist who published the first theoretical work on this topic. The equation in question is now commonly known as *Ohm's law*, and it may be formulated as

$$\text{Strength of current} = \frac{\text{Potential difference}}{\text{Resistance}}$$

or, in symbols,

$$I \text{ (amperes)} = \frac{V \text{ (volts)}}{R \text{ (ohms)}}$$

Ohm's law is a highly useful equation, since it enables us to predict in advance the strength of a current from the known resistance of the conductor and the potential difference available. When we say that the current is proportional to the voltage, $1/R$ is, in fact, the proportionality constant. It must be regarded as a natural phenomenon that the resistance of a wire is constant as long as its temperature is constant.

JOULE'S LAW

By combining Ohm's law with the equation for electric power we obtain another useful relation known as Joule's law, which describes the rate of converting electrical energy into thermal energy when charges flow through a conductor. Since

Power = Potential difference × Current strength

$$P = VI$$

and

Potential difference = Current strength

× Resistance

$$V = IR$$

by substitution we obtain

Power = Current strength^2 × Resistance

$$P = I^2R$$

which is *Joule's law*.

To illustrate, suppose the resistance of a wire is 500 ohms and, because of this resistance, the potential drop along the wire amounts to 200 volts when a current of 0.4 amp is set up in the wire ($I = {}^{200}\!/_{500} = 0.4$ amp).

Then the power lost is evidently

$P = VI$ or $P = I^2R$

$P = (200)(0.4)$ or $P = (0.4)^2 500 = 80$ watts

From the foregoing it appears that the power consumed in transmission depends more on the strength of the current than it does on the resistance to be overcome. For example, if the current is increased tenfold, the power consumption increases a hundredfold.

When it is desired to convert electrical power into some other form such as heat, this disparity is of no consequence. But, if electrical power is to be transmitted over power lines from a generating station to a group of consumers, such conversion into thermal power represents loss in the line. In order to minimize such losses, it is obvious from Joule's law that the wire cables should have the lowest possible resistance but, especially, that the current should be of the lowest possible strength. The way in which currents are kept small during transmission and then increased for use at their destination will be explained later (p. 230).

RESISTANCE AND TEMPERATURE

In developing Ohm's law we assumed that the temperature of a conductor does not change during conduction and that the resistance re-

mains constant. Actually a conductor becomes warmer by the passage of electrons through it, especially if it is highly resistant material. Electric heaters depend on just this characteristic. But metallic substances increase in resistance as they become hotter. The mobile electrons in a wire must experience greater difficulty in getting through the porous material when the kinetic agitation of the atoms making up the wire increases.

RESISTANCE AND DIMENSIONS

We might also expect a long wire to be more resistant than a short one and a stout wire to be less resistant than a thin one. Experiment proves both expectations to be correct, and an equation embodying them can be written as follows:

$$\text{Resistance} = \frac{K \times \text{Length}}{\text{Cross-sectional area}}$$

where K is a constant whose magnitude depends on the material of which the wire is made.

THE OERSTED EFFECT

Volta's invention of the electric battery was soon followed by numerous useful applications of the electric current. It also stimulated the investigation of many fundamental problems. One of these was the possible relation between electric currents and magnetism. H. C. Oersted (1777–1851), a Danish engineer, was one of those who suspected that moving charges might produce a magnetic effect. His deliberate efforts to prove the connection were unsuccessful until 1820 when he discovered that a magnetic field of force formed around any conductor through which electric charges flowed. This can be demonstrated by connecting a long, insulated wire to a battery and then holding the wire near, and parallel, to a magnetic compass. The compass immediately turns and after a few oscillations comes to rest in a direction perpendicular to the wire. If the demonstration is repeated with the electric current in the reverse direction, the compass swings through 180° so that it is again transverse to the wire but pointing in a direction opposite to its former one.

Let a straight segment of the same wire be made to pass through a hole in a piece of cardboard, held horizontally as shown in Fig. 106a, and iron filings sprinkled around the wire will arrange themselves in concentric circles centered around the wire (Fig. 106b). A small compass will indicate the direction of these circles as clockwise if the current is from the positive terminal of a battery downward through the cardboard. If the current is reversed in direction, the

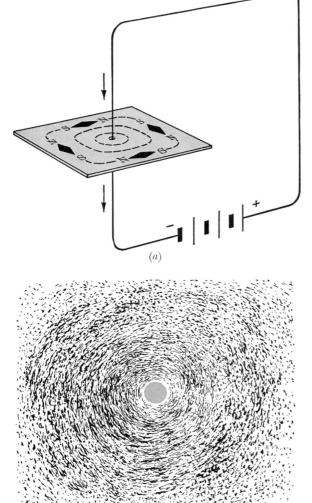

(a)

(b)

FIG. 106. (a) The Oersted effect. (b) Pattern of iron filings around a wire carrying a current.

magnetic lines of force reverse their direction also, forming counterclockwise concentric circles. Put in terms of a convenient rule, if the conductor is grasped by the right hand with the thumb pointing in the direction of positive current, the fingers will encircle the wire in the same direction as that of the magnetic lines of force.

Oersted's discovery was of extraordinary im-

portance. Before 1820 there was no known connection between electric and magnetic phenomena. His celebrated experiment showed them to be intimately connected, as in fact they must be. Philosophers and scientists share the conviction that all nature is a unity, and that all its manifestations are related to one another. It is now believed that the fundamental mechanism responsible for magnetic behavior in any material is the motion of electric charges. There is no other known cause of magnetism, and the magnetic properties of a substance such as iron are believed to be due to minute electric charges spinning around within the very atoms of the element. This clears up a difficulty encountered before, when we questioned the existence of magnetic poles. The Oersted discovery makes it evident that magnetism is not due to small separate north and south poles but is a manifestation associated with moving charges.

THE ELECTROMAGNET

Oersted's discovery of the magnetic field that accompanies moving electric charges led to important practical applications. One such application grew out of the realization that the weak fields surrounding every segment of wire could be added together to make a strong field by simply coiling the wire into a spiral shape. Suppose, for example, that a spiral of insulated wire is threaded through holes in a piece of cardboard, as shown in Fig. 107a, with its free ends attached to the terminals of a battery represented conventionally by long and short lines. When there is a current, the resulting magnetic lines are directed, as usual, perpendicularly to the wire, with the consequence that inside every loop all lines point toward the right-hand end of the coil, which thus becomes a north pole of augmented strength. The pattern produced by iron filings sprinkled over the cardboard resembles the magnetic field around a bar magnet (Fig. 107b). A coil of this design, called a solenoid, can exert very great magnetic force, particularly if the current through it is a strong one and the number of turns of wire is large. The magnetic field is greatly intensified if a bar of soft iron is placed inside it.

The magnetic field associated with an electric current is in every respect like the field produced by a permanent magnet. It can, for example, exert either attractive or repulsive force on the field surrounding a nearby conductor.

If there are currents flowing in the same di-

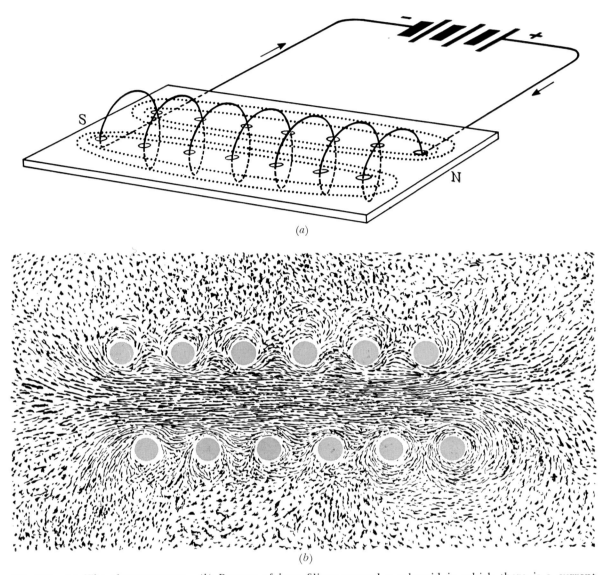

FIG. 107. (*a*) The electromagnet. (*b*) Pattern of iron filings around a solenoid in which there is a current.

rection through two parallel wires which pass through perforations in a slab of cardboard, iron filings sprinkled on the cardboard will form a pattern as shown in Fig. 108. From our experience with the pattern around permanent magnets we infer that the two wires, through which electric currents are in the same direction, attract each other. If the card is removed, the motion of the wires toward each other confirms this prediction.

Conversely, if the currents in the wires are in opposite directions (Fig. 109), the iron filing pat-

tern is denser between the wires than it is elsewhere, just as it was between bar magnets having like poles abreast of each other. The inference that in this case the wires repel each other is likewise borne out when the card is removed.

THE MOTOR EFFECT

Magnetic fields interact with one another whatever their origin. In Fig. 110 a positive current is shown directed downward between the poles of a permanent magnet. The flow of charges creates a circular magnetic field around the wire.

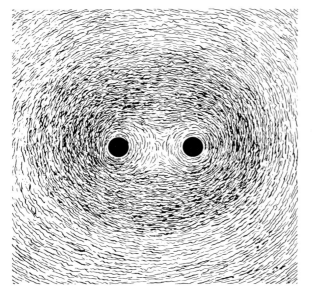

FIG. 108. Magnetic field around parallel wires, currents in the same direction.

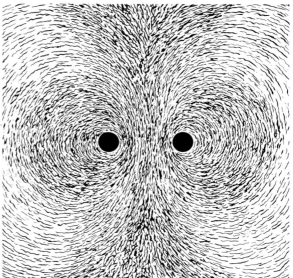

FIG. 109. Magnetic field around parallel wires, currents in opposite directions.

The direction of this circular field is such as to strengthen the permanent field immediately behind the wire and weaken it in front of the wire. In consequence, the wire experiences a thrust forward toward the observer. Looking downward, as in the right part of the diagram, it appears as if the magnetic lines were acting like stretched elastic bands to push the wire forward.

Such forces are used practically in many ways. Instruments for measuring current strength (ammeters) or for measuring potential differences (voltmeters) are common examples (Fig. 111).

A strong magnetic field is provided, usually by a permanent magnet of the horseshoe type. Within its field, a coil of fine wire is so mounted that it can turn on an axis. The little coil of wire becomes an electromagnet when electrons flow through it, its north pole being repelled by

the north pole of the permanent magnet and attracted by the south pole of the same. Yielding to these forces, the coil turns on its axis, while a pointer attached to the coil swings across a graduated scale. A fine watch spring at one end of the coil restrains it from making a complete rotation.

The stronger the current in the movable coil the greater is the magnetic force it exerts against the field of the permanent magnet and the larger is the angle through which the pointer swings. Thus, by calibration of the instrument with known currents it becomes an ammeter for measuring the strength of unknown currents. The thick bar or *shunt* between the terminals of the ammeter has low resistance; hence it carries most of the current, only a small but known fraction of the total flowing through the delicate wire

FIG. 110. The motor effect.

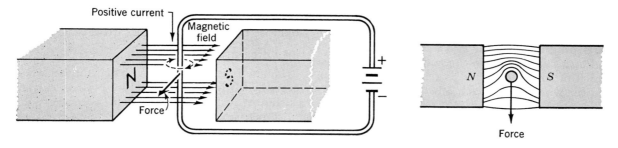

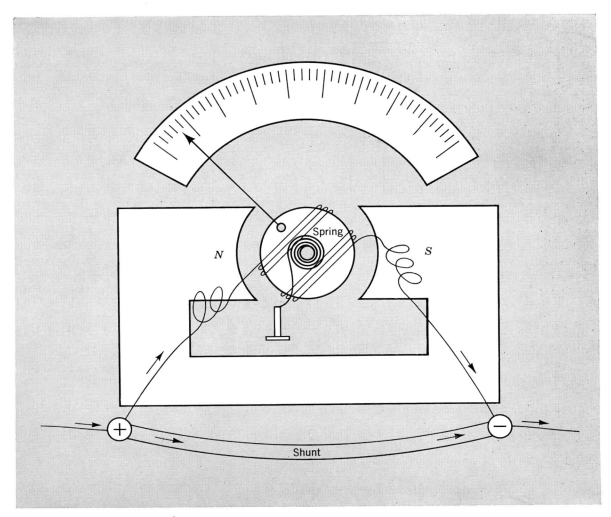

FIG. 111. The ammeter or galvanometer.

spiral. The sensitivity may be greatly increased by suspending the coil by a fine fiber instead of mounting it on an axis.

THE MOTOR

The forces that drive our electric motors are the forces of interaction between magnetic fields. Figure 112*a* shows in perspective a rectangular loop of insulated wire wound lengthwise around an iron core which is mounted in bearings so that it is free to rotate between the poles of a magnet (usually an electromagnet). The turning shaft is equipped with a brass collar split into two separate halves. A pair of conductors, *B* and *B'* (called brushes), connected with the source of electric energy, press lightly against this collar.

If positive current enters at *B* and flows back along the left-hand segment of the loop, it produces a clockwise magnetic field around this part of the wire, so that the magnetic field already existing between the pole pieces is strengthened immediately above the wire and weakened below it. On the right, where positive current is approaching the reader, it produces a counterclockwise pattern of magnetic lines which strengthens the existing field below the wire and weakens it above. The left segment of wire is thus urged downward and the right one upward; hence the entire loop begins to rotate counterclockwise. After a partial turn, however, when the right segment of wire has entered the left half of the field, that part of the collar to which it is connected has also crossed over and is now touching brush B through which positive current continues to enter. At the same time, the left-hand segment has reached the right side and its part of the collar has broken contact with brush B and instead is touching brush B', which is the point of exit for positive current. The split collar, or *commutator,* is thus an automatic switching device which insures that the direction of current flow through opposite sides of the loop shall always be such as to give continuous rotatory motion to the moving part (the armature) of the motor.

The force of interaction between the constant magnetic field between the pole pieces and the variable magnetic field produced by the current depends on the strength of the current and on the strength of the steady magnetic field. It depends also on the number of turns of wire in the moving loop, since every segment of wire along the armature contributes an equal amount of magnetism when the electric current flows through it. Hence it is desirable to have many windings of wire on the armature so that their cumulative magnetic effect will be large. In

practical designs many coils are compactly arranged in slots along the sides of the armature (Fig. 112b). Each coil is connected to a pair of oppositely situated segments of the commutator, which then consists not of two halves but of twice as many segments as there are coils. There are still, however, only two brushes.

ELECTROMAGNETIC INDUCTION

Oersted's discovery that an electric current can cause motion in nearby magnets immediately raised the question of a possible inverse effect. Can the motion of a magnet cause electric current in a conductor? This question can be answered affirmatively and conclusively with the aid of just such a direct-current (d-c) motor as we have described. Turning the armature by hand produces relative motion between the conductors along the armature and the field of the magnet. It should not, and does not, matter whether the actual motion is performed by the magnet or by the conductors.

For this experiment, the source of electric current is absent and the wires leading away from brushes B and B' are connected instead to a

FIG. 112. (a) The electric motor.

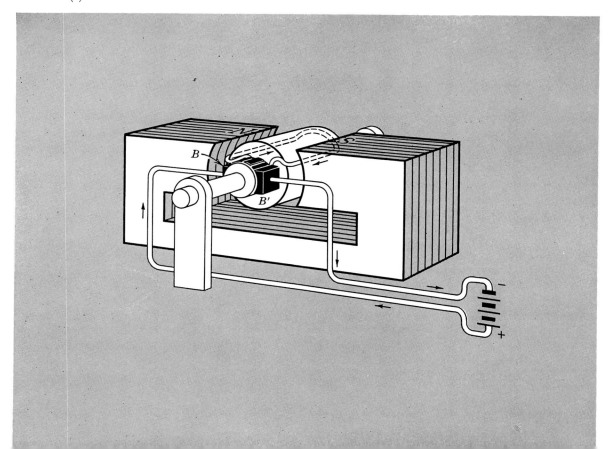

galvanometer, an instrument for detecting current, like an ammeter. When the armature is turned, the galvanometer needle immediately deflects, showing that electric charges are flowing through the circuit. If the speed of turning is increased, the needle deflects through a larger angle, thus indicating a stronger current.

Currents developed by the relative motion of a conductor and a magnetic field are said to be *induced,* and the phenomenon is called *electromagnetic induction.* Further experimentation shows that this induction will occur even if the conductor and the magnet are both stationary, provided the magnetic field is somehow made to change in strength. This method of producing currents was first detected during the 1830's by Joseph Henry (1797–1878) in the United States and by Michael Faraday (1791–1867) in England, who were working independently of each other. Two of their experiments can be reproduced easily.

1. A considerable length of insulated wire is wound into a coil of many turns, and the bare ends are connected to the terminals of a galvanometer. One pole of a bar magnet is pushed through the open center of the coil. There is an immediate sharp deflection of the galvanometer needle, which returns to zero, however, as soon as the magnet ceases moving. On withdrawal of the magnet the galvanometer again shows a sharp deflection, but in the opposite direction.

Evidently the current induced by a moving magnetic field takes a direction that depends on the direction in which the magnetic field is moving.

If the magnet is repeatedly thrust into the coil and withdrawn again, the current is observed to alternate, surging through the coil in one direction when the magnet enters and then in the opposite direction when the magnet is removed. A current which reverses in direction periodically is called an *alternating current* (a-c).

The same result ensues if the magnet is held stationary and the coil of wire is moved toward and away from it.

2. A coil of insulated wire is connected to a battery through a switch or key that permits rapid closing and opening of the circuit. Surrounding this coil is a second one, made also of insulated wire, whose ends are connected to a galvanometer. When the switch is closed so that charges flow through the inner coil, the galvanometer shows that there is a current momentarily through the outer coil. This induced current ceases almost immediately, however, even if the direct current is allowed to continue through the inner coil. Opening the switch causes a galvanometer deflection in the opposite direction, also of only momentary duration. Evidently the induced current is generated only during the brief time when the battery current is growing to full strength or else dying out. This plainly suggests that electromagnetic induction can be achieved in a practicable way without the physical motion of either magnet or conductor merely by fulfilling the condition that the inducing magnetic field shall continually fluctuate in strength. Just such means of inducing currents are used in the operation of the *transformer.*

Before examining this application, let us inquire more searchingly into the induction phenomenon as exemplified by a moving magnet, for at first thought it may seem to violate the conservation of energy law. We therefore at-

FIG. 112. (*b*) Armature with commutator.

Courtesy of General Electric Co.

Bettmann Archive

PLATE XXIX. The laboratory of Michael Faraday, one of the great experimenters of the nineteenth century. Note the simplicity of the apparatus, in contrast with that of a modern laboratory.

tempt to circumvent this law by a clever experimental arrangement (Fig. 113).

Suppose a very strong magnet to be suspended by fine threads and set oscillating so that one end of it swings into and out of an open coil consisting of many turns of insulated wire. The whole system may even be placed in an evacuated inclosure so as to eliminate air resistance in the hope that the magnet may continue to oscillate for a long time once it has been started. Each time the magnet moves into the coil, and again when it moves out, a current will be induced in the coil, and this current may be made to do useful work such as generating heat, lighting a lamp, or running a motor. Will not this useful energy greatly exceed the small amount of work we did in starting the magnet swinging?

Actually, we find that the magnetic pendulum comes to rest very quickly—much sooner than it would have done if the coil of wire had not been there. We must therefore seek some force that opposes its motion. The cause of the opposition is not hard to find if we recall that every electric current, induced or otherwise set up, is attended

by a magnetic field. As the north pole of the bar magnet moves into the coil, thereby inducing current in the coil, the induced current sets up its own magnetic field, which turns out to be so directed as to repel the entering magnet. In other words, the coil becomes an electromagnet having its north pole at the side facing the advancing bar magnet. The momentum of the bar magnet carries it into the coil nevertheless, but the repelling force decelerates it greatly. If we expect this same force to accelerate the exit of the bar magnet from the coil, we are again deceived, for, as the bar starts moving to the right, there is induced in the coil a current directed oppositely to the first, and this causes the right-hand face of the coil to become a south pole. The bar magnet is accordingly resisted in its exit from the coil, and its motion suffers a further deceleration. We can, of course, offset these retarding influences and keep the magnetic pendulum moving, but only by giving the bar an additional push at each oscillation. That is to say, we must supply mechanical energy for all the electrical energy that is generated in the coil.

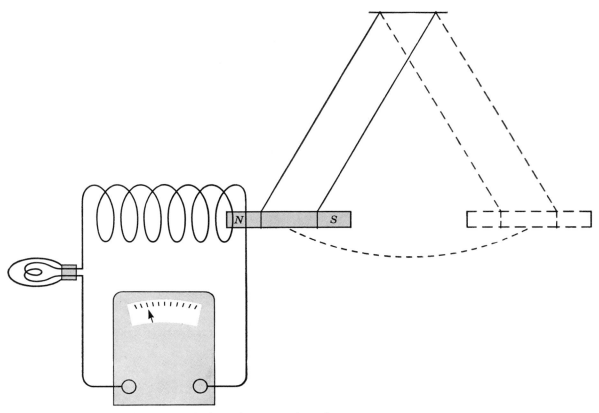

FIG. 113. An effort to circumvent the law of conservation of energy.

LENZ'S LAW

An important law, discovered in 1833 by the Russian physicist H. F. E. Lenz (1804–1864) covers the foregoing and similar experiences in the words: Whenever a current is induced in a conductor that is moving relative to a magnetic field, the current direction is such that its attendant magnetic field opposes the motion.

To illustrate the application of Lenz's law, consider the straight segment of wire AB (Fig. 114), which we propose to push between the magnet poles in a direction away from the reader. When we do so, a current is induced in the wire and a local magnetic field forms around the wire. According to Lenz's law, this field must create a force directed toward the reader, that is, a force (F) tending to prevent the motion of the wire. Such a force does result if the induced magnetism is directed as shown by the small circular arrows, and comparison with earlier diagrams will show that this requires that the induced current must have a positive direction downward.

If Lenz's law did not apply in this instance, no work would be needed to push the conductor between the magnet poles and we should then get our induced electric current at no expense of energy. The conservation of energy principle would be invalidated, and a perpetual motion machine would be realized.

FIG. 114

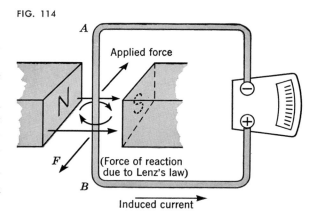

ELECTRICAL POWER TRANSMISSION

With these few phenomena as background, we are now able to describe the generation of electrical power and the way in which this power is distributed to consumers over a wide area. An electric alternator, sometimes called a dynamo, consists essentially of an efficient arrangement of many coils of wire which are kept rotating in very strong magnetic fields produced by electromag-

Con Edison

PLATE XXX. The Pearl Street Station, Thomas Edison's first commercial electric plant, was put into operation on September 4, 1882. There were six generators, or dynamos, each one of which could light 1750 lamps of 16 candlepower or approximately 50-watt rating.

nets. The intricate details of design need not concern us; it is sufficient to consider one rectangular loop and the manner in which it is connected to the outside circuit (Fig. 115). When such a loop (*ABCD*) is made to rotate clockwise in the field of the electromagnet (*NS*), a voltage is induced whose positive direction is shown by the arrows. Each end of this coil is connected to a metallic ring which is fixed on the same rotating shaft (not shown) as the coil is. Graphite blocks (*E* and *F*) are so mounted as to press against the rotating rings so that the current induced in the coil can flow through these blocks to the external circuit. The induced voltage and resulting current will reverse in direction periodically, since, in every revolution of the coil, the segments *AB* and *CD* are cutting across the magnetic field upward half the time and downward the other half. The effect may be conveniently depicted in graphical form (Fig. 116)

by plotting the alternating voltage against time and representing the voltage induced in one direction above the horizontal line; the voltage in the reverse direction is shown below this line. The graph is very nearly a perfect sine wave. The current may also be plotted against the

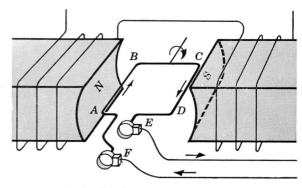

FIG. 115.   A simple alternator.

time, yielding a curve of the same shape. In modern electrical design there are 60 complete cycles or rotations of the coil every second, and the product is called a 60-cycle alternating current.

Aside from friction between the moving parts of the alternator, the operation of Lenz's law requires work to be done in turning the coils of the machine. The greater the current generated, the larger will be the force needed to keep the moving parts rotating. The necessary force has to

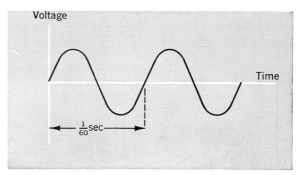

FIG. 116.   Graphical representation of an alternating voltage.

be supplied by an engine of some kind. It may be a turbine driven by falling water or one driven by steam derived from a boiler which is heated by burning coal or oil. Whatever the primary source of energy, it always exceeds the amount of electrical energy obtained from the generator.

The locations of electric generators are determined by such economic factors as availability of fuel or water source, cost of setting up power lines, and concentration of consumers. Where water at good elevations is abundant, huge installations like those of the Hoover Dam, the Grand Coulee Dam, and the Tennessee Valley Authority make it practicable to generate large amounts of electrical power for transmission over long distances.

The sending of electrical power over considerable distances aggravates the problem of power loss in transmission. Although many metals are good conductors, having low intrinsic resistance, the total resistance of a metallic cable that is many miles long is large, and in flowing through such long cables the electric power must inevitably decrease considerably because of useless thermal power. The transmission lines become heated, but to no one's advantage. It is therefore important to make the conducting wires of materials having the lowest resistance possible. Copper is better than steel in this respect. Silver and gold are even less resistant than copper, but they are too costly to be economically feasible. Aluminum is a little more resistant than copper, but the cost of producing it has so decreased in modern times that a good deal of power line in the United States is now made of aluminum wire supported by steel cable to give it greater strength. The resistance of all conductors is lowered by increasing the cross-sectional area, but to use very stout wires for long distances would make the cost of the metal prohibitive.

We come then to the much more impressive economy that can be achieved by reducing the intensity of the current during its passage from the alternator to some distant distributing station. It has already been shown that the conversion of electrical into thermal power is governed by the simple law of Joule:

$$\text{Power lost} = (\text{Intensity of current})^2 \times \text{Resistance}$$

or in symbols

$$P = I^2 R$$

and in units

$$\text{Watts} = \text{Amperes}^2 \times \text{Ohms}$$

But if a large amount of power is to be transmitted to customers, must not the current transmitted be large also? The answer is that it need not be large if the voltage is high, since the power

transmitted equals the product of current times voltage and this product may be large even though the current is small.

THE TRANSFORMER

The device by which a given amount of power is adjusted to high voltage and low amperage is

General Electric Co.

PLATE XXXI. Generators in the hydroelectric power station at Boulder Dam. Each generator has approximately 1000 times the capacity of one of the Edison generators shown in Plate XXX.

the transformer. The principle of its operation can be understood from Fig. 117. A frame made of numerous layers of soft iron is wound on two sides with coils of insulated wire. One coil, say, the left one, functions as the primary winding by being supplied with an alternating current from a 60-cycle alternator. The graph of such a current shows that it fluctuates continually, rising to a maximum and then decreasing to zero every

$\frac{1}{120}$ of a second, after which it reverses its direction and varies in the same way for the next $\frac{1}{120}$ of a second. The magnetic field which is set up within the frame varies in the same manner. In consequence, a displacement of electric charges occurs in the right hand, or secondary, coil because it encircles this fluctuating magnetic field, and an alternating voltage is induced across its terminals.

If the ends of the secondary coil are connected to a closed circuit, an alternating current flows

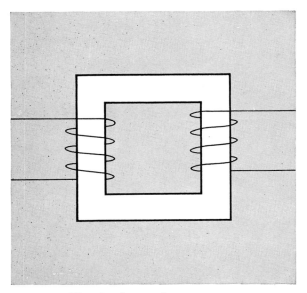

FIG. 117.   The simple transformer.

through this circuit because of the voltage induced across the coil. If the secondary circuit is open, however, not only is there no flow of current through it but the current in the first or primary coil practically ceases to flow. This is an effect of Lenz's law. The fluctuating magnetic field causes induction even in the primary coil, and this takes the form of a countervoltage that prevents all but a very small current from flowing through the primary coil. The establishment of this countervoltage is called self-induction, and it has the very useful effect of practically stopping the primary current automatically except when the secondary current flows, at which times the countervoltage decreases automatically.

The transformer's great usefulness stems from the fact that the induced voltage depends on the number of turns of wire in the secondary coil in comparison with the number in the primary.

Thus, if the secondary coil consists of 1000 times as many turns of wire as the primary does, the induced voltage across the secondary will be almost 1000 times the voltage impressed across the primary. ($V_2 = 1000V_1$.) But the total power (VI) through both coils is the same, or very nearly the same. Hence, the intensity of the current flowing through the secondary coil and out to the external circuit will be $\frac{1}{1000}$ as strong as the current flowing through the primary coil. It is apparent from the earlier discussion of line losses that here is a means of cutting them down to a bare minimum. Recalling that the power loss is I^2R, we need only diminish I to a small value by stepping up the voltage at the generating station with the aid of a transformer. Conversely, at the distributing station many miles away, this low current is fed into another transformer. Here it enters the coil having a large number of turns and induces a low voltage across the coil of few turns. The stepping down of the voltage results in a proportionate increase in the current strength. Thus the consumer receives current at the relatively low voltage suitable to his appliances and in the relatively high strength that he desires.

It must not be supposed that voltage in a power line can be increased without limit. High-voltage wires are dangerous and must be so carefully insulated that this feature alone represents great expense. The lines must be suspended from elaborate porcelain insulators high above the ground on tall steel towers. Sometimes in damp weather a luminous glow or corona discharge is visible at night around high-voltage lines. This is an electrical discharge directly into the surrounding air, and it is such power losses that set the upper limit of voltage for practical transmission.

Figure 118 shows a simplified transmission system. Inasmuch as high voltages cannot be safely generated in a power plant, an alternating current at low voltage is set in motion by the alternator G. Outside the plant the voltage is stepped up by a transformer (T_1) whose secondary coil has many more turns than its primary. The high-voltage secondary coil is connected to the long line L. In practice only one wire need be used for each circuit; the other conductor is the earth itself, which has sufficiently low resistance to carry current with negligible loss. The other end of the secondary coil is therefore "grounded," i.e., connected to a stout metallic conductor buried deeply in the moist earth.

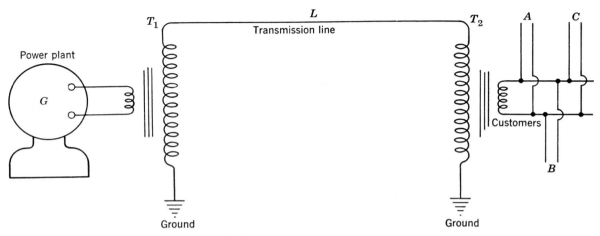

FIG. 118. A simple electric power transmission system.

At the distributing end of the line the single wire connects with one end of a coil having many turns of wire at transformer T_2, and the induced current drawn from the other coil of few turns has its voltage stepped down to a safe and usable magnitude. *A*, *B*, and *C* represent pairs of wires leading to the homes of different users.

SUMMARY

The foregoing account scarcely hints at the outstanding benefits man has derived from those fundamental experiments which gave rise to the huge electrical industry of the present day—the systems of communication which link us efficiently with all parts of the world, the improved means of travel and of transporting goods, the contributions to medicine and sanitation, and the applications to countless devices for safe and intelligent living. Now it is appropriate to take a backward look and to note the sequence of those discoveries which we have discussed and which contributed so richly.

We began with seemingly unimpressive facts—the attracting properties of amber and lodestone. No one could have foreseen the extraordinary consequences of investigating such simple phenomena, but a few individuals, having the curiosity characteristic of the scientist, began to experiment with them. Out of these experiments came not only a host of useful devices but also a penetrating understanding of the structure of matter.

Surely this furnishes proof that nothing in nature is trivial. Every part of the physical universe in all its manifestations is teeming with clues to its ultimate character.

Each one of the experiments in our sequence was simple in principle but was, in practically every case, preceded by other experiments which set the stage for the next steps. Each new discovery made possible a large assortment of related discoveries. The reality of static electric charges had to be established before the electric battery could be discovered; and the magnetic fields associated with electric currents (the Oersted effect) could not be realized and described until batteries were available to produce steady currents. The discovery of electromagnetic induction by Faraday and Henry followed Oersted's discovery quite naturally, since induction is merely the inverse of the Oersted effect. The electric motor and the generator are applications of the discoveries of Oersted and Faraday.

Each discovery was so prolific in consequences that, once the experimental method was applied freely, new facts were recorded with increasing frequency. This is an instance of the cumulative advantage that is so impressive in the experimental sciences.

It is not sufficient, however, to focus attention only on the accumulation of experimental data; the scientific structure is much more than a stockpile of facts. These facts must be related to one another; they must be fitted into a pattern or model. Principles and theories must be made consistent with them. In this process, mathematics and logic are necessary and a vocabulary of precisely defined terms must be agreed upon.

PROBLEMS

1. In an ordinary a-c circuit, the current is, in effect, turned on and off 120 times every second. Why do we not see a constant flickering of our electric lights?

2. If a particular radio set draws ½ amp from a 110-volt source, how many amperes will a comparable set draw from a 6-volt car battery?

3. In household circuits it is common to have the total current flow through a *fuse* which consists of a wire made of a low melting point metal or alloy. Currents above the rated value of the fuse will melt the wire or "blow" the fuse, thus protecting the rest of the circuit from excessive currents and heating which might cause fires. Suppose that on a 110-volt line you have connected a 150-watt radio, a 250-watt flatiron, five 60-watt lamps, and a 75-watt refrigerator. How large should the fuse be?
Ans.   8 amp.

4. Using general facts presented in this chapter, make a list of the items which you consider important in determining the cost of electric power generation and distribution.

5. A common household voltage is 110. (*a*) How many amperes will flow through a 60-watt lamp designed for such a voltage? (*b*) What is the electrical resistance of such a lamp? (*c*) What would be the cost of burning such a lamp steadily for 24 hr at the rate of 7 cents per kilowatthour?
Ans.   (*a*) 0.545 amp.   (*b*) 201 ohms.   (*c*) 10 cents.

. . . .

REFERENCES

1. *A Source Book in Physics*, W. F. Magie, McGraw-Hill Book Co., 1935, pp. 436–519.
2. *The Autobiography of Science,* Forest R. Moulton and Justus J. Schifferes, Doubleday & Co., 1950, pp. 288–292.

23 Conduction of Electricity through Gases

Any two specimens of unlike material become equally and oppositely charged when brought into intimate contact with each other. From this fact we have concluded that atoms of matter contain positive and negative electric charges. From the ease with which their electrical neutrality is upset we may assume further that atoms and molecules are rather fragile structures. It is reasonable to expect, therefore, that in any large assemblage of freely moving particles, such as the molecules of a gas, there would be a certain proportion of damaged ones that have lost electrons through some energetic encounter. Others may have captured free electrons that happened to be in their path. Any particle, atomic or molecular, that bears an uncompensated charge, whether positive or negative, is called an *ion*.

The existence of occasional ions in any body of gas is amply shown by experiment. For example, suppose a carefully insulated electroscope to be charged positively or negatively and left for several hours. It will be found that, even with the greatest care in design and in the driest weather, the leaves of the electroscope will slowly converge; the device eventually loses its charge, no matter what gas surrounds it. This is proof that there must exist in all gases under normal conditions both positive and negative ions. These are the charged particles which occasionally collided with the oil drop in Millikan's experiment.

If a lighted match is brought near the knob of the charged electroscope, the discharge rate is greatly accelerated, thereby indicating that the surrounding gas has become a better conductor. Experiment reveals that any rise in temperature will facilitate electrical conduction through a gas. This is to be expected; the high temperature of the flame increases the kinetic energy of the molecules, and some of their mutual collisions become forcible enough to break up the neutral structures.

We conclude that any violent agitation or any increase in the severity of the molecular collisions should also facilitate electrical conduction in gases. Let us try to produce such agitation electrically.

Let two metallic electrodes be sealed into the opposite ends of a long glass tube which has an outlet leading to a vacuum pump (Fig. 119). If, at atmospheric pressure, a potential difference of about 1000 volts is applied between the elec-

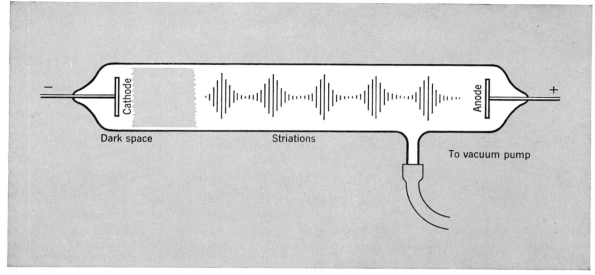

FIG. 119. Striations in an electrical discharge through a gas.

trodes, we find that no current flows. As air is pumped from the tube, however, a diminished pressure is reached at which current suddenly begins to flow. Such an electrical discharge must be seen for an appreciation of its beauty and detail, but here we need only concern ourselves with certain of its features. First a pink glow appears, and this light gradually fills the entire tube as exhaustion of the air continues. A dark region appears in front of the cathode (the negative electrode), and the rest of the tube is filled with equally spaced bands of colored light (striations). As the evacuation proceeds, the dark space lengthens and the striations move toward the anode, eventually disappearing. At this time a green fluorescence can be observed on the glass walls of the vessel. When the vacuum has become very great, this fluorescence vanishes also.

The color of the electrical discharge varies markedly with the gas. Air, a mixture of nitrogen and oxygen, gives a pale-pink color; hydrogen, blue; neon, a brilliant orange red. These colors, in fact, are so characteristic of the elements involved that a careful analysis of the light makes a very sensitive test for the elements present.

The probable mechanism of the electrical conduction is easily described. Although air and other gases are practically non-conductors at ordinary pressures and temperatures, nevertheless, when a potential difference is impressed between the electrodes, the occasional ions in the gas must respond and begin moving toward the appropriate electrodes. The electric current begun in this way must be extremely feeble, since the congestion of gas molecules is so great that every moving ion is certain to be stopped by collision within a very short distance. As the molecular population is diminished by continued operation of the pump, however, the ions can be accelerated over longer distances and thus attain higher speeds and greater kinetic energy. When sufficiently fast-moving ions hit neutral molecules, the collisions will be forceful enough to disrupt these molecules, thereby producing more ions which join in the two-way migration toward the electrodes. Not only is the number of conductors increased by such encounters, but the fresh ions so formed are themselves accelerated by the electric field and they become agents for the production of still more ions.

The result is an avalanche of positive and negative ions moving rapidly in opposite directions and constituting a comparatively strong current.

The fracturing of a neutral atom or molecule requires energy. This is supplied by the moving ions, which lose kinetic energy by collision with particles in their path. It must be expected that many recombinations will occur among the swarm of positive and negative ions produced by the collisions. On recombination, the energy previously imparted to the fragments should be evolved again if the law of conservation of energy holds. We find this energy reappearing in the form of light—the colored light emitted by the excited gas. Later we shall examine the possible mechanism of light radiation. It will be found that the character of the radiation is uniquely identified with the kind of atoms of which the gas consists.

CATHODE RAYS

Additional information about the particles responsible for these effects is revealed if we change the shape of the discharge tube to that shown in

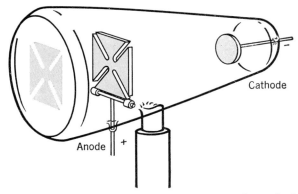

FIG. 120. A metal cross casts a shadow on the end of the glass tube.

Fig. 120 and evacuate the tube to the point where the glass emits a greenish fluorescence. A metal cross is hinged on its support in front of the cathode so that it can either stand upright or be dropped down out of the way. When the cross is down, the nearby end of the tube is uniformly green, but when the cross is upright, a sharp shadow of it is cast on the glass directly behind it. At once it is apparent that the fluorescence must be due to something emitted by the cathode—something which is intercepted by the metal cross. Does this something consist of light, or is it a stream of material particles? If the latter, are the particles electrically charged or are they neutral? If neutral, are they perhaps magnetic?

These questions can be answered by a single test—the reaction of the cathode rays to a magnetic field. If the north pole of a bar magnet is brought near the discharge tube, the shadow is deflected markedly in a direction at right angles to the magnetic field. The south pole deflects it, also at right angles to the field, but in the opposite direction. From these observations we draw the following conclusions:

1. The cathode rays do not consist of light, for light never exhibits such marked reaction to a magnetic field. Tentatively, we assume the rays to consist of particles.

2. Cathode rays cannot consist of magnetic particles, for in that case the deflecting forces would be parallel to the magnetic field.

3. Cathode rays cannot consist of neutral particles, since these would not respond to the magnetic field. Evidently they are electrically charged.

4. From the direction in which the wires of a motor armature are displaced we can deduce the direction in which charges are flowing through the wires. Applying the same criterion to the deflection of cathode rays, we infer that they consist of negatively electrified particles.

Presumably the metallic negative cathode in the discharge tube is crowded with electrons delivered there from the source. When the cathode is struck by fast-moving positive ions that have been attracted to it, many of these electrons must be dislodged and, once free of the electrode, they should be repelled by it and should take up the race toward the positive anode. In the course of their progress, being acted on continually by the electric field, they may be expected to attain very high velocities. The stream of electrons passing swiftly through space as cathode rays constitutes an electric current which is just as real as if the electrons were passing along a wire. The cathode rays set up magnetic fields around themselves, and these can interact with other magnetic fields to yield observable forces.

Further experimentation permits additional inferences about the cathode rays:

1. A delicately mounted paddle wheel in the path of the rays is set spinning. This indicates that the electronic constituents of the rays possess inertia.

2. A concentrated beam of cathode rays focused on a piece of thin metal foil heats the foil to incandescence. Evidently the particles possess considerable kinetic energy.

3. The cathode rays can be collected in a metal box and tested with an electroscope; the sign of the charged particles making up the rays proves to be negative.

4. Various minerals emit characteristic colored lights when struck by the cathode rays. The origin of this radiant energy can hardly be anything other than the kinetic energy of the cathode ray particles.

The foregoing experiments establish certain qualitative characteristics of cathode rays. The next step is to obtain quantitative information about them. How great a negative charge do these cathode particles bear, and how much mass does each possess? The classical experiment that we shall describe, first performed in 1897 by the celebrated British scientist Sir J. J. Thomson (1856–1940), does not answer these questions separately, but in a single datum it gives the ratio of charge to mass for the electronic particles which Thomson believed even then to constitute the cathode rays. His work, performed long before the oil-drop experiment, is regarded as the first experimental proof that electrons exist, even though he did not prove that cathode rays consist of identical charges.

A glass tube like the one shown in Fig. 121 is evacuated to the stage where the glass fluoresces green. The anode has a small hole drilled through its center, so that, although most of the cathode rays are stopped by the anode, those which are moving along the axis of the tube can pass through the hole and ultimately strike a screen, S, which is coated with fluorescent material. Normally, a bright fluorescent spot appears on the screen at A from the impact of the narrow beam of cathode rays.

Two parallel metal plates are sealed into the tube, and these can be oppositely electrified so that the cathode beam must pass through a uniform electric field of known strength. The symbol E for the field strength represents the number of dynes of force which this field exerts on every

unit of negative charge passing through it. If e represents the amount of charge carried by one electron, the product Ee gives the force with which every moving electron is impelled toward the upper plate.

The fundamental laws of mechanics show that a force produces acceleration according to

$$F = ma$$

or in this case

$$Ee = ma$$

$$a = Ee/m$$

But we have also found that a body moving under a constant force for a time t moves through a distance

$$h = \tfrac{1}{2}at^2$$

so that here

$$h = \frac{1}{2}\frac{Ee}{m}t^2$$

How shall we express the time t, which of necessity must be exceedingly short? This turns out to be simple enough, for, once the cathode rays have passed through the channel in the anode, they are no longer accelerated forward and may be presumed to be traveling to the right at constant speed. At this horizontal speed (v) they must traverse the length of the plates (l) in conformity with the equation

$$l = vt \quad \text{or} \quad t = \frac{l}{v} \quad \text{and} \quad t^2 = \left(\frac{l}{v}\right)^2$$

FIG. 121. Experiment to determine e/m for electrons.

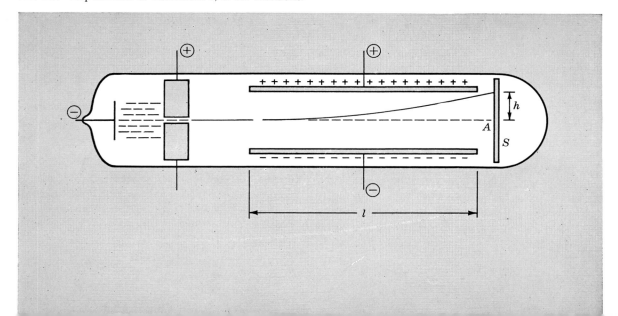

hence the displacement becomes

$$h = \frac{1}{2}\frac{Ee}{m}\left(\frac{l}{v}\right)^2$$

which may better be written as

$$h = \frac{1}{2}E\left(\frac{l}{v}\right)^2\left(\frac{e}{m}\right)$$

or

$$h = K(e/m)$$

The value of the constant K is readily determined by an auxiliary experiment, which need not be described here. Repeated measurements of the displacement h under varying conditions gives the result that $e/m = 5.3 \times 10^{17}$ esu per gram.

This very large number may seem surprising at first glance, seeming to suggest that the electronic charge is enormous. On reflection we recall, however, that the charge is actually very small. Using the value of e now known from Millikan's determination, we may compute the mass of the electron to be

$$m = \frac{e}{e/m} = \frac{4.8 \times 10^{-10}}{5.3 \times 10^{17}}\frac{\text{esu}}{\text{esu/gram}}$$

or

$$m = 9 \times 10^{-28} \text{ gram}$$

The magnitudes of both e and m are of course inconceivably tiny. No human mind can possibly visualize quantities so far out of line with familiar standards, any more than the mind can appreciate the monstrous distances that separate celestial bodies. It is only when we compare the charges and masses of other atomic particles with those of the electron that the relative figures acquire meaning. Such comparisons will become available as we proceed.

It must be emphasized that Thomson's experiment does not deal with single electrons, but with billions of them in a compact stream. Neither does it measure the charge or mass separately but only their ratio. Considered as an identification of the electron, the Thomson experiment does not have the logical strength of that performed by Millikan, which reports on individual charges. On the other hand, Millikan's oil-drop experiment reveals nothing about the mass of the electron. Together, the two experiments furnish very impressive arguments for the existence of electrons having a unique mass and a unique charge.

It is equally revealing to produce cathode ray deflections by means of magnetic fields. Suppose in the Thomson experiment that we subject the entire path of the electron stream to a constant and uniform magnetic field directed horizontally but perpendicular to the path of the beam. Then deflections, either upward or downward, will again occur, and it may be shown that the displacement from the center of screen S will again be proportional to the ratio e/m. The magnitude of the ratio as determined in this manner agrees with that obtained from the electrostatic deflections, thereby strengthening our confidence in the fundamental assumptions.

THE THERMIONIC EFFECT

Electron streams may also be produced in other ways. In 1883 the American inventor Thomas Edison (1847–1931) made a discovery which, although unexplained by him, proved to be of great importance. The early electric lamps developed by Edison were highly evacuated glass bulbs, which tended to become blackened with use. In his investigation of this failing, Edison constructed a lamp having an electrode or plate opposite the hot filament (Fig. 122).

FIG. 122. The Edison, or thermionic, effect.

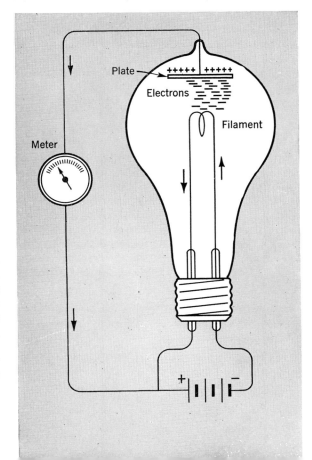

When this plate was charged negatively, no unusual result was observed, but, when connected with the positive side of a battery, it became part of an extra circuit through which a small current was found to flow. Later it was learned that this was due to electrons emitted by the hot wire, and these free electrons responded to the strong attraction of the plate and moved across the intervening empty space. This ability of electrons to escape from the solid conductor is possible only because the filament is hot; a cold conductor does not exhibit this Edison, or *thermionic, effect.* The negative charges, or *thermions,* which leap from hot filament to positive plate can be identified by determination of their charge to mass ratio. This turns out to be identical with the e/m ratio for cathode ray particles. Hence we conclude that the thermions are also electrons.

Apparently the thermionic electrons are originally free to move about from atom to atom within the metal wire. It is their orderly motion in response to a potential difference that constitutes the electric current in a wire. As relatively independent particles, they may be expected to share in the thermal agitation of their environment, that is, they should possess kinetic energy comparable with that of the atoms in their vicinity. Under ordinary conditions this energy is small, whereas at high temperatures the electrons acquire much more energy, enough to enable them to escape from the metal surface. The electrons behave somewhat like molecules escaping from the surface of a liquid during evaporation. If the wire is hot enough and the vacuum high enough, the current so produced may be a strong one. Radio tubes, X-ray tubes, and television picture tubes use just such a hot filament for generating electron beams.

A structure employing a hot cathode and positive accelerating electrodes is called an *electron gun.* It is used a great deal in experimental work where an easily controlled electron source is needed. The number of electrons emitted is controlled by varying the temperature, and their speed (v) is determined by the total potential difference (V) through which the electrons are made to fall. Applying the law of conservation of energy

$$10^7 \cdot Ve = \tfrac{1}{2}mv^2 \qquad \text{or} \qquad v = \sqrt{\frac{2Ve \cdot 10^7}{m}}$$

where V is in volts, v is in cm/sec, $m = 9 \times 10^{-28}$ gram, and $e = 1.6 \times 10^{-19}$ coulomb. This equation gives the speed of the electron for all cases where the voltage is not so high that the electron speed begins to be comparable with the speed of light.

POSITIVE RAYS

Inasmuch as a hole drilled through the anode of a gas discharge tube made possible a quantitative study of the negative rays, one is encouraged to hope that, by reversing the electrode signs in Thomson's apparatus, a similar study of positive rays might be made. With a perforated cathode, a luminous stream does emanate from the aperture, and it travels in a straight path to strike the center of a screen at the far end of the tube. For a permanent record, the screen may be replaced by a photographic plate, whose sensitive emulsion is affected by the impinging particles in the same way as it would be by rays of light.

The beam is readily shown to consist of positive ions of the gas originally left in the vessel. The positive rays differ from cathode rays, however, in two important respects: (1) The constituent ions do not all have the same velocity; inasmuch as they are produced chiefly by cathode ray bombardment, those ions formed near the anode are accelerated to higher speeds than the ones formed near the cathode. (2) When the positive rays pass between oppositely charged plates, it requires several thousand times as strong a field to deflect them appreciably. Just as with cathode rays, the charge to mass ratio for a single particle is inversely proportional to the field strength necessary for producing a given deflection. The ratio e/m is therefore much smaller for all positive ions than it is for electrons. But, since we cannot assume the positive ionic charge to be any smaller than the electronic charge, the smaller ratio must be due to larger mass. The e/m determination evidently offers a means of measuring the mass of any positive ion, provided the element or compound which it represents can be put into the gaseous state.

Many designs of apparatus have been used for determining the charge to mass ratio e/m of positive ions. The instruments are known as mass spectrographs, and they differ from one another chiefly in the geometry of the ion paths through various combinations of electric and magnetic fields. Since, essentially, they are all refinements of the apparatus used by Thomson, we need only concern ourselves here with a description of his original design (Fig. 123).

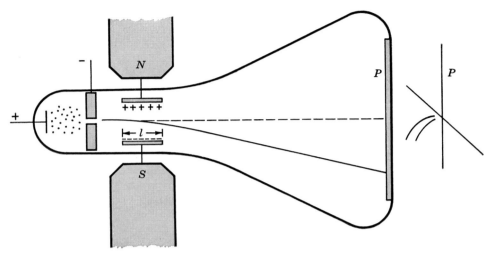

FIG. 123. The mass spectrograph of Sir. J. J. Thomson.

A potential difference of some 30,000 volts between the anode and the perforated cathode produces a swarm of positive ions, some of which travel through the cathode aperture at high speeds. Here they must pass through an electric field maintained by charged plates, as well as a magnetic field having the same direction as the electric field. The electric field deflects the positive rays downward, but the magnetic field deflects them horizontally in a direction away from the reader into the page. At the end of the apparatus the ions strike a photographic plate, P.

It will be recalled from the description of the electric motor that a current flowing across a magnetic field is displaced in a direction perpendicular to both the field and the current.

The actual photograph which the ions take of themselves by impact at P is never a single spot, however. Instead it is a curved line or, usually, several curved lines. The points on any one line are made by ions having the same charge and mass but different one from another in speed. The fastest-moving ions naturally suffer the least displacement from their original course, and these therefore strike the plate at points nearest the center, whereas the slower ions, being deflected more by both fields, hit the plate farther from the center.

It is not necessary for our discussion to derive the exact equation of the ion paths from the cathode to the photographic plate P. We need only to understand that both the horizontal and vertical deflections are proportional to the charge to mass ratio e/m for each ion. However, the differences in velocities among the ions of any kind have a greater influence on the vertical deflections than on the horizontal deflections, and that is why the traces on the photographic plate are parabolas rather than straight lines. If we draw a convenient horizontal line intersecting the parabolas, the distances of these intersections from the central vertical axis will be proportional to the values of $\sqrt{e/m}$ for each kind of ion represented by a parabola.

If we now examine the parabolas formed by an actual discharge through hydrogen gas (Fig. 124), we find two curves, one representing a value of

FIG. 124. Parabolas formed by hydrogen, using the Thomson mass spectrograph.

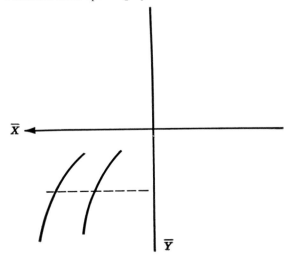

e/m twice as great as the other. The charge is known to be the same in both cases, but the ions which produce the parabola closer to the Y axis have twice the mass of those which form the other curve. We now recall that hydrogen atoms normally combine in pairs to form hydrogen molecules (H_2). Calculation indicates that the one curve is due to ions (H_2^+) formed from these diatomic molecules, whereas the other curve is produced by ions of individual hydrogen atoms (H^+). No matter what voltage is used in a tube containing hydrogen gas, there is no ion type represented by H^{++}. We are therefore obliged to conclude that no hydrogen atom can lose more than one electron, for the reason that all hydrogen atoms contain only one electron.

Hydrogen is the lightest element known. The ion H^+ must therefore be the lightest of all ions. It is known as the *proton,* and its positive charge is exactly equal numerically to the negative charge of the electron. From the measured value of e/m for protons, we find that the mass of this particle is 1836 times as great as that of the electron. If the neutral hydrogen atom consists of one proton and one electron, it is evident that almost all the mass of the hydrogen atom belongs to the proton. Among heavier elements an even greater proportion of the atomic mass belongs to the positive ion which remains when one or more electrons have been sheared off, so that a determination of ionic masses is virtually a determination of the atomic masses.

Next let us analyze the element oxygen. Here the problem becomes more complex because several types of oxygen ion are possible; ions having the formula O^+, O^{++}, O_2^+, and O_2^{++} are commonly observed. The first and last of these yield the same parabola, however, since type O_2^{++} has twice the mass and also twice the charge of type O^+; hence the ratio e/m is identical for both types.

ISOTOPES

After these ions have been identified by the mass spectrograph, there remain still other faint parabolas to be accounted for. Their positions indicate that they are produced by ions of greater mass than that of the first set. Inasmuch as the containing vessel held nothing but pure oxygen, one is forced to the conclusion that there must be two distinct varieties of oxygen, differing from each other only in mass. If they differed at all in chemical behavior, the two varieties would

have been detected and separated during the preparation of the specimen.

Atoms having different masses but identical chemical properties are called *isotopes* of the same element. The relative atomic masses of these oxygen isotopes are about 8:9 or, more precisely, 16.0000:18.0037. By the use of exceptionally sensitive mass spectrographs, a third isotope of oxygen has been discovered with a relative mass of 17.0045.

The mass spectrograph affords an extremely sensitive method for determining the mass of any small charged particle without regard to the chemical properties of the particle. The instrument was the unforeseen outgrowth of the investigation into the electrical conductivity of gases.

Nearly all elements exist in more than one isotopic variety; for some elements the number of stable isotopes is as high as ten! In nature the several isotopes of any one element occur together in constant proportions, irrespective of the state of combination or of the geographic source. Such uniformity could have been established only in a system which was originally gaseous and so hot that all atoms were thoroughly intermingled by diffusion among one another.

The determination of atomic masses by chemical means always involves a very large number of atoms of the element under investigation. Consequently the result is an average of the masses of the isotopes present in the specimen. That the chemically determined values are the same no matter where the element has been obtained indicates how constant the isotopic mixtures must be throughout the world. There are, for example, two isotopes of chlorine having relative atomic masses of 35 and 37 respectively. The lighter one preponderates in all compounds of chlorine obtained from natural sources, comprising about 75% of the mixture. Accordingly, the atomic mass of the blend as determined by chemical analysis always comes out to be

$$0.75 \times 35 + 0.25 \times 37 = 35.5 \quad \text{(approx.)}$$

In 1932 the American chemist Harold Urey discovered an isotope of hydrogen almost twice as heavy as the ordinary variety. This heavy isotope of hydrogen is now called *deuterium,* and its positive ion D^+ is known as a *deuteron.* A still heavier isotope of hydrogen, namely, tritium, having three times the mass of the lightest variety, has been discovered more recently.

Experimental research has also revealed cases of different elements where a certain isotope of one has the same mass as one isotope of the other. These occasional examples of two dissimilar atomic types that nevertheless agree in the one characteristic of mass are known as *isobars*.

Table 14, which we shall find useful later on, illustrates the extraordinary precision of atomic mass determinations. The figures are based on a standard value of 16.0000 for the relative mass of the lightest isotope of oxygen and are not to be confused with chemists' atomic weights.

TABLE 14

The electron	0.00055
The proton	1.00758
The lightest hydrogen isotope	1.00813
Deuterium (heavy hydrogen)	2.01472
The helium atom	4.00388
Lithium^6	6.01690
Lithium^7	7.01804
Beryllium	9.01497
Carbon^{12}	12.0040
Oxygen^{16}	16.0000
Oxygen^{17}	17.0045
Oxygen^{18}	18.0037

PROBLEMS

1. Since electrons do have mass, a charged body does not have the same mass as it does when uncharged.   Suppose a body to be charged negatively by 10^{-9} coulomb.   How much does its mass change?

2. List the facts about the electron that we have encountered so far, and for each fact note the experiments which have yielded that particular information.

3. How would you arrange the electric and magnetic fields of Sir J. J. Thomson's mass spectrograph (Fig. 123) so that the resultant deflections would be zero?

4. Draw the parabolas, as in Fig. 124, which you would expect for the following ions of an element X: X^+, X_2^+, X_2^{+++}, X_3^{++}.

5. In Fig. 122, what would the current through the meter be like if, instead of the battery shown, an a-c source of current were used?   Can you think of any practical use for this arrangement?   Explain.

6. Calculate the speed of an electron which has been accelerated by a potential of 100 volts.
Ans. 6×10^8 cm/sec.

. . . .

REFERENCE

1. *A Source Book in Physics,* W. F. Magie, McGraw-Hill Book Co., 1935, pp. 561–600.

24 *Light*

What would be our concept of the physical universe if we could not see? Would we have discovered the stars or the planets? What strange turns would our thoughts and philosophies have taken? What would be the state of our civilization if mankind had not been endowed with the sense of sight? A little speculation of this kind reveals the extent to which sight dominates our sensory experiences and therefore influences our thinking. A large share of our knowledge of the external world comes to us visually, and this fact alone would justify an inquiry into a few simple phenomena concerned with light and the mechanism of seeing.

In those instances when the eye is deceived, it is important to note the extent of the deception and the manner in which the errors are rectified by other sensory experiences. Optical images are illusions, to be sure, but they are not hallucinations, and, once the laws governing their formations are known, they can be interpreted as reliably as any other sensory stimulus. The sense of sight becomes, in fact, an extension of the sense of touch, so that we can reach out into space and apprehend objects beyond our immediate reach. Thus, we have come to believe that the moon and the sun and the planets exist in reality even though we cannot touch them, and we believe that the distant stars and nebulas are realities, although perhaps forever beyond our tactual sense.

In the classical poem *Concerning the Nature of Things,* composed by Lucretius in the first century B.C., there is a strange description of the process of seeing. The whole poem was an attempt to explain all natural phenomena in terms of the Epicurean or atomist school of philosophy which, in turn, was founded on the atomic speculations of Democritus in the fifth century B.C. Optical images were thought to be "shapes which, being separated, like membranes, from the surfaces of the bodies of objects, flit hither and thither through the air." Visible objects were supposed to throw off thin skins or films composed of the "numberless minute particles on the surfaces of the objects," and retaining the contours of the surfaces like a mask. The impacts of these thin atomic films upon the eye were supposed to stimulate the sensation of sight.

Plato, Euclid, Ptolemy, and many others thought that the eye emitted something like tentacles, though of a very subtle kind, and that vision resulted when these *feelers* reached out through space and touched the object. This idea became so firmly established that it persisted throughout most of the Middle Ages, and remnants of it remain to this day among those who believe in the *evil eye* and kindred superstitions. Aristotle, characteristically, sought an explanation in the *quality* of the medium through which the vision occurred. The belief that radiations were emitted by the eye persisted until the

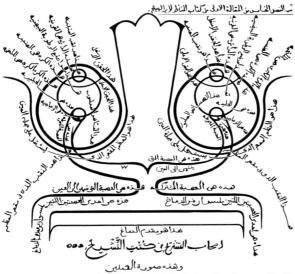

Bausch & Lomb Optical Co., Rochester, N. Y.

PLATE XXXII. Diagram of the visual system taken from the *Book of Optics* of Alhazen, written in 1083. Many of the known components and parts of the related nervous system are shown in this early drawing.

Arabian scholar Alhazen (about 1000 A.D.) wrote his *Treasury of Optics*. Such were the beginnings of optical theory.

THE STRAIGHT-LINE PROPAGATION OF LIGHT

It was no accident that Euclid concerned himself with optics. Whatever the true nature of vision might be, the paths of communication between the external object and the eye lay along the same straight lines whose spatial relationships he was so fond of investigating. No wonder that Euclid's *Optics*, written about 300 B.C., consisted largely of a series of exercises in perspective.

Thus originated the first abstraction in optics—the *ray* of light. Actually, there is no such thing in nature as an infinitely thin ray of light which can be completely represented by a geometrical line, and yet the analogy proved to be so useful that it persists to this day and serves as a basis

for the whole field of geometrical optics. There are many such abstractions in the natural sciences; they are mathematical-physical half-truths which serve as starting points for rational analysis.

The idea of a ray of light is suggested by many observations. Light rays trace visible paths from a bright exterior through the dust-laden air of a darkened room. Occasionally, straight streamers of sunlight emerge from apertures in clouds to form an impressive sunburst. A searchlight forms a straight luminous pencil on a dark night. These common observations all suggest that the path of a beam of light is a straight line. As a matter of fact, the most useful physical definition of a straight line is that it is the path of a beam of light through a homogeneous medium, rather than the Euclidean "shortest path between two points" concept. We sight along the edge of an object to determine whether or not it is straight; engineers sight through levels and transits to lay out straight lines in surveying; astronomers locate distant objects in space by assuming straight paths for the light beams through the axes of their telescopes.

The pinhole camera furnishes a simple and beautiful illustration of the straight-line propagation of light (Fig. 125). Suppose that O is a small aperture or pinhole which admits light from a luminous object AE into a darkened box. Though light rays will pass out in all directions from the luminous point A, only that light which moves in the direction AOA' will fall upon the darkened screen at the back of the box. To someone inside the box, there will be an image at A' which represents the source A both in color and intensity. Similarly, every luminous point source on the object duplicates itself on the screen. The result is an inverted image of the object whose size depends on the relative distances of the object and screen from the pinhole O. With increased exposure times, one can get excellent photographs by substituting such a pinhole for the lens in an ordinary camera (Plate XXXIII). The sharpness will, however, be considerably reduced.

The pinhole image is admittedly a deception in the sense that there is no real object where there appears to be one on the screen. However, there are real beams of light striking the screen and thence scattered to the eye, and the image is a faithful, though inverted, replica of the real source, so that, once we are aware of the nature of the illusion, we may study the real object by an examination of its image.

But, to prepare for a later difficulty, it must be stated here that the image in the pinhole camera will not become sharper and sharper as the pinhole becomes smaller and smaller without limit, although it should do so if the paths followed by light were truly straight lines. This fact, which is not consistent with the straight-line concept, serves to remind us again that we are dealing with an abstraction that must not be confused with the ultimate physical reality—the passage of real light through space.

THE SPEED OF LIGHT

The problem of the speed of light is not easy to attack experimentally. Galileo, in his *Dialogues Concerning Two New Sciences,* recorded an attempt to measure this property and also admitted the inadequacy of his method. At a distance of less than one mile from each other, two observers with covered lanterns tried to measure the time lag in the passage of a light signal from one station to the other and back again. The first observer suddenly uncovered his lantern. The second observer, seeing the distant light, immediately uncovered his own lantern. The first observer, receiving the light signal from the second observer, was then in a position to estimate the time required for the passage back and forth. Since there appeared to be no perceptible time difference, Galileo concluded that the velocity of light must either be infinite or, at least, extremely great.

In 1675 the Danish astronomer Olaus Roemer (1644–1710) made an interesting observation which showed for the first time that light has a finite speed and which gave an estimate of that speed (Fig. 126). Roemer was engaged in determining the period of Io, the innermost of the many moons of Jupiter. This he was able to do by noting the time intervals between successive eclipses of Io by Jupiter. This is the period of the moon and is known to be 42.5 hr. Since Jupiter is more than five times as far away from the sun as the earth is, there will be times when the earth is moving away from Jupiter in its orbit and at other times the earth will be moving towards Jupiter. Roemer found that the period of revolution for this inner moon of Jupiter was lengthened when the earth receded from Jupiter and shortened when the earth approached Jupiter. The total discrepancy in time amounted to about 22 min in approximately ½ yr while the

earth traveled from A to B. The effect was explained by Roemer as due to the extra time required for light to travel approximately the diameter of the earth's orbit, the difference between JA and JB. This reasoning is now considered quite sound, but the time is more nearly $16\frac{2}{3}$ min, yielding a speed for light equal to about 186,000 mps. No wonder that Galileo failed in his crude attempt! Though Roemer's explanation was not accepted at once, it was brilliantly confirmed by Bradley's observation of aberration in 1726, already described in the section on astronomy.

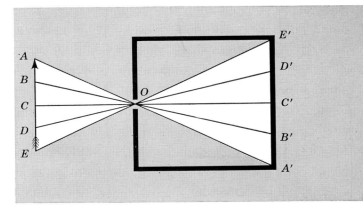

FIG. 125. The pinhole camera.

Since the time of Roemer and Bradley, there have been numerous determinations of the velocity of light. Some of these have achieved extraordinary accuracy through the use of mechanical or electrical timing devices with far faster response than Galileo's lantern observers.

Whatever the nature of light may be, it is certainly a form of energy. That small fraction of the radiant light energy from the sun which is intercepted by the earth is our only source of energy except for that which comes from radioactive or nuclear processes. It is the energy from the sun that keeps up the earth's temperature. It is energy from the sun which is changed to chemical energy when carbon dioxide and water form carbohydrates in our vegetation, and these carbohydrates, in turn, furnish the energy for animal life. Fuels like oil and coal have animal and vegetable origins, whereas water and wind power owe their energy rather directly to the heat of the sun.

When light strikes the surface of a body, some of its energy may be transmitted through the

(a)   (b)

PLATE XXXIII. Pinhole photograph. (a) Photograph taken with good camera lens. (b) Photograph taken with ½-mm pinhole substituted for the lens.

material as in the case of glass. We say then that the material is transparent. But no material is perfectly transparent; some of the light energy is lost to the material itself. The energy so removed increases the internal energy of the material and usually causes a small rise in the temperature of the material. Black bodies, which are opaque, absorb almost all the light energy incident upon them. Some bodies which are

FIG. 126. Roemer's method for determining the speed of light.

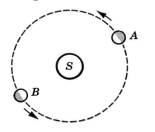

white or have polished metallic surfaces reflect a great deal of the incident light. Of special interest is the plane reflecting mirror because it enables us to study another simple case of image formation.

THE REFLECTION OF LIGHT

There is a simple law governing the geometry of reflection which is so old that it was known to Euclid. A beam of light *CB* (Fig. 127) will be reflected from a plane surface *B* so that the reflected ray *BD* and the incident beam *CB* make equal angles with *AB,* the perpendicular to the surface. The law is summarized by saying that *the angle of incidence (CBA) equals the angle of reflection (ABD).* Also *CB, AB,* and *BD* lie in the same plane. This innocent-looking relation serves to explain the formation of all types of image produced by mirrors of every kind.

Consider, for instance, the plane mirror *EF* in Fig. 128. Let an illuminated object *AB* be set up in front of it. Each point on the luminous object radiates rays of light into space, and some of these will strike the mirror and be reflected. A ray AC which is perpendicular to the surface will be reflected back perpendicularly, since the angle of incidence is zero and the angle of reflection must also be zero. Another ray AD, selected at random, will be reflected from the mirror towards G, again paying respect to the law of equal angles made with the perpendicular at D. Obviously no rays of light can penetrate

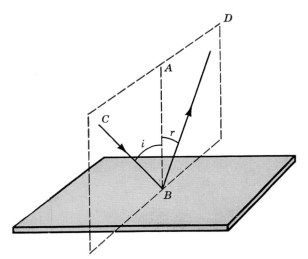

FIG. 127. In reflection, angle i equals angle r.

the mirror—it is opaque. But to an eye at H, looking in the direction of the mirror, the two rays CA and DG appear to have come from a common point A' which is as far behind the mirror as A is in front of it. The two rays CA and DG are not the only pair we might have chosen; it requires only simple geometry to show that any ray drawn from A will, upon reflection, seem to have come from A'. At this point a defect in the whole visual process becomes apparent. The eye is not able to discern what the previous path of a light ray has been; it can judge only the intensity, the color, and the direction of the ray. The eye is therefore deceived into thinking that there must be a source of light at A'. That is what we mean by an image; A' is an image of the source A. But the luminous object AB consists of many point sources of light, for each of which the preceding argument applies. Thus an image $A'B'$ of the same size as the object AB is formed. This image is really a greater illusion than the pinhole image already discussed,

because if we go behind the mirror we shall not find any rays of light coming from $A'B'$. Nevertheless, being fully aware of the nature of such images, we use plane mirrors frequently and with confidence that they reveal the true appearance of the source.

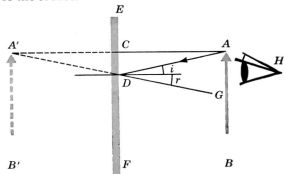

FIG. 128. Construction of an image formed by a plane mirror.

When the surface is curved, we may still apply the same arguments essentially by making use of a geometrical trick. We regard the surface as a composite of tiny plane mirrors set at small angles to each other and behaving like the plane mirror just discussed. This makes it possible to construct the images even though the surfaces are concave or convex.

THE REFRACTION OF LIGHT

It is a familiar fact that our eyes deceive us with regard to the depth of a pool of water. The true depth is always greater than we suppose it to be. Also, a stick, partially immersed in water

FIG. 129. Refraction of a beam of light.

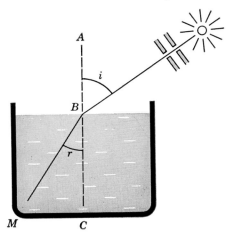

and held obliquely, seems to be broken at the water surface. These phenomena were known so long ago that Ptolemy and other Greek geometers concerned themselves with the explanation. Light travels in straight lines in a homogeneous medium, but, on passing obliquely from one medium to another of different properties, the

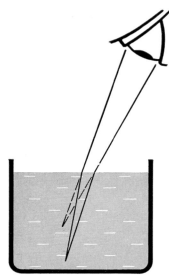

FIG. 130. Apparent displacement of an object due to refraction.

rays bend sharply at the boundary. Experimentally, the problem of measuring the angles of incidence and the angles of bending is a simple one, and yet it was not until the seventeenth century that the correct relation between these angles was stated in mathematical form.

Consider a thin beam or ray of light proceeding from an aperture toward the surface of water in a glass vessel (Fig. 129). If the room is somewhat darkened, the broken path of the ray will be plainly visible from outside the vessel. The change in direction of the oblique light ray as it

enters the water is called *refraction,* and the angle *CBM* between the refracted ray and the perpendicular to the surface is called the *angle of refraction.*

If the light travels the other way, that is, from *M* at the bottom of the tank upward, it follows an identical bent path. Thus, an observer looking along the direction indicated in Fig. 130 can see an object on the bottom of the tank by means of the refracted light ray, although the object will appear to him to be displaced upward because he is accustomed to seeing objects as if they were always in a straight line with the eye. An amusing demonstration of such refraction can be made by placing a coin at the bottom of an opaque drinking glass and, after taking a position a little to one side so that the coin cannot be seen, pouring water into the glass. The coin will become visible when the glass is full of water, even though the eye is still out of line with it.

THE INDEX OF REFRACTION

When a ray of light passes obliquely from air (or from empty space) into glass, water, or any other transparent medium, its direction always changes in such a way that the incident angle exceeds the refraction angle. Larger angles of incidence result in larger angles of refraction (Fig. 131). We seek a relationship between the two. Measurements made by Ptolemy in the second century persuaded him that the ratio of these two angles was constant. This is not true, however. The correct relation, as discovered in 1621 by Snell (1591–1626), is as follows:

SNELL'S LAW

The ratio between the sines of the angles of incidence and refraction is a constant for two given media. The numerical value of the constant changes when either medium is changed.

$$\frac{AB/AC}{ab/ac} = \frac{\sin i}{\sin r} = \mu$$

FIG. 131. Illustration of Snell's law.

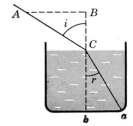 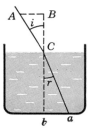 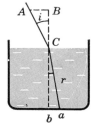

where μ is a constant known as the *index of refraction*.

Failure to discover this simple law sooner indicates an extraordinary lack of experimentation

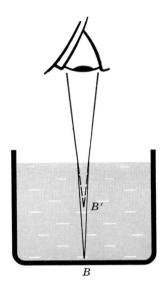

FIG. 132. An image of B at B' is formed due to refraction.

during the fifteen centuries from Ptolemy to Snell.

The index of refraction of light between air and water is 1.33; between air and glass it ranges from 1.5 to 1.7; between air and diamond the index of refraction is 2.42.

EXAMPLES OF REFRACTION

We are now prepared to understand why a vessel containing any transparent liquid appears to be shallower than it really is.

In Fig. 132, imagine the eye to be viewing a small object B which lies at the bottom of a

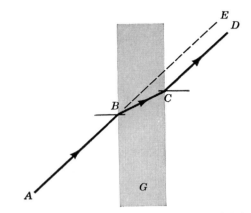

FIG. 133. Lateral displacement of a beam of light due to refraction.

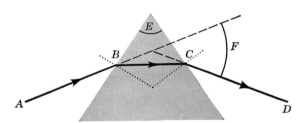

FIG. 134. Refraction of light by a prism.

FIG. 135. Convergence of light by a positive lens.

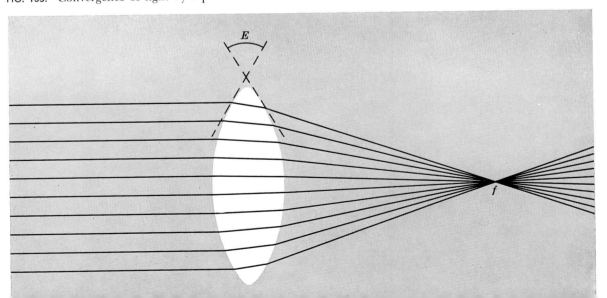

vessel of water. The cone of light rays which enters the eye makes a larger angle in air than it does in the water. But the observer, from experience, judges the source of light to be at the apex of the cone of rays which enters his eye, since this is the most common situation. The observer is thus deceived into thinking that the object B is really at B'.

The path of a ray of light through a glass plate with parallel sides is shown in Fig. 133. At each of the faces the refraction can be calculated from Snell's law, if the index of refraction of the glass is known. The path $ABCD$ is such that the emergent ray CD is parallel to the entering ray AB, and the net effect is merely to shift the ray laterally. For a thin glass plate this lateral shift is very small, and this explains why objects are not seriously distorted when seen through a windowpane. If the ray AB were incident perpendicularly, there would, of course, be no lateral shift at all.

The result is quite different, however, when a ray of light passes through a glass with nonparallel sides, such as a prism. The path $ABCD$ shown in Fig. 134 indicates that the ray has been strongly deflected from its original path AB through the angle F. The extent of this deflection depends on the angle E of the prism, the index of refraction of the glass, and the angle of incidence of the ray AB. By varying these factors we may deflect a beam of light into any direction we choose. This provides us with an excellent method for forming real images.

The *converging* or *positive* lens which is used so frequently in practical optics can be considered as a composite of very small prisms with gradually varying angles E. As shown in Fig. 135, such a system can be made to converge a number of parallel rays of light to a single common intersection or focal point f. It turns out practically that this is very nearly true if the sides of the lens are spherical. We can now understand how such a lens can be used to form a real image on a screen (Fig. 136).

A point B on the object will radiate light in all directions, but we need only consider two typical rays to locate the image. If one of these passes through the center of the thin lens, it will not be appreciably deviated and will reach the screen at B'. Another ray from B may be drawn parallel to the central axis of the lens, and this will pass through the focal point, by definition, and proceed to B', where it intersects the previous ray. The position of the screen may easily be adjusted so that it coincides with this intersection. It turns out that any ray from B which passes through the lens is refracted so that it intersects the other two approximately at B'. Since there are actual light rays falling on the screen, the luminous spot B' represents the point B faithfully in color and intensity. Every point on the object forms an image of itself on the screen from B' to A'. The image is therefore inverted and, depending on the relative object and image distances, may be either larger or smaller than the object.

FIG. 136. Formation of a real image by a positive lens.

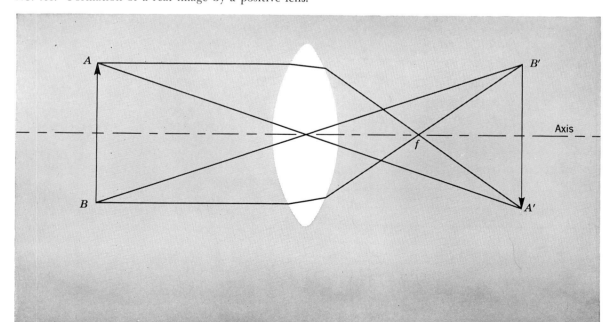

THE HUMAN EYE

The images projected on motion-picture screens are of the nature just described; so are the images formed on photographic films by camera lenses. Perhaps the most wonderful example of all is found in the human eye, in which a lens of variable focal length forms inverted real images on the retina.

The important refracting mechanism in the human eye is the crystalline lens *L* (Fig. 137). It is made up of transparent plastic cells inclosed in

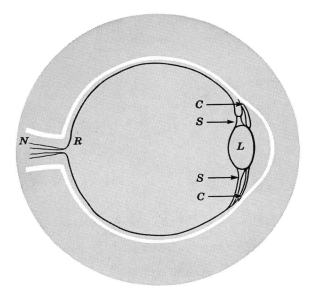

FIG. 137. The human eye.

a transparent membrane which is attached to suspensory ligaments *S*. The tension in these suspensory ligaments may be increased or relaxed by the ciliary muscles *C* arranged circularly around the inside of the eyeball. When the tension in the ligaments increases, the lens *L* flattens out and its focal length increases; when the tension is relaxed, the lens, like a liquid drop, tends to become more rounded and shortens its focal length. This focusing mechanism goes on quite automatically and enables the eye to form a sharp image on the retina *R*, which covers the inside back of the eyeball. In the retina are imbedded tiny light-sensitive organs called rods and cones, and the nerves from these sensory receivers join in a compact bundle called the optic nerve, which leaves the eye at *N*, a little off the central axis. The amazing fact is that these thousands of nerve impulses can be integrated in the brain into a reliable impression of the exterior object.

Not only do we learn to interpret an image which is upside down, but we detect subtle variations in color and intensity with extraordinary sensitivity.

DISPERSION

In Book I of the treatise which he called *Opticks,* Newton described, with extraordinary attention to detail, some experiments in which sunlight was refracted by glass prisms. Sunlight entered his darkened room through a hole *O* (Fig. 138) in the window shutter and was allowed to pass through a prism *ABC* and then to fall upon a white screen or piece of paper *S*. Upon this screen he observed the white light *dispersed* into the rainbow array of colors, or spectrum, from red to violet. If any part of the spectrum was allowed to pass through a hole *H* in the screen *S* and to fall upon a second prism, there was no further separation into any new colors. From this Newton concluded that white light was a complex mixture of many colors of light each having a different "refrangibility" or index of refraction. Since there was refraction and dispersion at each of the prism faces *AB* and *AC*, it was clear that the index of refraction increased for the spectral colors from the red end toward the violet end of the spectrum. That white light was a blend of colors was also confirmed by causing a dispersed beam to pass through a second prism inverted with respect to the first, as in Fig. 139. If the second prism was properly designed, the colored beams were reunited into a narrow beam which gave the eye the sensation of white.

The analysis of white light into colored components and their subsequent resynthesis are conclusive proofs of the composite character of white light. The eye itself is incapable of singling out the individual colors in this blend, however, until they have actually been separated. Indeed, the eye is a rather unselective instrument, and it can be deceived by a combination of two or three colors into seeing the mixture as white. Thus, if a source of yellow light and a source of blue light are arranged to project overlapping beams on a screen, that portion of the screen that receives illumination from both sources will appear white.

From the increasingly greater refraction of the red, orange, yellow, green, blue, and violet components, it is apparent that the index of refraction between air and glass is not identical for

Chaufourier del. *Herisset Sculp.*

TRAITÉ
D'OPTIQUE,
SUR
LA LUMIERE
ET LES COULEURS.

LIVRE SECOND.
TROISIE'ME PARTIE.

*Des Couleurs permanentes des Corps Naturels, & de l'a-
nalogie qui se trouve entre ces Couleurs & celles
des Plaques minces transparentes.*

E voici parvenu à une autre Par-
tie du Dessein de cet Ouvrage :
c'est d'examiner quel rapport il
y a entre les Phenomenes des
Plaques minces transparentes, &

N n ij

PLATE XXXIV. Page from the second French edition of Newton's *Opticks,* Paris, 1722. The engraving shows Newton's experiment on the dispersion of light by a prism.

light of different colors, being least for red and greatest for violet. The same is true when light passes between air and other transparent materials such as water. That medium in which the rays bend nearer to the perpendicular, for the same angle of incidence, is referred to as the *optically denser* medium. Water is optically denser than air, and glass in turn is optically denser than water. But air itself is the denser medium when compared with empty space, and light entering the earth's atmosphere obliquely across the vacuous space which separates the earth from the sun is refracted and dispersed to a small extent.

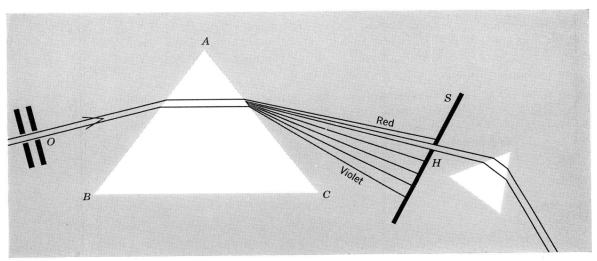

FIG. 138. Newton's experiment on the dispersion of light by a glass prism.

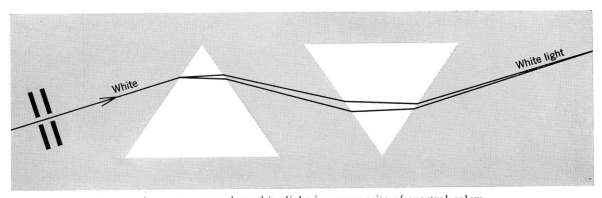

FIG. 139. Newton's experiment to prove that white light is a composite of spectral colors.

PROBLEMS

1. Using the geometry of Fig. 128, prove that the object and image distances from the mirror must be equal.

2. In Fig. 136, the thickness of the lens is supposed to be very small with respect to the object and image distances. Why is the light ray BB' through the center of the lens not appreciably deviated?

3. In Fig. 133, prove that the light rays AB and CD are parallel.

4. In old people the eye tends to become farsighted, i.e., near objects are not clearly seen. Using Fig. 136, does this mean that the crystalline lens of the eye has too short or too long a focal length? Would a positive spectacle lens help for a far-sighted eye? Explain.

5. By studying Fig. 136, answer the following questions: (*a*) How does the position of the image $A'B'$ change when the object AB recedes from the lens? (*b*) How does the size of the image change as the object AB recedes from the lens? (*c*) Can you see a simple geometrical relation between distances and sizes of the object and image? (*d*) What happens to the image when AB gets very close to the lens?

. . . .

REFERENCE

1. *A Source Book in Physics*, W. F. Magie, McGraw-Hill Book Co., 1935, pp. 265–280, 298–308, and 335–344.

Theories of Light

In Chapter 24, the description of certain light phenomena such as reflection, refraction, and dispersion supplied no hint as to the nature of light itself. Let us now consider some attempts at theoretical explanation of these observed facts.

THE CORPUSCULAR THEORY

Numerous hypotheses concerning the mechanism of light propagation have been proposed, two of which developed into theories which were able to account for some of the familiar properties of light in a reasonable manner. We shall therefore consider in some detail the corpuscular theory and the wave theory of light. The former assumes that incandescent bodies eject particles or corpuscles of light energy like a machine gun discharging bullets. The corpuscles move outward from the source in all directions in straight paths and at enormous speed. When they encounter a reflecting surface, the corpuscles rebound, whereas translucent materials allow the corpuscles to penetrate them.

What of the quantitative laws of reflection and refraction according to this hypothesis? Isaac Newton, who is generally believed to have advocated the corpuscular theory, although his writings show that he was not entirely satisfied with it, tried to account for reflection and refraction by the following arguments.

REFLECTION

Let a stream of light corpuscles impinge obliquely on a smooth, opaque surface. The opaque surface repels the light in the same way that a hard, elastic plate would seem to repel a hail of steel balls. In Fig. 140, such a ball is shown about to collide with the plate. The velocity of the ball is here represented by an oblique arrow. Mechanical experience tells us that the oblique velocity is equivalent to the combination of two smaller velocities—one perpendicular to the plate and one tangent to it as shown, the two forming sides of a rectangle which has the oblique arrow as its diagonal. In other words, the ball is actually moving to the right and downward simultaneously with speeds which, properly compounded, are equivalent to the oblique speed of the missile.

If the collision is elastic, mechanical experience also teaches us that the tangential part of the velocity is unaffected, but that the perpendicular part is reversed, as indicated in the diagram at the right. The combination of these two velocities again gives a diagonal velocity, this time away from the plate, thus accounting for the reflection of the ball at an angle equal to the incident angle. Note that the angles labeled i and r are the angles of incidence and reflection.

According to this explanation, the reflection of light is governed by the same principle as the one which operates in the reflection of a billiard ball when it strikes a cushion.

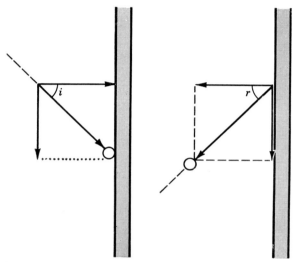

FIG. 140. Newton's theory for the reflection of light corpuscles.

REFRACTION

The refraction which a beam of light undergoes on striking the surface of a plate of glass was explained by Newton on the assumption that glass attracts light. Suppose a stream of light corpuscles to be directed at a glass surface as shown in Fig. 141. At the left the velocity of a single corpuscle is again represented by an oblique arrow. The perpendicular and tangential components of the velocity are drawn at the point where the corpuscle is about to enter the glass.

Now, if the corpuscle is attracted by the glass, the effect must be to increase the perpendicular part of the velocity without influencing the tangential part, and in the right-hand diagram we represent this increase by adding a small vertical arrow to the original one. But if the resultant velocity of the light particle is obtained as before by drawing the diagonal of a rectangle having the increased vertical velocity and the unchanged tangential velocity as sides, this resultant diagonal will be not only longer but steeper than the corresponding arrow of the left-hand figure.

Accordingly, the path of the light corpuscles through glass must be more nearly perpendicular to the glass surface than their incident path through the air was. Moreover, the speed of the light corpuscles in glass must be greater than their speed in air.

The first of these consequences is in obvious agreement with experience. A ray of light passing obliquely from air into glass or from air into water, is, in fact, bent so as to take a steeper path. Nevertheless, a thoughtful student will immediately wonder how glass, for example, which simultaneously reflects part of the impinging light and transmits the remainder, can at the same time repel those corpuscles which are reflected and attract those which are transmitted.

The second consequence of Newton's hypothesis provides the idea for a crucial experiment. If light actually travels through glass or water faster than it does through empty space or through air, it should be possible to settle the issue by direct measurement of the speed of light in various media. Newton's assumption that light had a greater speed in water and glass than it had in air may have been prompted by his

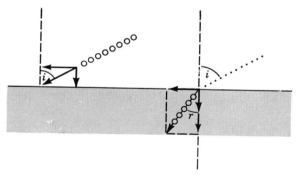

FIG. 141. Newton's theory for the refraction of light corpuscles.

knowledge that sound travels more than four times as fast through water and about fifteen times as fast through glass as it does through air.

THE SPEED OF LIGHT; MICHELSON'S METHOD

The speed of light has been determined by several methods since Roemer's time. It is generally conceded that one of the most accurate values is that obtained by the American physicist Albert Michelson (1852–1931) in experiments conducted by him from 1878 to 1927. Michelson used a rotating mirror of eight sides and subsequently a rotating prism of thirty-two sides to reflect a beam of light to a distant fixed mirror, which reflected the light back again to another face of the rotating prism. The essentials of Michelson's original apparatus, as shown in Fig. 142, are almost self-explanatory.

Although the fundamental character of the light does not matter, the experimental principle is most easily understood if we imagine the light to consist of little corpuscles. Let us follow the journey of any one corpuscle as it leaves the

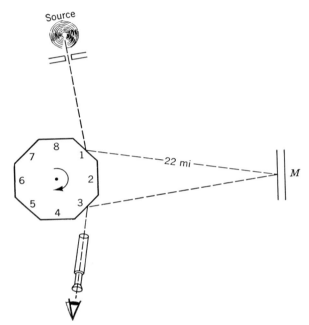

FIG. 142. Michelson's method for determining the speed of light.

upper aperture and strikes face 1 of the octagonal mirror. After reflection from this face it travels outward to the distant mirror M, 22 mi away, and back again, returning to face 3, from which it is reflected into the observer's telescope. If the octagonal mirror has rotated a little during the 44-mi trip, the returning corpuscle will still be reflected from face 3 but not along the axis of the telescope. If, however, the octagon is turning fast enough to bring face 2 into the position of face 3 by the time the light corpuscle returns, then the observer will receive it at the center of his eyepiece. What has been described for one particle will, of course, be true of the entire beam of light. The calculation is extremely simple. Suppose the mirror had to be spun at 530 rps in order to bring about the result described. Then $\frac{1}{8}$ of $\frac{1}{530}$ of a second, or 0.000236

sec, elapses while the light is making a 44-mi journey. Hence the speed of light through air is

$$c = \frac{44}{0.000236} = 186,000 \text{ mps or } 3 \times 10^{10} \text{ cm/sec}$$

Later Michelson determined the speed of light in vacuum and found it to be only slightly more than its speed through air.

THE SPEED OF LIGHT THROUGH WATER

Earlier, in 1850, the French physicist Foucault had determined the speed of light through water and found it to be only $\frac{3}{4}$ as great as the speed through air. Foucault used a rotating mirror having only one reflecting face, and the total path allowed for the light beam in his experiments was only a few meters. Nevertheless, with extraordinary skill, he measured the angle between the outgoing beam and the returning deflected beam as the datum needed for calculating the speed of light. A long cylinder of water placed between the fixed and the rotating mirrors compelled the light to make practically its entire round trip through water.

These experimental results are clearly inconsistent with the simple Newtonian explanation of refraction in terms of corpuscles.

THE WAVE THEORY

Considerably before Newton's optical investigations, it had been supposed by some that light traveled away from a luminous source as a train of *waves*. Newton himself considered this alternative, but was apparently unable to accept it for the reason that the edges of opaque objects seem to cut off light sharply and cast geometrically simple shadows. Now an obstacle in the path of *water* waves does not block the passage of the water waves effectively. They simply bend around the object, the fragments of the intercepted wave front rejoining on the other side of the obstacle and proceeding onward almost as if no interruption had occurred. Sound energy, which is also known to be transmitted in waves, is likewise relatively indifferent to obstacles. Sound produced in one room can be heard distinctly by listeners in an adjoining room even though they are in the geometrical shadow of the wall and the sound must bend around one or more corners in order to reach them. In other words, the straight-line propagation of light, by which the region behind an opaque object remains unilluminated, seems at first thought to be at variance with an assumption that light travels in waves.

It will be shown presently that there is really no inconsistency in attributing a wave character to light, that light *does,* in fact, bend slightly around opaque obstacles so that the shadows of such obstacles are actually not sharply bounded.

GENERAL WAVE PROPERTIES

It is a common observation that when a quiet water surface is suddenly disturbed, circular

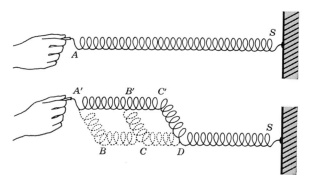

FIG. 143. Transmission of a pulse along a spring.

waves travel outward from the source of the disturbance. It is perhaps not so commonly observed that there is no transfer of water progressively in the direction of the wave movement. If some fragments of cork are strewn on the water, they will be seen to experience only up and down motions and to have no tendency to move progressively with the waves. This characteristic of waves may perhaps best be illustrated by considering how a wave is set up in a simpler medium.

Suppose the long wire spring of Fig. 143 to be held by the hand at A and fastened firmly to a rigid support at S. Suddenly the hand is moved

up from A to A'. The part of the spring very near A' must, of course, follow the upward movement of the hand, but the parts not so near, having inertia, resist motion, and the spring stretches in the region from A' to B. This stretch exerts a force on the parts of the spring near B, and they begin to move upward toward B'. In moving upward, the spring must stretch in the region $B'C$ and this causes parts of the spring near C to begin moving upward also. All of this takes time, however, because the parts of the spring are reluctant to move. The entire spring does not stretch at once, and no section will rise until the section just left of it is stretched. The result is that the original kink $A'B$, produced by the sudden upward movement of the hand, travels to $B'C$, $C'D$, and so on until it reaches the rigid support S. Here the stretch in the spring cannot move the support S, hence the stretch produces a backward pulse of the spring toward A'. In other words, the kink in the spring is reflected at the rigid support. If the hand is now held rigid, the kink is reflected also at A' and it is possible to observe several reflections backwards and forwards across the length of the spring. Eventually friction causes the movement to die out.

A little thought will make it clear that the velocity with which the kink travels will depend on at least two factors:

1. The stiffness of the spring.
2. The mass per unit length of the spring.

The stiffer the spring, the larger will be the velocity; the more massive the spring is per unit length, the lower will be the velocity.

If now the hand is moved up and down regularly, a series of kinks will travel down the spring as shown in Fig. 144. The distance between neighboring crests is called the wave length, usually represented by the Greek letter λ (lambda).

FIG. 144. Transmission of a transverse wave along a spring.

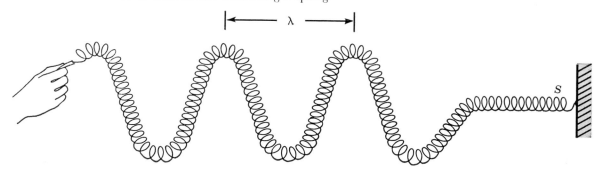

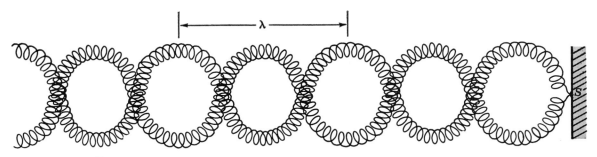

FIG. 145.   A standing wave.

When these regular waves are reflected from the support S, the sum of the two displacements in the spring form a pattern called a standing wave, as shown in Fig. 145, provided the wave length is such that one-half of a wave is contained a whole number of times in the length of the spring.

The kind of wave we have just described is called a *transverse* wave. In such waves the parts of the medium vibrate at right angles to the direction of propagation. Such *mechanical* waves cannot be transmitted through liquids or gases because fluids have no transverse forces comparable to those of the spring in the previous cases. But another kind of wave motion is possible.

Suppose that the experimenter takes hold of the spring at B as in Fig. 146 and pulls it toward his other stationary hand at A. When B is now released, a compressional pulse will then be transmitted down the spring and will be reflected at the support S. The explanation is the same as before except that the parts of the spring now vibrate back and forth in the same direction as that of propagation. Such waves are said to be *longitudinal* or *compressional,* and they can be transmitted through liquids and gases as well as through solids. Sound waves are of this nature.

In order to discuss waves with efficiency and clarity we need to add a few new words to our scientific vocabulary.

Phase. Two particles are said to be in the same phase if they are in the same relative positions in the vibrational cycle. In Fig. 147, A and A', B and B', and C and C' are, by pairs, in the same phase. Two waves are said to be in phase with each other if the parts of each wave which are in the same phase coincide in space.

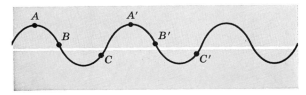

FIG. 147. A and A' are in the same phase.   So are B and B' and C and C'.

Wave Length. The distance between any two particles in the same phase is called the wave length. The distance between successive wave crests conforms to this definition and is perhaps the most convenient designation of wave length.

Frequency. The number of cycles completed by a particle of the medium in 1 sec is known as the frequency (f) of the waves. This is evidently the same as the frequency with which the original disturbance at the source occurs. Moreover, the greater the frequency at which a disturbance is generated, the closer together will be the ensuing wave crests and hence the shorter the wave length.

FIG. 146.   A compressional wave is started along the spring.

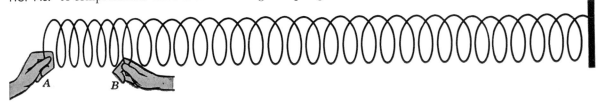

Frequency and wave length are thus proportional to each other in the inverse sense.

Speed. Suppose that the disturbance which generates the waves occurs 20 times each second at the source. Then by the end of 1 sec the first wave produced will be 20 wave lengths away from the source. If each wave is 50 cm long, the disturbance has evidently traveled $20 \times 50 = 1000$ cm during this second. But the distance traveled in 1 sec is the *speed* of the waves. The

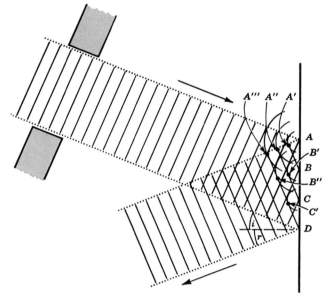

FIG. 148. Reflection of a plane wave according to Huygens' principle.

speed in this example is consequently 1000 cm per second.

In general, if f is the frequency and λ the wave length, the speed, V, of any wave is:

$$V = f\lambda$$

Note that this is *not* the velocity of the particles comprising the medium. It is only the *configuration* of particles which moves along at the rate V. Each particle remains in its own neighborhood notwithstanding the steady advance of the disturbance.

Amplitude. As particles of the medium through which waves are moving go through their various phases, the amount of displacement of each particle from its normal position depends upon its phase. The *maximum* displacement, i.e., the displacement which forms the peak of a crest or the base of a trough, is called the

amplitude of the wave. Waves of large amplitude convey more energy than do waves of small amplitude. In the case of sound waves, large amplitude signifies greater loudness; in the case of light waves, large amplitude signifies greater brightness.

We are now prepared to attempt explanations of a few phenomena on the assumption that light consists of waves rather than particles.

REFLECTION

If the source of any train of waves is a point, the wave crests may be regarded as a series of concentric spheres extending outward from this point. As the waves get more remote from the source, their curvature diminishes until it is so nearly negligible that any small portion of a wave front is practically plane, just as the earth's surface over a short range is practically plane.

Suppose a train of such plane waves to pass through an opening and approach a flat reflecting surface, as represented in Fig. 148. When the foremost wave front strikes the flat surface, reflection occurs, like the reflection of the kink in the spring at the rigid support. According to a principle first enunciated by Christian Huygens (1629–1695),

all points on a wave front behave as if they were sources of the same periodic disturbance which brought them into being and, if the wavelets emanating from such points are joined by a continuous tangential surface, this surface is also a wave front.

Let us apply Huygens' principle and determine whether or not it is consistent with experimental facts. Thus, for the case represented in Fig. 148, point A, where the incident wave first strikes the reflector, becomes a source of waves proceeding toward the left. By the time a wavelet from A has reached position A', another point B of the reflector has been struck, and this also becomes a source of reflected wavelets. When the lower edge of the advancing wave has struck the point D, the wavelets reflected from A, B, and C have reached positions A''', B'', and C' respectively, and a tangent drawn to these wavelets specifies the location of the reflected wave front. In actuality, the points A, B, C, and D lie extremely close to each other, so that the reflected wave front is quite smooth. Reflected waves move backward in a direction such that the angle of reflection equals the angle of incidence, a relation which can be established by simple geometry.

This is a law of reflection which we have already found to be true for light, thus strengthening our belief in the validity of Huygens' principle. Later we shall encounter additional experimental proof.

REFRACTION

In explaining refraction by the wave theory, we have to assume that light slows down when it passes from air into a denser medium, such as glass or water. Newton had to assume the op-

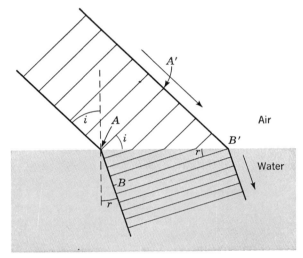

FIG. 149. Refraction, according to the wave theory.

posite—a speeding up—in his attempt to account for refraction by the corpuscular theory.

Imagine a train of plane light waves moving obliquely toward a water surface as represented in Fig. 149. As each part of the wave front enters the water, it is retarded and consequently forced into a new direction which is more nearly perpendicular to the surface than the incident direction was. This is precisely what happens when a platoon of marching soldiers wheels into a new direction while attempting to preserve its alignment. Their change in direction requires that the man at the pivot, and subsequently the men next to him, slow down until the entire front has swung into the new direction.

THE INDEX OF REFRACTION

By simple geometry we can show that the ratio between the sines of the incident and the refraction angles is the same as the ratio between the speed of light in air and the speed of light in water.

Let AA' be a wave crest which is about to leave the air, and let BB' be the same wave crest after it has entered the water. Then $A'B'$ is the distance traversed in air by one end of the wave during the same time that the other end of the wave has moved a distance AB into the water. Since speed is distance divided by time, the ratio between the speed of light in air and the speed of light in water (using the symbols V for speed and t for time) must be

$$\frac{V_a}{V_w} = \frac{A'B'/t}{AB/t} = \frac{A'B'}{AB}$$

But note that the incident angle (i) and the refraction angle (r) have their respective counterparts in angles $A'AB'$ and $BB'A$. We can therefore represent the ratio $A'B'/AB$ as

$$\frac{A'B'/AB'}{AB/AB'} \qquad \text{which is the ratio} \qquad \frac{\sin i}{\sin r}$$

Finally, since the index of refraction is the ratio of these sines, we have

$$\text{Index of refraction} = \frac{\sin i}{\sin r} = \frac{V_a}{V_w}$$

Alternatively, the explanation of refraction can be given in terms of Huygens' principle, which states that any point on a wave front may be regarded as a fresh source of waves. In Fig. 150, choosing points such as A, B, C, D on any one of the wave fronts advancing through air as point sources of light, we draw arcs of equal radius, using each of the points as a center. The common tangent to these arcs marks the new wave front in air an instant later. This process is continued for subsequent instants of like duration until one edge of the beam has reached the water surface at A'. During the next equal instant a wavelet constructed about B' in the air will extend to B'', but a wavelet constructed in the water with A' as its center will extend only to a, where $A'a$ is ¾ the length of $B'B''$. This is because we know by actual measurement that the speed of light in water, V_w, is ¾ the speed of light in air, V_a.

As successive points on the original wave front reach the boundary at C'' and D'', these points become centers of shorter wavelets in the water. The tangents drawn to the wavelets in water mark the new wave front of the light beam as it proceeds through the water. Just as in the previous explanation, the incident angle exceeds the refraction angle and the ratio of their sines is the ratio of the velocities in the two media.

DISPERSION ACCORDING TO THE WAVE THEORY

We have been leading up to the most interesting property of white light, namely, its dispersion into colored components. When a beam of white light enters any translucent body whose boundaries are not parallel, it always emerges in a dispersed condition and produces a colored spectrum on the other side. The various components of white light undergo refraction in different degrees, the violet component most and the red component least. We shall see presently that the wave length of violet light is considerably less than that of red light, and that orange, yellow, green, and blue light all have wave lengths intermediate between these extremes. Since refraction, according to the wave theory, is due to the slowing down of light as it passes from one medium into an optically denser medium, it must follow that the speed of violet light is even less than that of red light in translucent substances. This inference has been confirmed by experiment.

Let us pause to review some of the points for and against the rival theories of light. If we take the hypothesis that a ray of light is a swift procession of corpuscles, the phenomena already described are explainable only on the assumption that light moves with greater speed through optically dense materials like glass and water than it does through optically rare ones like air, or through space devoid of matter. Since the assumption about its relative speed is incorrect by experimental proof, the corpuscular hypothesis fails. There is the further objection, pointed out by Huygens, that light beams from two sources can cross without disturbing each other —a fact impossible to reconcile with the corpuscular hypothesis. Alternatively, if we take the hypothesis that a ray of light represents a wavelike disturbance moving rapidly through a medium, there are still certain objections to be overcome. Two of those raised by Newton have been answered satisfactorily:

(1) If light travels in waves, how can it persist in straight paths when some opaque barrier cuts off part of the beam? In Fig. 151, the edges of the opening cast a sharply bounded shadow on the screen beyond. Waves on the surface of water, Fig. 152, or sound waves passing through air, habitually bend around obstacles which they cannot penetrate and spread into the region of shadow.

The answer depends on the experimental fact now known, that the wave lengths of light are extremely short—a few hundred-thousandths of a centimeter. Very short waves do undergo slight spreading around the edges of an obstacle. For a clearly noticeable effect, however, the aperture through which they pass must be very small—of a size comparable with their small wave length.

(2) Newton's second objection was due to a general misconception that prevailed in his day.

FIG. 150. Refraction explained by Huygens' principle.

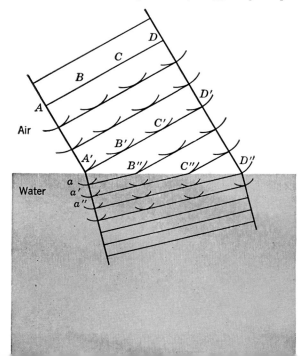

FIG. 151. A circular aperture seems to form a cone of light with sharp boundary.

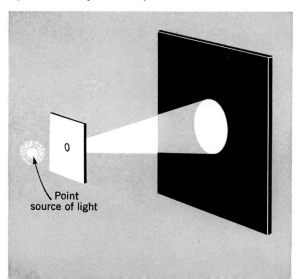

Point source of light

It was commonly supposed by the proponents of the wave theory that light waves were longitudinal like those of sound. That is to say, a train of waves was thought to be a succession of com-

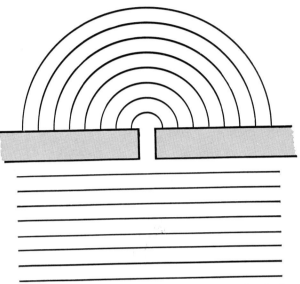

FIG. 152. Water waves tend to spread into the shadow.

pressed and rarefied regions in the medium which carried the disturbance.

POLARIZATION

But light is capable of *polarization,* as Newton and his contemporaries knew, and this capability is impossible in longitudinal waves like those of sound. Polarization of light is now familiar to everyone through the modern material called Polaroid. This material consists of translucent sheets in which millions of tiny crystals have been imbedded, nearly all of them oriented in the same direction. When two such sheets are held parallel to each other in front of a light source, an observer can see the source through them if the crystal axes in both sheets happen to be aligned in the same way. If either sheet is rotated, however, the view of the light source is gradually diminished until, after a 90° rota-

tion, it is practically obliterated. Many crystals produce the same effect on light. The explanation of this remarkable behavior was first offered by the French scientist Augustin Fresnel (1788–1827). Let us assume that light consists of waves in which the crests and troughs are perpendicular to the direction of advance, like the waves first described in a spring. Figure 153 represents two such transverse wave trains with the displacements in one train all at right angles to those in the other.

It is evident that a grating of vertical bars set astride this combination would permit the vertical vibrations to pass and prevent the horizontal ones from doing so. In optical terminology we would say that the composite wave was *polarized* by the grating.

A beam of light is thought to consist similarly of transverse waves with the vibrations occurring

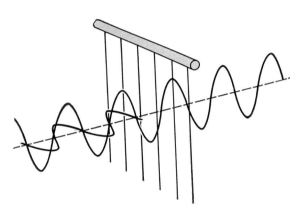

FIG. 153. Polarization of transverse waves.

not just in two but in many planes perpendicular to the direction of advance. When such a composite beam impinges on a crystal of the type whose molecules form an optical grating, only those vibrations which are parallel to the grating can get through. The beam is thereby polarized. If the transmitted polarized light now encounters a second crystal which lies at right angles to the first, it cannot pass and the beam is extinguished.

PROBLEMS

1. When a beam of light moves from one medium to another of different index of refraction, which of the factors (velocity, frequency, wave length) change?

2. Sound is known to travel through air with a speed of about 1100 fps. What is the wave length of a sound having a frequency of 550 vibrations per second?

3. Refraction of sunlight by the earth's atmosphere extends the hours of daylight a little. Show by a drawing how plane waves from the sun are retarded by the atmosphere so as to cause such a refraction.

4. Suppose a glass prism to be totally immersed in water. If a beam of white light is now incident on the prism, will the refraction and dispersion of the white light be greater or smaller than if the prism had been in air? Explain. Will the focal length of a positive glass lens be increased or decreased if used when completely immersed in water?

5. Polaroid is used in photography and other applications to cut out reflected light from shiny surfaces. What can you conclude about the nature of light reflected from such surfaces?

6. Draw a diagram to show how the position of a star is distorted owing to refraction by the earth's atmosphere.

·   ·

REFERENCE

1. *A Source Book in Physics,* W. F. Magie, McGraw-Hill Book Co., 1935, pp. 283–294.

Some Important Light Phenomena

THE AETHER

With Newton's objections answered by experiment, is there any remaining reason to withhold acceptance of the wave theory? Later we shall present evidence that there is. Meanwhile let us consider a very serious gap in the picture. What is the medium by which light is transmitted through empty space? Water waves, sound waves, and all other energy transfers that we know with certainty to be wavelike consist of oscillations in some material medium. To many physicists it seemed inconceivable that any wave disturbance which was transmitted hand to hand, as it were, over great distances at a large but finite speed, could propagate itself through space that was entirely empty. Adherents of the wave theory of light have always been troubled by the apparent absence of a wave-carrying medium, and so they invented one. Borrowing a term of Aristotle's, they assumed all space to be filled with a highly rarefied substance which they called the *aether*. This "aether," which was supposed also to pervade all matter, was the hypothetical medium by which light waves were transmitted.

There were serious inconsistencies in the now-discarded aether concept. Notwithstanding its supposedly pervasive character, it defied all attempts to detect it, even by the most ingenious and delicate experiments. Worse than that, the aether had to be assigned a set of highly contradictory properties. If it could pervade solid matter such as glass, it had to be exceedingly light and tenuous, especially as it apparently offered no resistance to the passage of bodies through it. The best vacuum pump could not remove it from a vessel. Yet, in order to transmit waves with the enormous speed of light, it had to be more elastic than steel and, indeed, to be like a rigid solid, for fluids do not have the kind of elasticity that allows transverse waves to pass through them. Since there is no experimental evidence that any such medium as the aether exists, scientists have somewhat reluctantly abandoned the concept.

DIFFRACTION OF LIGHT

There remain to be described two other properties of light that are explainable by the wave hypothesis alone. Suppose a train of plane waves proceeding across a smooth body of water encounters a small opening in a wall (see Fig. 152). After the disturbance has passed through this aperture, it is seen to have changed its pattern. The wave crests, which formed a series of parallel lines before, now emerge as a set of concentric arcs diverging from the opening. Instead of advancing in just one direction from the wall, the waves now expand in all directions as if the opening were a point source at which the disturbance originated. This is the phenomenon of *diffraction*. Light always exhibits diffraction when it passes through a very small opening.

INTERFERENCE

Now suppose that the wall has in it two small openings close together. Each wave will now undergo diffraction after passing through the

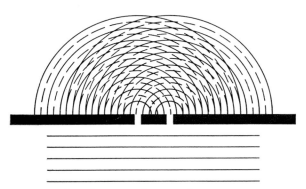

FIG. 154.   Interference of waves from two apertures.

openings. But the two diffracted wave trains must overlap each other, and we notice a result which is of the greatest importance. In Fig. 154, continuous lines represent wave crests and broken lines represent wave troughs. Wherever the wave crests of one train cross those of the other, there forms a crest larger than the normal height. Similarly, wherever the troughs of each train intersect, there is a deeper trough than before. But at those points where a crest of one train meets a trough of the other train, there is no agitation of the water at all! The water, which is being urged upward by the disturbance advancing from one opening, is simultaneously urged downward by the disturbance advancing from the other. This is the phenomenon of *interference*, and it is possible only in the case of energy which is being transmitted in *waves*. A demonstration of interference calls to mind the age-old question: "Do not 2 and 2 always make 4?" To which our answer must be: "No; if one is +2 and the other is −2, they make zero."

Interference between water waves is very easily

demonstrated. Let a wide, shallow pan, preferably dark colored, be partially filled with water. With the first two fingers of one hand touch the smooth surface of the water at rapid, equal intervals. The overlapping ripples will show a pattern of interference quite distinctly.

In 1801–1803 the English physician Thomas Young (1773–1829) announced the results of similar experiments performed with light. A modification of his earliest experiment will be described first, for Young used sunlight, which is a blend of many components and therefore more complex in behavior than light of a single color. Suppose then that a source of green light S is placed behind an aperture in a screen (Fig. 155), beyond which is a second screen parallel to it and perforated by two very narrow, vertical slits. Still further from the light source stands a third screen to receive the images. It is necessary to have a single source of light to make this experiment succeed. The room is darkened.

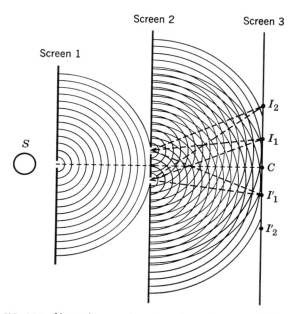

FIG. 155.   Young's experiment on interference of light.

Now, although the middle of the third screen, through C, lies in the geometric shadow of the opaque section between the slits of screen 2, a bright green line appears at this place. Only if light consists of waves is this to be expected, since a line through C is equidistant from the slits, so that two wave trains which are in the same phase at the slits must arrive in phase with each other at C. Hence they reinforce each other at C and produce a brighter line than a single slit would have yielded. Reinforcement of the light waves does not demand that both disturbances necessarily travel the same distance, however. Any point on screen 3 so situated that waves from the two apertures arrive there in the same phase will also receive reinforced illumination. Thus, at places like I_1 and I'_1 there will be other bright images. As the diagram shows, each is receiving two wave crests simultaneously, as it will receive all subsequent crests and troughs simultaneously. That one train is always a full wave behind the other train at such points does not hinder the reinforcing process. The same reasoning applies to I_2 and I'_2, where another pair of green lines appears. This time the waves of one train are reinforced by waves of the other which are two wave lengths behind them.

It should be equally clear that the spaces halfway between the bright lines are dark because the waves arriving from the two slits interfere destructively and cancel each other. At such points crests and troughs will be superimposed.

DETERMINATION OF WAVE LENGTH

It is apparent that the diffraction images enable us to calculate the wave length of the light used in this experiment. Consider Fig. 156 show-

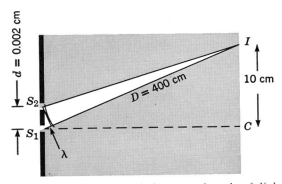

FIG. 156. Measurement of the wave length of light.

ing only the central image at C and the first diffraction image at I. Reinforcement occurs at I because that point is just one wave length further from slit S_1 than it is from slit S_2. With I as a center and a radius of length IS_2, construct a short arc cutting off equal distances on IS_2 and IS_1. The residual distance, IS_1-IS_2, must be the desired wave length λ. A tangent to the arc forms a small right triangle similar to the large right triangle CIS_1. Since the sides of the two similar triangles are mutually proportional, we

can easily compute the value of λ. Using the figures which appear on the diagram,

$$\frac{\lambda}{d} = \frac{CI}{D}$$

therefore

$$\lambda = \frac{0.002 \times 10}{400} = 5 \times 10^{-5} \text{ cm}$$

When violet light is used, the diffraction images fall closer to the central one at C; hence the wave length of violet light is shorter. The shortest visible violet light proves to have a wave length of about 4×10^{-5} cm. When red light is used, the diffraction images fall farther from the central one and the wave length is accordingly known to be greater. The longest visible red light has a wave length of about 7×10^{-5} cm.

DIFFRACTION GRATINGS

In actual laboratory determinations of wave length the light is never sent through just two slits; the resulting images would then be entirely too faint. Instead, a grating of several thousand narrow slits is customarily used. Such a grating is made by ruling lines on a slab of glass at equal but very short distances. In the example just worked out there would have to be 500 lines per centimeter in order to provide apertures of 0.002 cm between every pair of lines. When placed in the path of a luminous beam, the grating allows light to pass only between the rulings, which are themselves opaque. Gratings are also made by ruling lines on bright, metallic surfaces so that light directed at such a surface undergoes reflection only from the equally spaced, unruled portions.

Mechanical difficulties prevent the ruling of diffraction gratings with spaces narrower than about 0.0001 cm, but it is interesting to speculate on the effect of continually decreasing the interval between adjacent slits. From the foregoing numerical example, we see that the distance CI must increase as d becomes smaller. If d could become as small as λ, then λ and d would no longer form sides of a triangle at all and the diffraction image would fail to appear on the screen. In other words, diffraction images vanish when the obstacle to the light waves approaches the same length as the light wave itself. Obstacles of such small size are ineffectual in changing the course of the waves, just as a slim, upright pole is unable to change the course of water waves. But it is by the effect of an object on impinging light that we are able to see the object. Hence we conclude that particles as small as the wave length of light, or smaller (i.e., a few hundred-thousandths of a centimeter in diameter), must be invisible to the eye. There is excellent evidence that atoms are about a thousand times smaller than this, and so it seems as if we must abandon the hope of detecting individual atoms by optical means.

INFRARED AND ULTRAVIOLET SPECTRA

Considering the enormous range of wave lengths which radiant energy can have, the human eye is extraordinarily limited in its range of sensitivity. The radiation emitted by the sun includes wave lengths from about a millionth of a centimeter up to a few hundredths of a centimeter, the greatest being more than 10,000 times as long as the smallest. Yet red light, with the longest waves in the visible spectrum (about 7.5×10^{-5} cm), has less than twice the wave length of violet light, which has the shortest waves in the visible spectrum (about 4×10^{-5} cm). Beyond this narrow range are the infrared radiation at the longer end and the ultraviolet radiation at the shorter end. Infrared radiation was first reported in 1800 by Sir William Herschel, the astronomer who discovered the planet Uranus. He noticed that a thermometer bulb held in the region beyond the visible red end of a solar spectrum showed a marked rise in temperature. The faculty of undergoing conversion into thermal energy when it strikes matter is the outstanding characteristic of infrared radiation. Because of it infrared radiation is often called radiant heat. It was Herschel who found, too, that a prism cut from rock salt was much more satisfactory than a glass prism for separating infrared radiation from the other varieties of radiant energy arriving from the sun.

Beyond the violet end of the solar spectrum is the extended range of ultraviolet radiation—the short wave energy that is responsible for numerous chemical changes, especially in living organisms. First reported in 1801 by the German chemist Ritter (1776–1810), it was much more completely revealed in 1842 in a photograph of the sun's spectrum made by the French physicist Edmond Becquerel (1820–1903). Ultraviolet radiation, although invisible to the eye, acts even more energetically than visible light does on photographic emulsions. Nowadays the therapeutic claims for ultraviolet light are well known.

LINE SPECTRA

We have already referred to the solar spectrum as a continuous spectrum because each color band merges gradually into the adjacent one, so that no boundaries between them are detectable. White-hot solids, like the filament of an electric lamp, yield the same continuous spectrum. But if the spectrum of the sun is examined carefully, it will be found to have a great many thin, dark lines distributed through it, each at a particular place and hence corresponding to a unique wave length (Plate XXXV). These thin stripes, which are known as Fraunhofer lines, constitute what is called an *absorption spectrum,* and their origin will be explained farther on (p. 271). There are thousands of these lines, several hundred of which were first observed in about 1814 by the German optician Joseph Fraunhofer (1787–1826).

EMISSION SPECTRA

Of particular importance to the investigation of atomic structure are the line spectra obtained from incandescent gases. Chemically similar elements emit line spectra which show certain similarities—a sure indication that from an elemental spectrum we may hope to obtain some clue as to the constitution of the atoms themselves. It is common knowledge that, if a volatile salt of

PLATE XXXV. Part of the Fraunhofer, or absorption, spectrum of the sun.

Mount Wilson and Palomar Observatories

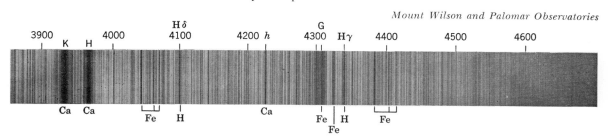

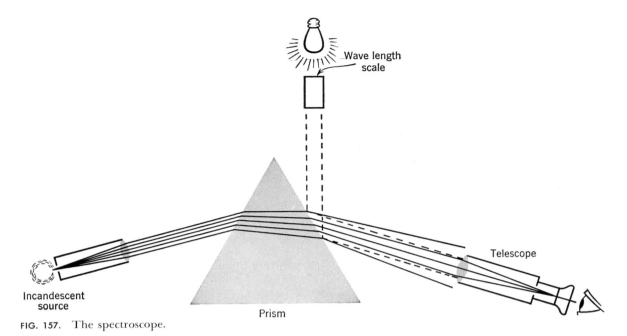

FIG. 157. The spectroscope.

certain metals such as copper, strontium, sodium, or potassium is placed in a flame, the flame emits a distinctively colored light: green for copper, red for strontium, yellow for sodium, violet for potassium. Such flame colorations have long been used as quick tests for detecting the elements responsible for them. Much more reliable information is obtainable, however, by analyzing the colored light with the aid of a spectroscope. This is a very useful instrument which was invented by two eminent German chemists, G. R. Kirchhoff (1824–1887) and R. W. Bunsen (1811–1899). Its essential parts are illustrated in Fig. 157, which shows the light of an incandescent vapor being dispersed by a triangular glass prism into a number of colored lines, which appear at different places in the field of view of the observing telescope. The image of a scale is usually projected into the telescope also, by means of which the observer can read directly the wave lengths of the colored lines. With a chart showing the principal lines in the emission spectrum of any element and their corresponding wave lengths, the spectroscopist can identify the elements in an incandescent vapor even when several elements are present in a mixture or a chemical combination. Moreover, the characteristic lines appear when the merest trace of the element responsible is present.

The value of the spectroscope in original investigation is illustrated in the discovery of rubidium and cesium by Bunsen and Kirchhoff, who first detected the hitherto unknown spectral lines of these elements in 1860–1861 with the aid of this instrument. The discovery by Lockyer in 1878 of helium in the spectrum of the sun has already been mentioned (p. 185).

THE HYDROGEN SPECTRUM

In order to understand the significance of spectral lines in revealing the structure of matter we need to study some one elemental spectrum in detail. Since hydrogen is the lightest element, its atoms are presumably the simplest of all atoms, and it seems reasonable to choose the spectrum of hydrogen as the starting point for our exploration. In describing the discharge of electricity through elemental gases at low pressure, we recall that one of the attendant phenomena was the rich glow of colored light emitted by the gas. That this luminosity is due to the gas rather than to the cathode ray electrons becomes certain when we use different elemental gases and obtain light of different colors. Furthermore, this light becomes steadily fainter as more and more of the gas is pumped from the tube.

When the gas remaining at low pressure is hydrogen, the spectrum shows a red, a blue, and numerous violet lines whose wave lengths are approximately as follows:

6.562×10^{-5} cm	Red	Hydrogen alpha line
4.861	Blue	Hydrogen beta line
4.340	Violet	Hydrogen gamma line
4.101	Violet	Hydrogen delta line

(and many other closely placed lines beyond the hydrogen delta)

Examining the spectral lines with regard to spacing rather than color, one is struck by a certain regularity in their distribution (Plate XXXVI). As the wave lengths become shorter, the lines crowd closer and closer together in a way that suggests a pattern of some kind. If there is such a pattern, it must be representable by an equation. In seeking such an equation, we might start with the formula that applies to related musical notes. If a violin string is bowed so as to emit simultaneously two notes an octave apart, the sound waves which carry these notes are found to have wave lengths in the ratio 2:1. Every doubling of the frequency or halving of the wave length produces a rise in pitch of one octave. If we try such a rule on the lines of the hydrogen spectrum, say, by assuming the successive wave lengths to be representable by K, $\frac{1}{2}K$, $\frac{1}{4}K$, $\frac{1}{8}K$, etc., we see at once that there is no agreement with the facts, for each wave length is much more than half the next longer one. Letting the frequencies increase in some simple ratio proves to be no better. In the course of our groping for a formula, we might hit on the device of expressing each relative frequency in terms of the *difference* between a constant and a series of decreasing numbers, and, with a suitable choice of numbers, we would obtain at last a general formula which agreed almost perfectly with the experimentally determined values. It was doubtless by some such trial and error method that the Swiss investigator J. J. Balmer (1825–1898) succeeded in finding an equation by which the wave lengths of the lines in the visible hydrogen spectrum could be represented. Balmer's report,

published in 1885, set out to deal with only the first four of these lines, but the agreement between his formula and the actual wave lengths was so good that he was encouraged to predict numerous additional lines. When the wave lengths of these additional lines were determined, they too were found to fit the formula with remarkable exactness.

Balmer's equation for the visible spectrum of hydrogen is now usually written in a form that emphasizes its possibilities:

$$\frac{1}{\lambda} = R \left[\frac{1}{2^2} - \frac{1}{n^2} \right]$$

Here $1/\lambda$ is known as the *wave number*, which is the number of waves per centimeter; λ, as usual, represents the wave length in centimeters corresponding to any line; and R is a constant, called *Rydberg's constant*, the present value of which is 109,678. The letter n stands for any whole number greater than 2; clearly it could not be 2 or less, for then λ would be infinite or negative.

We call attention to the extraordinarily close agreement between the two sets of figures in Table 15, one column listing the wave lengths determined experimentally and another the wave lengths calculated from Balmer's formula.

TABLE 15. PRINCIPAL LINES IN THE HYDROGEN SPECTRUM

Line	n	Wave Length by Experiment	Wave Length by Balmer's Formula
H_α	3	6.56210×10^{-5} cm	6.56208×10^{-5} cm
H_β	4	4.86074×10^{-5} cm	4.86080×10^{-5} cm
H_γ	5	4.34010×10^{-5} cm	4.3400×10^{-5} cm
H_δ	6	4.1012×10^{-5} cm	4.1013×10^{-5} cm
.	.	.	.
.	.	.	.
.	.	.	.
(Limit)			
H_∞	∞	3.64581×10^{-5} cm	3.64560×10^{-5} cm

The measured wave lengths of more than 30 additional lines have been found to conform to Balmer's equation when n is made successively larger by one number at a time. If n becomes so

PLATE XXXVI. Spectrum of the star HD 193182 showing hydrogen absorption lines near the limit of the Balmer series.

Mount Wilson and Palomar Observatories

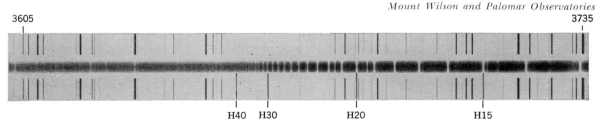

3605

3735

H40 H30   H20   H15

large that $1/n^2$ can be neglected, there results the limiting value of the series,

$$\lambda_{lim} = 4/R = 3.6456 \times 10^{-5} \text{ cm}$$

Balmer realized that this limit should exist. He also realized a point which our modern way of writing his equation strongly suggests. Suppose the fraction $1/2^2$ in the equation were replaced by $1/3^2$, $1/4^2$, or even $1/1^2$. It is to be expected that these changes should yield the wave lengths of several new series of spectral lines for hydrogen. Does incandescent hydrogen actually produce such lines?

It is gratifying to report that these series have indeed been found. Using $1/1^2$ instead of $1/2^2$, the modified formula becomes

$$\frac{1}{\lambda} = R \left[1 - \frac{1}{n^2} \right]$$

where n can now be any integer greater than 1. Since the differences are now larger in every case than before, the wave lengths must evidently be shorter than those of the Balmer series. In about 1906 the American astronomer Lyman discovered such a set of lines in the ultraviolet region of the hydrogen spectrum. They are now known as the Lyman series.

When, on the other hand, $1/2^2$ is replaced by $1/3^2$, $1/4^2$, $1/5^2$, or $1/6^2$, the final fraction in the equation must start as $1/4^2$, $1/5^2$, $1/6^2$, or $1/7^2$, and the smaller differences lead to larger wave lengths. The series of lines resulting from each of these substitutions has since been discovered in the infrared region of the hydrogen spectrum, the first by Paschen in 1908, the next by Brackett in 1922, and the next by Pfund in 1924. Another series of infrared lines of still longer wave length than the Pfund series has been found by Humphreys.

This procedure illustrates the power of the mathematical attack in natural science. On the one hand, the close concordance between the calculated and the measured wave lengths removes any possible doubt that Balmer's empirical formula is a correct summary of facts. On the other hand, the formula and its modifications have met the most severe and valuable requirement of any natural law, namely, the ability to predict facts not previously known. Like Kepler, who has been called "the legislator of the heavens," Balmer was a great empiricist. The Balmer equation is analogous to the elliptical orbits of Kepler, who summarized planetary data so brilliantly

without offering any hypothesis or model to explain them.

It was soon found that formulas designed on the Balmer pattern were helpful in describing the spectra of elements other than hydrogen. Any extension of this account, however, would lead us into excessive complexities, and we shall therefore set aside the emission spectra for the time being and consider briefly another type of spectrum.

ABSORPTION SPECTRA

Returning for a moment to Fraunhofer's discovery of dark lines in the solar spectrum, it has been learned since how to produce such lines artificially; hence we now know how they are caused in the sun. We have already remarked on the simplicity of the spectrum derived from sodium compounds when they are volatilized in a flame. Two yellow lines, falling so close together that they look like one, are the strongest in the spectrum. Their wave lengths are 5.890×10^{-5} and 5.896×10^{-5} cm. The continuous spectrum of sunlight shows two dark lines in the same positions occupied by the two bright yellow lines, thus giving rise to the inference that sodium is present in the sun. But why should the sodium radiation in the sun's light produce dark lines? Kirchhoff answered this question by directing white light from a very hot laboratory source through a flame in which sodium chloride was being vaporized. The lines of sodium appeared in the spectrum, reversed, just as they are in the solar spectrum, i.e., as dark lines in the otherwise continuous colored spectrum of the source. The phenomenon is evidently a case of *resonance* similar to the resonant behavior of a piano string. If a piano key is gently depressed and the note which it ordinarily emits is sounded by some other source, the piano string will begin to vibrate and give off this note as if the key itself had been struck. The string absorbs some of the sound energy passing over it, since it is tuned to vibrate at that same frequency. So, too, do the sodium atoms in the flame absorb radiation of their own characteristic frequency from the immense collection of frequencies in the light sent out by the white source. Hence the dark lines are due to selective absorption, and they form what is called an absorption spectrum.

X RADIATION

The closing years of the nineteenth century were marked by a number of discoveries so remarkable as practically to launch a new era in physical science. One of these was the first observation of X rays in 1895 by Professor W. K. Roentgen (1845–1923) of Munich. The extraordinary benefits to diagnosis and therapy which the modern world has derived from this radiation are common knowledge. The designation X rays was used by Roentgen himself for want of knowledge of their nature.

Roentgen was investigating the properties of cathode rays in a darkened laboratory when he noticed a fluorescent glow appearing on a distant screen which was coated with the mineral barium platinocyanide. He immediately began a study of the cause and traced it to the spot on his discharge tube where the narrow beam of cathode rays was striking the glass. When the beam was deflected so as to strike another part of the glass, that spot in turn became the source of the X rays. Roentgen tested particularly the unusual penetrating power of the new radiation, finding that wood, paper, and even thin sheets of metal were transparent to it. Dense metals, such as lead, absorbed X radiation entirely.

Suspecting that X rays were a kind of light, because they affected photographic plates and cast shadows as light does, Roentgen was, nevertheless, unable to get any evidence of reflection, refraction, or interference.

PRODUCTION OF X RAYS

Although X rays do emanate from the glass walls of an evacuated chamber when cathode rays strike the glass, this is not an efficient way of producing them, as Roentgen quickly realized. It is far better to let the cathode rays bombard a target made of some dense metal, such as platinum or tungsten. In the modern method of X-ray production, due to the American scientist W. D. Coolidge, the electrons are emitted by a hot tungsten filament and are pulled at high velocity toward the target in consequence of a large potential difference between the filament and the target. Urged by the strong attraction of the positively electrified target, the electrons attain enormous speeds and strike the target with great force. The X radiation generated by their impacts passes easily through the walls of the vessel.

To confirm the early suspicion that X rays were a kind of invisible light, it was necessary to prove, among other things, that X rays could be diffracted. Roentgen's own attempts to obtain such

proof had been unsuccessful. This failure is not surprising, inasmuch as X rays have extremely short wave lengths—less than a billionth of a centimeter for the shortest of them—and we recall that the degree to which waves can bend around obstacles is less, the shorter their wave length. Our geometrical analysis of the conditions governing the diffraction of visible light showed that the separation between central and diffraction images was $(D/d)\lambda$, where D was the distance from grating to the image, and d the distance between the slits of the grating. The applicability of this relation to X rays having wave lengths perhaps 10,000 times smaller than the wave lengths of visible radiation would evidently require a grating so closely ruled as to exceed mechanical possibility. Nevertheless, X-ray diffraction by reflection from metallic gratings has been successfully achieved in recent years, and the spectra so produced give excellent measurements of the wave lengths. The technique is to direct a thin sheet of X rays toward the ruled reflector at such a small angle (less than half a degree from the surface), that the effect is similar to more oblique reflection from a grating with finer rulings.

LAUE'S METHOD

In 1912 the eminent German physicist Max von Laue, also of Munich, proposed a most ingenious method of determining the wave lengths of X rays, whereby the regularly spaced atoms in a natural crystal were to serve as reflectors (see Plate XXXVII). A modification of this method, devised by Sir William H. Bragg (1862–1942), will be described briefly.

The symmetry of crystals indicates that their component atoms are regularly spaced to form relatively simple patterns, and that in numerous parallel layers throughout a single crystal the same pattern is repeated. One can even estimate the distance between atoms, a distance which turns out to be a few hundred-millionths of a centimeter. Figure 158 is designed to show a sectional view of such a crystal greatly enlarged. The small circles represent atoms, and the intervals between them are supposedly empty space. The oblique lines show the parallel paths of several X rays of the same λ in a narrow beam of this radiation. Intermediate rays, not impinging on atoms of the crystal, are omitted.

According to the law of reflection, those rays which rebound from atoms, should do so by

PLATE XXXVII. Electron micrograph showing regular arrangement of the individual molecules on the surface of a crystal of catalase. The large patch is one molecular step above its surroundings. This substance is a protein enzyme obtainable from liver and has a molecular weight of 250,000. Magnification 150,000 times. Courtesy of Dr. C. E. Hall, Massachusetts Institute of Technology.

paths which make the same glancing angle (θ) with the crystal planes as the incident rays do. The pertinent question is: will the reflected waves which take the direction of these rays reinforce or destroy one another? Comparing the waves following path 1 with those following path 2, it is clear that the second path is longer than the first by the distance $AB + BC$ or $2AB$. Now if $2AB$ happens to equal the wave length of the radiation, or some whole multiple of the wave length, the extra distance along path 2 will cause no hindrance to mutual reinforcement. The waves reflected from B will emerge in phase with those reflected from P. The same will be true of waves reflected from all atoms below P and B. This required condition will not be fulfilled in general but only for certain angles of incidence, among which we assume θ to be one. If the angle is suitable for the reinforcement of waves following two of these paths, it must, of course, permit all waves following parallel paths to rein-

force one another provided they all have the same wave length.

How can we best express the required condition? Let d be the distance between successive layers of atoms in the crystal. Then AB/d is the sine of the angle θ, and the path difference $AB +$

FIG. 158. X-ray reflection from a crystal.

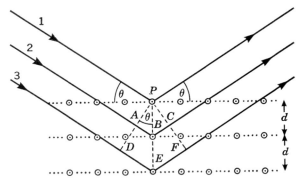

BC is $2d \sin \theta$. If this path difference equals the wave length λ, or some multiple of it, say, $n\lambda$, then

$$n\lambda = 2d \sin \theta$$

This formulation is known as *Bragg's law*.

Now we are ready to apply this equation to experimental data. Let the crystal be mounted on a turntable so that it can be rotated and thus receive a narrow, parallel beam of X rays at any angle to its surface. Provide a receiver for the reflected radiation which will permit measurement of the reflected intensity. When the crystal has been turned to a position where it reflects a maximum of the X radiation, the angle between the impinging rays and the crystal surface is read off and its sine is obtained from a table of trigonometric functions. The distance *d* between the layers of atoms in the crystal can be found by independent means.

It is assumed that the smallest value of θ for which reinforcement occurs must correspond to $n = 1$.

NATURE OF X-RAY SPECTRA

The total range of X-ray wave lengths is large—from a few ten-billionths of a centimeter to about one hundred-thousandth of a centimeter. Ultraviolet radiation actually overlaps this range somewhat, for ultraviolet light from an incandescent source may have wave lengths as short as a few millionths of a centimeter. It has become customary to speak of X rays having relatively long wave lengths as *soft* X rays and those of relatively short wave length as *hard* X rays.

When the results of X-ray reflection are examined, it is found that the radiation has yielded a continuous spectrum, which has no importance in our present study, and also a line spectrum, which turns out to be very helpful in revealing some of the secrets of atomic structure. A unique line spectrum is obtained for each element used as a target—a fact that proves the target to be the source of the radiation.

There are two marked differences between X-ray line spectra and the line spectra obtained in the visible region. First, the X-ray spectra are, in general, much simpler, consisting usually of two groups of lines. One group, called the *K* series, comprises three lines (one of the lines is really two lines very close together) made by radiation of very short wave length; the other, called the *L* series, comprises many more lines made by radiation of about ten times as great

a wave length. The second and very significant difference is that the X-ray line spectra of all elements are much alike, whereas the visible line spectra of different elements differ greatly, except for related elements. Thus, if as targets we choose a succession of metals of increasing atomic number, practically the same *K* and *L* lines are obtained in every case, although their wave lengths are found to be progressively shorter for elements of increasing atomic number. This interesting fact was discovered in 1913 by the British physicist H. G. J. Moseley (1887–1915), who first photographed the *K*-line spectra of some 38 elements. The marked contrast between X-ray spectra and visible spectra is attributed in modern theory to the different seats of origin of these two varieties of radiation. Evidence indicates that X radiation comes from deep-seated disturbances in the inner structure of atoms, which are believed to be almost the same for all elements, whereas visible radiation is due to disturbances in the exterior parts of atoms, which vary considerably from one element to another.

When the X-ray spectral photographs of any series of elements, arranged according to increasing atomic mass, are displayed one below another, as in Fig. 159, it is evident that, usually, the same lines appear, although with progressively diminished wave lengths as the atomic mass increases. This regular shift of lines is violated in the cases of a few elements one of which, nickel, is included here. Such exceptions convinced Moseley and others that, in basing his arrangement of elements on their atomic masses, Mendelejeff had chosen the wrong fundamental property. If the elements really obey some natural law which dictates their systematic arrangement, there should be no exceptions to it. Therefore the atomic masses must be incidental to some yet more fundamental property of elements, which Moseley called the atomic number. For the present we can identify this number merely with the X-ray spectrum of an element by allowing the number to increase uniformly as the spectral series shift progressively to shorter wave lengths. After more electrical evidence has been considered, we shall identify the atomic number of an element with the number of protons in one of its atoms.

The discovery of isotopes has enabled us to account for the discrepancies that would occur in Mendelejeff's periodic table if the order of increasing atomic masses were rigorously adhered to. The atomic mass of an element, as deter-

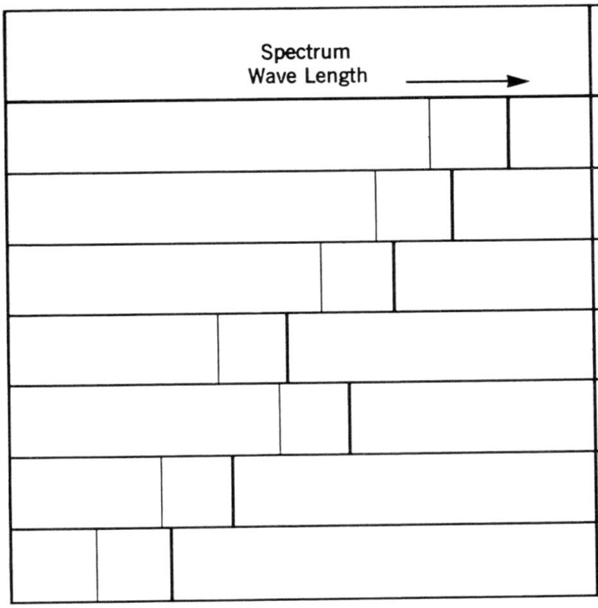

Spectrum Wave Length ⟶				Element	Atomic Mass	Atomic Number
				Chromium	52.01	24
				Manganese	54.93	25
				Iron	55.85	26
				Nickel	58.69	28
				Cobalt	58.94	27
				Copper	63.54	29
				Zinc	65.38	30

FIG. 159. Alpha and beta lines of the K series for several elements.

mined chemically, is an average of the masses of several isotopes, and any sample of the element obtained from natural sources will, in general, consist of the same isotopic mixture which was formed, no doubt, eons ago when the earth was fluid. If, in such a natural mixture, one of the heaviest isotopes, or one of the lightest, happens to be preponderant, the average atomic mass will be abnormally high or low. Hence, in a sequence of elements based upon average atomic masses, such an element will occur out of its proper order as far as other properties are concerned. The correct order of the elements is therefore the order of their atomic numbers, not of their atomic masses.

The regular decrease in wave length of any characteristic X-ray line with increasing atomic number suggests a mathematical relation be-

tween wave length and atomic number. One might discover such a relation rather easily by selecting one of the spectral lines and plotting the corresponding wave length for each element against the atomic number of that element. Such a graph shows that the wave length decreases faster than the atomic number increases. Moseley found that the reciprocal of the wave length agreed with a formula like the following,

$$1/\lambda = C(Z - b)^2$$

in which Z is the atomic number of the element, and C and b are constants. Hence, if the square root of $1/\lambda$ is plotted against the atomic numbers of successive elements, the various points lie on a straight line. When applied to the strongest line of the K series (called the K_a line), b in Moseley's formula has the value 1.

PROBLEMS

1. Making use of the information presented in this chapter, what would you expect to see when a strong distant point source of light, like a street lamp, is observed through the wire screen of a window? Confirm your conclusion by observation.

2. How many lines per centimeter must a grating have in order to make the angle IS_1C in Fig. 156 30° for the yellow sodium lines?

3. Using Balmer's formula, calculate the wave length of the first line in each of the spectral series known for hydrogen. Which of these lines are visible?

4. Using the information from Table 15, on p. 270, draw the first four lines and the limit of the Balmer series on a piece of graph paper so that the position of each line will be proportional to its wave length. This graph will present much the same order you would see in a spectroscope, viewing the hydrogen spectrum.

5. How does the crystal grating, used for X rays, differ from the plane optical grating in geometry?

6. How would you use X-ray spectra in the discovery of a new element?

The Quantum Theory

In the foregoing paragraphs we have described numerous radiation phenomena, both visible and invisible, and have explained them on the supposition that radiation is transmitted by waves. The wave speed as well as the wave lengths have been measured by different methods with consistent results. The facts that two beams of radiation can either reinforce or cancel each other and that, on passing through an opening, radiation can spread into the shadowed region seem to furnish conclusive proof of this wave character. Throughout most of the nineteenth century the wave theory of radiation was uncontested. Scientific theories are seldom very durable, however. We have seen that the caloric theory of heat had to be abandoned when it failed to account for the heat generated by friction, and that the phlogiston theory was abandoned when it fell short of explaining the quantitative facts of combustion. Yet the transitory character of scientific theories is not to be deplored. It is in keeping with the spirit of science that its theories shall not claim finality, for they are usually only models or analogies for the description of natural systems, and, in general, we lack the ability to verify such descriptions directly.

Radiation furnishes a peculiar and continuing example of contradictory theories. The wave theory, which appears to account for most optical phenomena so successfully, leaves others unexplained. One of these is the photoelectric effect, discovered in 1887, whereby light, falling on a polished metal surface, releases electrons from the metal. Another exception arose from the investigation of so-called black-body radiation at the turn of the present century.

BLACK-BODY RADIATION

A black body is anything whose surface absorbs all the radiation impinging upon it. No actual body meets this requirement, for all surfaces reflect some fraction of the radiation they receive, but dull velvet and lampblack are good approximations to perfect blackness, and a hole in a vessel with blackened interior conforms very closely to total blackness. By putting a source of heat into such an inclosure, one can study the emitted radiation at various temperatures and, in particular, find the amount of energy evolved at various wave lengths. For example, if the source is hot enough to glow, the radiation can be passed through a prism and the resulting spectrum of light allowed to fall on a photographic film or upon some device which measures temperature. Some parts of the spectrum will be very intense, indicating high energy at the corresponding wave lengths. Elsewhere the spectrum will be less intense, showing that little energy has been directed there. By plotting the measured intensity of energy against the wave length, we obtain a diagram like that of Fig. 160.

During the closing years of the nineteenth century several German scientists made experimental studies of the energy radiated by black bodies at various temperatures. They found that, even though the emitter was all at one temperature, the energy which it gave off extended over a wide range of wave lengths, but in strikingly different amounts. As Fig. 160 shows, the longest and shortest waves make up only a small fraction of the total energy emitted. At wave lengths between these extremes the amounts of radiation are seen to be increasingly greater from either end toward an intermediate wave length at which the emission is most copious. That is to say, although the radiant emission contains many wave lengths, it is richest in radiation of an intermediate wave length. The wave length corresponding to this maximum emission depends on the temperature of the black body in such a way that the hotter the body the shorter is the preponderant wave length.

If we put these findings into ordinary language, everyone will recognize them as consistent with common experience. When a bar of metal is held in a hot flame, it soon begins to glow dull red, then brighter red, then yellow, and ultimately it becomes white-hot—a description which means merely that enough blue light is being emitted to blend with the red, yellow, and green to give the appearance of whiteness. The red light is of long wave length, the yellow is shorter, and the blue still shorter, so it appears that, with rising temperature, the object radiates an increasing proportion of the shorter waves.

WIEN'S DISPLACEMENT LAW

The foregoing observation is only a crude endorsement of the experimental work to which it corresponds, for the human eye is incapable of dispersing light into its numerous components. Several years before the energy studies described, their result had been predicted by the German physicist Wilhelm Wien (1864–1928), who summarized his forecast in what is now known as *Wien's displacement law*. The law may be stated as follows:

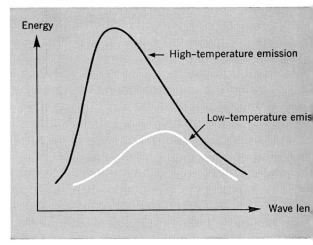

FIG. 160.   Black-body radiation.

The wave length of the most intense radiation emitted by a black body is inversely proportional to the absolute temperature of the body. For wave lengths expressed in centimeters the proportionality constant is 0.29.

$$\lambda_{max} = 0.29/T$$

Among the uses that can be made of Wien's law, there are the estimates of the sun's surface temperature, as well as the temperatures of stars. The sun and stars are not black bodies, but they approximate such a body well enough to permit a rough calculation. The sun's radiation extends over many wave lengths, but its greatest intensity is at a wave length of about 5.5×10^{-5} cm, which is green light. If we substitute this figure into Wien's equation,

$$T = \frac{0.29}{5.5 \times 10^{-5}} = 5270° \text{ abs}$$

It is fairly certain that the sun's surface is actually somewhat hotter than this, say, about 6000° abs, since our atmosphere absorbs a good deal of the short-wave radiation. If the shorter waves came through to the earth undiminished, the maximum of the energy curve would be shifted to a wave length somewhat shorter than 5.5×10^{-5} cm and the calculated temperature would accordingly be higher.

PLANCK'S INVESTIGATION

The shape of the radiation curve for a hot solid invited questions. Why should the body emit relatively small proportions of short-wave and long-wave energy when at some intermediate band of wave lengths its output is much more copious? Stranger still, why should the peak of emission shift with rising temperature to proportionately shorter wave lengths? Since at higher temperatures the radiating body must have more energy to give out, we are led at once to the inference that high energies and short wave lengths are related. Many able theorists tried to find answers to the questions just proposed prior to the beginning of the present century. Of numerous formulas devised to fit the radiation curves, two were partially satisfactory. One of these, which was derived by the British physicists Rayleigh and Jeans, agreed with the experimental results at long wave lengths. That is, the Rayleigh-Jeans equation, when plotted, gave a curve which coincided with the experimental one for large values of λ. For shorter wave lengths it failed. The other formula, due to Wien himself, gave satisfactory agreement for short wave lengths but not for long ones. Late in 1900 the German physicist Max Planck (1858–1947) announced a new formula which agreed with the experimental data very well over the whole range that had been studied. What interested him more, however, was a desire to probe to the root and cause of radiation. It was already known that the long-wave radiation that we now call radio waves was caused by the rapid oscillations of electric charges. When, for example, electrons oscillate back and forth in an antenna or aerial, radio waves are generated which travel outward through space with the speed of light. Radio waves are, in fact, a variety of light, although their wave lengths are much longer than those of visible light waves. It seems reasonable, therefore, to suppose that the radiation from a hot solid is due also to electrical oscillations, and, since even in Planck's time atoms of matter were suspected of containing electrons in very rapid motion, the emission of light by a hot solid was attributed to these electrons. Planck found, however, that, in order to derive a formula which would express the energy of these electrical oscillators in a way that agreed with experimental findings, he was obliged to assume that their energy was emitted in bursts or gushes. Each burst consisted of a definite amount of energy, the amount being inversely proportional to the wave length of the emitted radiation. This relation is more easily grasped in symbolic notation than in words, especially if we use, as Planck did,

the frequency of the radiation rather than its wave length. Remembering that the constant velocity of light equals frequency times wave length ($c = f\lambda$), we may write Planck's result in the form

$$\text{Energy} \propto \text{Frequency}$$

$$E \propto f$$

or

$$E = hf$$

where h, the proportionality constant, is a very small quantity, now called Planck's constant and equal to 6.6×10^{-27} erg-sec.

Planck's discovery was revolutionary, and every aspect of physical science has been affected by it. For all its deceptive appearance of simplicity, this equation means that some mechanism in the structure of matter compels it to emit energy, at least radiant energy, in package lots or *quanta,* as Planck called them. In other words, radiant energy, like matter and electricity, is discontinuous. There is, however, this striking difference between the unit of electricity and the quantum of energy: all electrons are identical, whereas energy quanta differ in magnitude according to their frequency. If an atom gives off red light, it can do so in quanta of about 2.5 million-millionths of an erg, but in order to emit light in the deep violet range it must deliver quanta of about 5 million-millionths of an erg. The difference must somehow be connected with the way in which atoms are constituted, and we shall see that Planck's quantum of energy proposal played a large part in the elucidation of atomic structure.

The really baffling feature of the quantum idea is this: if radiant energy is emitted in quanta, how can it exhibit the properties of waves? How, for example, can quanta of light, which pass through adjacent openings, as in Young's experiment, cancel one another at certain points on a distant screen and yet reinforce one another at other points? We have no answer to this, but it is certain that visible light and the other varieties of radiant energy do show certain corpuscular properties. We shall hereafter employ the now common terminology by referring to the minute quanta of light as *photons.*

THE PHOTOELECTRIC EFFECT

The most striking phenomenon that emphasizes the corpuscular nature of light is the photoelectric effect, now widely applied in the "electric eye" for controlling such mechanisms as door openers and burglar alarms. First observed in 1887 by Heinrich Hertz (1857–1894), the discoverer of radio waves, this effect was investigated more thoroughly soon afterward by Hallwachs, Lenard, and other noted German physicists. One of Hallwachs' experiments illustrates the photoelectric effect so clearly that it merits description here (Fig. 161). A zinc plate, freshly polished with emery cloth, is connected to the knob of an electroscope. The plate is charged negatively, and the leaves of the electroscope are seen to

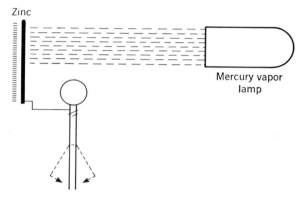

FIG. 161.   The photoelectric effect.

diverge. Now the light of a mercury vapor lamp with quartz window is allowed to shine on the zinc plate, whereupon the negative charge rapidly leaks away and the leaves come together again. When the plate is charged positively, the light has no apparent effect on it, and we conclude, therefore, that radiation can liberate electrons but not protons from the zinc. Hallwachs also showed that an uncharged metallic object acquires a feeble positive charge when illuminated.

Do all the colors of the impinging radiation contribute to releasing the electrons, or only some of them? This question occurred to Hertz when he first observed the photoelectric effect. He suspected that the ultraviolet ingredient of the light was mainly responsible. Since ultraviolet light does not pass through window glass, he placed a sheet of this glass before the light source and found that the photoelectric action ceased. So, too, in our repetition of the Hallwachs experiment, we can stop the discharge of the negative electroscope at any moment by inserting a piece of ordinary glass between the lamp and the zinc plate. The lamp itself is housed in a quartz, rather than a glass, vessel to

allow the ultraviolet light that it generates to get out.

Recalling Planck's equation $E = hf$, it is understandable that ultraviolet light should be more potent than the visible variety; ultraviolet photons are endowed with relatively large energies. This suggests that the photons of visible light, possessing smaller energies, should be effective if the metal which they strike is one that has a weaker grip on its atomic electrons. Much evidence exists to indicate that the alkali metals, lithium, sodium, potassium, rubidium, and cesium, fit this requirement. Their extraordinary chemical reactivity, for example, is directly attributable to unstable atomic structure in the sense that every atom of an element in the alkali class has one electron so weakly held that a minimum of energy is sufficient to dislodge it.

Here experiment bears out expectation, and we find that, when visible light falls on a specimen of alkali metal, electrons are set free and the metal becomes positively charged. Indeed, our reasoning leads to a useful generalization. If we expose all the elements in the activity series (p. 179) to light of various frequencies, we find that the less active the metal, the higher must be the frequency of the light in order to accomplish the release of electrons. This fact shows conclusively that chemical stability depends on the force with which electrons are bound to atoms.

The most revealing feature of the photoelectric effect is its primary dependence on the frequency of the light employed. The kinetic energy of the escaping electron does not depend at all on the brightness of the light, as we might expect it to. If the light is of sufficiently short wave length to produce the effect at all, then it will do so, no matter how feeble a beam is used. Increasing the intensity of the light merely increases the number of electrons that escape from the metal; it does not impart to them any increased speed. This point is so important that it is advisable to outline the experimental means by which this conclusion has been reached.

Suppose a metal with carefully polished surface is mounted in a vessel in such a way that it can be charged to various potentials, positive or negative. The vessel is evacuated, and a narrow beam of monochromatic light is allowed to strike the metallic strip. Suppose the light to be of high-enough frequency to liberate electrons from the metal. These will be attracted to a terminal which is kept positively charged for that purpose. Now let the metal be charged positively to a potential of a few volts so that no electrons can flow. With the light shining steadily on the metal, this positive potential is gradually reduced until the first small deflection of a galvanometer in the circuit shows that an incipient current of photoelectrons has begun to flow. Further reduction of the positive potential, followed by the imposition of a negative potential, merely makes the current larger. The experiment is repeated with monochromatic light of other frequencies until considerable data have been amassed. The most important items in these sets of measurements are: (1) the frequency of the light used and (2) the retarding potential, which is the

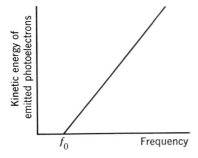

FIG. 162

name given to that positive voltage on the metal which just fails to prevent electrons from escaping. The reason for the latter's importance is that this retarding potential measures the minimum energy which the oncoming photons must possess in order to liberate electrons from the metal. When this potential, in ergs per esu, is multiplied by the charge in esu of one electron, the product is evidently the amount of energy in ergs required to ransom an electron from the metal. A plot of these energies against the frequencies of light to which the potentials correspond gives a graph like the one shown in Fig. 162.

The explanation of this straight-line relationship between energy and frequency appeared in a famous paper published in 1905 by Albert Einstein. He proceeded to account for the photoelectric effect in terms of Planck's quantum hypothesis. Assuming that an atom of any element contains electrons which are bound to it by electrostatic attraction, these electrons can be liberated only by the acquisition of a definite amount of energy. Presumably this energy requirement is the same for all atoms of the same element, and it must be greatest for the atoms of elements to which the electrons are most firmly bound and

least for the elements whose atoms contain weakly bound electrons. If a metal is irradiated with light of the frequency f, any surface atoms of the metal which happen to be struck will acquire energy in packages amounting to hf ergs from an impacting photon. If that quantity of energy is more than enough to dislodge an electron, and the liberated electron gets the excess, it will move away from the surface with kinetic energy amounting to $\frac{1}{2}mv^2$; hence the energy equation that applies is

$$hf = E_0 + \tfrac{1}{2}mv^2$$

where E_0 is that portion of the photon's energy which is needed merely for releasing the electron. As might be expected, it is this energy E_0 that differs for different elements, being small for metals like sodium and large for metals like platinum. This liberation energy, or *work function,* as it is called, resembles the heat of vaporization of a liquid, which is the energy required to convert a unit mass of substance from the liquid to the vapor state without raising its temperature.

Referring again to the straight line graph, we see that the intercept marked f_0, has an important significance also. If the photons of light have a lower frequency than the so-called threshold frequency f_0, no electrons escape from the metal regardless of the intensity of the light. Hence, hf_0, measures the work function or the bare minimum of energy that can effect their release. Other methods of removing electrons from metals, for example, by thermionic emission, require the same minimum energy in each case as that required of photons in producing the photoelectric effect. The minimum energy values for a few metals are listed in Table 16.

TABLE 16

Metal	Minimum Photoelectric Energy, ev
Platinum	6.30
Nickel	5.01
Gold	4.82
Silver	4.73

Finally we should note that the equation

$$\tfrac{1}{2}mv^2 = hf - E_0$$

has the same form as the standard equation for a straight line, $y = kx + b$. Hence, the coefficient of the independent variable f is the slope of the line plotted from the equation. Consequently, by measuring this slope, we can estimate the size of Planck's constant h, which turns out to have the value 6.6×10^{-27} erg-sec.

It appears now almost as if scientists have swung full circle back to the seventeenth century view of radiation which was held so stubbornly by the followers of Newton. Almost, but not quite, for we cannot ignore the wavelike attributes of radiation in transit from source to receiver. Its particlelike behavior is entirely restricted to interactions between radiation and matter. Physicists now ascribe a dual nature to radiant energy, whereby they think of it as consisting of photon packets which are attended by a wave disturbance in their passage from source to receiver. The useful features of each hypothesis are thus retained, and, although this makes it more difficult than ever to construct a mental image of what light is like, the dual theory does meet the obligation demanded of all scientific theories, namely, to suggest (we might almost say to prophesy) undiscovered phenomena. As an example, the dual character of radiation inspired Louis de Broglie in 1925 to pose this question: if light, which apparently travels in waves, can exhibit properties like those we associate with particles, is it not possible that the entities which we have heretofore regarded as particles may exhibit, when moving, the properties of waves? Such a proposal somehow seems especially fantastic, probably because we think we understand what particles are. Let us admit, however, that our understanding is limited to such particles as crumbs, sand grains, snowflakes, and other small bodies that can be seen or felt. About submicroscopic particles we know nothing at all directly. Indirectly, we can determine their inertia, their electric charge, when they have a charge, and their velocity. These, it must be acknowledged, are meager details—so meager that it is presumptuous to suppose that we understand particles. Just enough is known to make it certain that the ultimate corpuscles of matter bear little resemblance to the much larger bodies that can be seen with the naked eye or observed under the microscope.

To research physicists de Broglie's suggestion must have seemed highly speculative for there was no immediate attempt to investigate it experimentally. When the effect was finally discovered two years later (1927), it was stumbled upon accidentally by Davisson and Germer, two American physicists, who were experimenting with the reflection of electrons from nickel surfaces. Later, G. P. Thomson in England succeeded in demonstrating the same phenomenon. In both of these cases, electrons were diffracted as if they were beams of light whose wave lengths could be calculated from the observations. We shall consider these astonishing results in detail in Chapter 31.

PROBLEMS

1. Why should an insulated metal become positively charged when illuminated with light?

2. It has been observed that, in the normal human eye, the retina is sensitive to a stimulus of only 10–20 quanta of yellow-green light.   How many ergs of energy does this represent?

3. Summarize the experimental facts, presented in the section on photoelectricity, which seem to show that light is not absorbed as a continuous wave but in the form of quanta.

4. Assuming that a star is a black-body radiator, describe in some detail, using Fig. 160, how you would determine the temperature of a star.

5. When an electron is suddenly stopped by a metal target, a quantum of X radiation is emitted.   Assuming, from the law of conservation of energy, that the energy of the emitted quantum cannot be any larger than the kinetic energy of the impacting electron, write an equation which gives the upper limit of the frequency which the emitted X-ray quantum can have.

The Atomic Nucleus

RADIOACTIVITY

The evidence which we have presented so far has revealed the atom as a strong compact unit which does not lose its chemical identity even though jarred by collisions with other particles. To be sure, the atom may lose an electron or two in such encounters, but other electrons are easily acquired and the atom restored to neutrality. Assuming that the electrons are part of a relatively light outside structure, the heavy inside core of the atom is not so easily disturbed and so does not reveal any clues to its structure. It is also evident that, if we try to use the proton as a unit to build up atoms, we seem to violate the law of conservation of mass, since the elements immediately following hydrogen in the periodic table have masses which are not whole multiples of the proton's mass but slightly less. Thus if we take 1.00757 as the relative atomic mass of the proton and multiply this number by 4, 7, and 9 respectively, the products are seen to be greater than the relative atomic masses obtained by precise measurement for helium, lithium, and beryllium.

	Experimental Mass
$1.00757 \times 4 = 4.030$	4.004 for He
$\times 7 = 7.053$	7.018 for Li
$\times 9 = 9.068$	9.015 for Be

In order to probe into the internal structure of atoms, we shall consider a number of experiments which had their origin in an accidental discovery in 1896 by the French physicist Henri Becquerel (1852–1908). Some photographic plates, wrapped as usual in opaque paper, were found to have been blackened by uranium salts placed in the same drawer. Metal objects placed between the uranium salts and the photographic plates had cast shadows upon the plates as if some penetrating radiation had been emitted from the salts. Since the time of this discovery by Becquerel, a number of heavy atoms at the end of the periodic table have been found to behave like uranium. One of the most dramatic of these early discoveries was the isolation of radium from the mineral pitchblende by Marie and Pierre Curie (1867–1934, 1859–1906). Such atoms are said to be radioactive, and the phenomenon has come to be called radioactivity.

What was this strange new radiation? It produced the same effect on photographic plates as light, but its extraordinary penetration distinguished it from ordinary light. One of the first experiments performed with these rays showed their response to magnetic fields and turned out to be very revealing (Fig. 163).

A slender hole was drilled in a block of lead, and some radioactive salt was placed in the bottom. Lead was chosen because it was found to have great stopping power for the radioactive radiations, and the block thus acted as a small cannon, shooting out rays from the radioactive salt. The whole block was then placed in a magnetic field whose direction was perpendicular

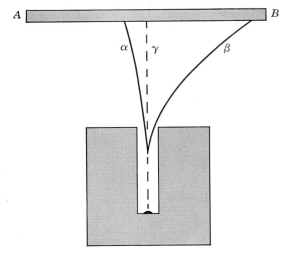

FIG. 163. Deflection of radioactive rays by a magnetic field.

to the path of the rays as they emerged from the block. A photographic plate *AB* was used to detect any deflections of the rays.

This simple procedure revealed the fact that, in general, the radioactive radiations were of three kinds. One component was very slightly deflected, another component was strongly deflected and in the opposite direction, and a third was not deflected at all. For convenience, these three kinds of rays were called alpha, beta, and gamma rays respectively.

The fact that the gamma rays were not deflected by either magnetic or electric fields suggested at once that they were like light. Later experiments proved conclusively that this was true except that their wave lengths were very much shorter than those for visible light. In other words, they were very hard X rays (see p. 274).

On the other hand, the deflections of the alpha and beta rays recalled the deflection experiments performed with positive and negative ions

(charged particles) in passing through magnetic and electric fields. The opposite deflections of the alpha and beta rays suggested that they were oppositely charged particles. But what were the particles?

The particle nature of the alpha rays was dramatically demonstrated by a simple technique used by Sir Ernest Rutherford (1871–1937) and his students. When a zinc sulfide screen, with a bit of radioactive material in front of it, was observed in the dark, the screen appeared to scintillate with little flashes of light scattered over its surface. Each alpha particle produced a tiny flash of light as it crashed into the screen! What could be more convincing than such an observation? If the strength of the source was properly chosen, one could actually count the number of alpha particles emitted by the source in a given time. Then, knowing the number of alpha particles emitted within a given solid angle, and measuring the total electric charge which they transferred to a metallic cup during an extended time interval, one could calculate the average charge on each particle. Such measurements showed that a single alpha particle carried the equivalent of two proton charges.

Another simple, and yet conclusive, experiment was performed by Rutherford in 1909. The apparatus is shown in simplified form in Fig. 164. Some radioactive element like polonium, which emits alpha particles, was introduced into a glass tube *A* with walls so thin that the high-speed alpha particles could pass through them into the space *B*, which was highly evacuated. At the beginning of the experiment a high voltage applied between the terminals *C* and *D* produced no electrical discharge. However, after a few days sufficient gas had accumulated in *B* to allow an electrical discharge. In the light emitted by this discharge the characteristic spectrum of helium was unmistakably observed. The alpha particles had picked up electrons from the walls and surroundings and become neutral helium atoms. In other words, the alpha particles were shown to be doubly charged helium ions.

Later, when the charge to mass ratio was determined from deflections of alpha rays in electric and magnetic fields, the results were consistent with the assumption that each alpha particle had a mass equal to that of the helium atom and carried the equivalent of two proton charges.

When beta rays were subjected to electric and magnetic fields, the charge to mass ratio was found to be the same as for cathode rays. In other words, they were found to be electrons.

The velocities for both alpha and beta particles were extremely high, those for beta particles coming very close to the velocity of light!

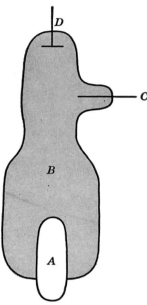

FIG. 164. Rutherford's experiment which identified alpha particles with helium nuclei.

THE GEIGER COUNTER

Another useful device which registers the effect of a single particle is called the Geiger counter (Fig. 165), in honor of its inventor. It consists essentially of a chamber with a central pin P which is supported in an insulating plug C and charged electrically with respect to the metallic case A. Some gas like argon at a few centimeters of pressure is allowed in the chamber, but the voltage is not high enough normally to cause an electrical discharge. However, if a single fast particle enters the chamber through the thin window W, it leaves a trail of ions, and there is a momentary flow of current through the gas and through the high resistance R. As soon as these ions have been collected, the current stops, but, while it flows, the potential drop across R can be made to flash a neon lamp, produce an audible sound, or actuate a counting device. Such Geiger counters can be made to count very rapidly, and the geometry of construction may be such that only particles from a known direction will enter the chamber and be counted.

With several counters properly arranged, a great deal of information about fast particles and their interactions with matter may be obtained in a short time. Such counters may even be made portable for use in detecting natural deposits of radioactive minerals or in searching for lost radioactive materials.

The photographic plate is also useful in such investigations. If, after exposure to radioactive particles, one examines the developed photographic emulsion under a microscope, the paths of these particles are observable in three dimensions as trails of black silver grains throughout the thickness of the emulsion.

THE WILSON CLOUD CHAMBER

Frequently, in experimental research someone suddenly sees how a very simple and well-known principle or phenomenon can be applied with great effectiveness. The cloud chamber, invented by the British physicist C. T. R. Wilson (1869–), is a brilliant example.

Fog, which is so common in nature, is due to the condensation of water on small dust or smoke particles in the air. This occurs when there is a decrease in temperature so that the

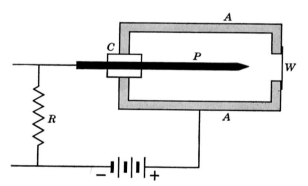

FIG. 165. The Geiger counter.

relative humidity of the air momentarily exceeds 100%. The excess water must then precipitate in the form of rain or fog. All this had been known for a long time, but it remained for Wilson to discover that charged ions will also serve as nuclei in the formation of fogs, although neutral atoms and molecules will not. However, particles as large as those of smoke or dust will precipitate fogs even if they are neutral.

Let us first describe a simple model of the cloud chamber to illustrate its principle of operation. A glass apparatus like that in Fig. 166, containing water to the level A, is connected to a rubber bulb B which can be squeezed so as to compress the air in the space C. When the pinchcock D is closed, the relative humidity of the air in C is 100%; in other words, the inclosed air is saturated with water vapor. If the bulb is then squeezed, the temperature of the air will rise and more water will evaporate into the space C to make the relative humidity of the air again 100%. If the bulb is then suddenly released, the

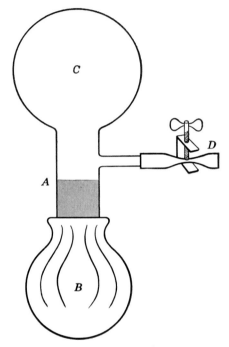

FIG. 166.   Model of a cloud chamber.

temperature will drop and the air becomes momentarily supersaturated (more than 100% humid). If the air is clean and free of ions, the excess moisture will eventually settle out on the glass walls, but if nitrogen or oxygen ions are present, a fog immediately fills the tube. When the air is compressed once more, the fog disappears just as suddenly as it formed. This makes an effective demonstration. When the air is clean, compressions and expansions produce no visible effect, but, when a little of the ionized air which surrounds a burning match is admitted through D, a dense fog forms every time the expansion occurs and disappears upon compression. This process may be repeated many times before the fog-inducing particles settle out.

Suppose now that we introduce into C a glass pin P which has on it a bit of radioactive polo-

nium emitting alpha particles. These high-speed alpha particles fly through the air, colliding with thousands of atoms and leaving a trail of ions in their wake. If the air is supersaturated at the instant when the alpha particles streak through the gas, a droplet of water condenses around each ion, tiny though it may be, and these droplets are visible as fog tracks which clearly mark the paths followed by the fast particles. This is an enormous advantage in that thousands of fog tracks may be observed and photographed in a short time. One precaution must be taken. Since alpha particles are continually ionizing the gas, and since the ions do not immediately recombine into neutral atoms, a cloud of fog would fill the entire chamber, due to the old ions, if they were not removed. Fortunately, the removal

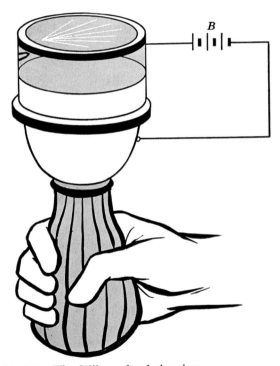

FIG. 167.   The Wilson cloud chamber.

is easy; by connection with an external battery, an electric field is applied between the top and bottom of the chamber and this field continually sweeps away the old ions.

The complete cloud chamber, including the external battery B, is shown in Fig. 167. The compressions and expansions are frequently achieved by means of a mechanically driven piston rather than by the squeezing of a bulb manually, and

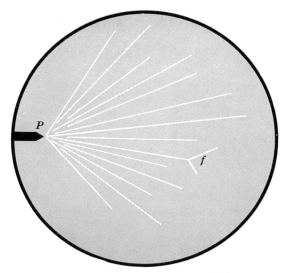

FIG. 168. Alpha-ray tracks from a cloud chamber.

two cameras are arranged to photograph the cloud chamber from different angles so that the geometry of the paths may be reconstructed in three-dimensional space. Such devices may be made quite automatic, taking thousands of photographs in a short time. These photographs serve as permanent records and may be studied at leisure. In a single investigation, the noted British physicist, P. M. S. Blackett (1897–) examined over 400,000 tracks obtained from such photographs of a cloud chamber.

Most of the alpha-particle tracks are straight lines a few centimeters long, as shown in Fig. 168,

but occasionally a forked track *f* occurs. This represents a kind of collision quite different from that which merely knocks off an electron or two; it signifies a collision with some particle comparable in mass to that of the alpha particle itself. Each little fog droplet represents a collision with an atom, but such collisions, even though there are hundreds of them, do not appreciably deflect the alpha particle. Since the forked tracks are so rare and since ionizations are so numerous, we are forced to conclude that the atom consists of two compartments: a relatively large and loose exterior structure made up of electrons, and a central, small, massive, and strong nucleus. Since an alpha particle is more than 7000 times as massive as an electron, we would not expect the outside structure to deflect it seriously but a collision with the massive tough nucleus is like the case of one billiard ball hitting another. The alpha particle and the struck nucleus each fly off at angles which depend on the closeness of the collision and the relative masses of the particles (see Plate XXXVIII). In fact, by measuring these angles in three-dimensional space, and applying the laws of conservation of energy and of momentum, it is possible to show that, for a collision with oxygen atoms, for example, the struck particle is very nearly four times as heavy as the alpha particle. But the total mass of an oxygen atom is four times that of a helium ion. From this we conclude that practically all the mass of the atom resides in its nucleus.

Although such experiments provide convinc-

PLATE XXXVIII. Cloud chamber photographs. (*a*) Collision of an alpha particle with a helium atom. (*b*) Collision of an alpha particle with a hydrogen atom.

(*a*)

(*b*)

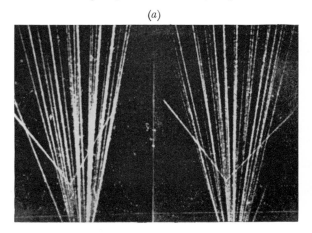

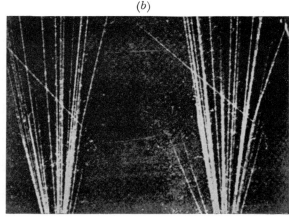

ing evidence that an atom consists of a massive nucleus surrounded by light electrons, we need more detailed information about that nucleus. What particles does it contain, and what energy is stored in its structure? Obviously, the nucleus must be positively charged to neutralize the negative charge of the exterior electrons, but how large is this charge?

RUTHERFORD'S EXPERIMENT ON THE SCATTERING OF ALPHA PARTICLES

The conclusion in the foregoing section, seeming to point to a nuclear atom, was easy to reach in retrospect, but this was not the way in which Rutherford arrived at his nuclear model for the atom. Retrospective reasoning of this kind is not only interesting but instructive because it reveals the unpredictable turns which scientific history (like all history) has taken. The develop-

ment has certainly not always been logical, and one is tempted to speculate on the strange theories which might have arisen if personalities and circumstances had been different. To be sure, Rutherford also concluded that the atom must have a very small heavy nucleus, but, in addition, his method of attack made it possible to calculate the electric charge on the nucleus and to estimate the nuclear dimensions.

In 1911 Rutherford and his students were performing experiments on the scattering of alpha particles by thin metallic foils. They found to their great surprise that some alpha particles were deflected through very large angles and that a few actually bounced backwards after collision with the foil. This was not at all what they had anticipated for the heavy, high-velocity alpha particle, and it led to speculation about what sort of structure atoms must have in order to

FIG. 169.   Scattering of alpha particles by a heavy nucleus.

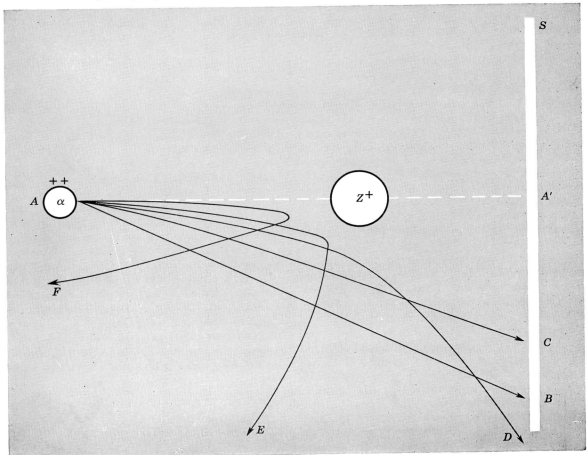

make such large deflections possible. Let us try to duplicate Rutherford's reasoning.

A radioactive source emitting alpha particles is placed at *A* in Fig. 169. The nucleus under investigation is represented as a single particle of charge *Z*+, but actually it is part of a very thin metallic foil made of that element. Consider now what happens when a stream of alpha particles approaches a positive nucleus at various angles. If an alpha particle does not get very close to the nucleus, there will be no appreciable deflection as shown by path *AB*, but, for closer and closer approaches, the repulsive forces between the positive alpha particles and the positive nucleus become greater and greater and cause larger and larger deflections. These paths are represented progressively by *AC*, *AD*, *AE*, and finally by *AF*, which would be very rare, for almost a head-on collision.

The total angular distribution in three-dimensional space is obtained by rotating the diagram about the axis *AA'*. If the nucleus were not charged at all, there would be very few appreciable deflections. The more positive the nucleus, the larger must be the deflections. In fact, it becomes possible to calculate the amount of charge on the nucleus from measurements of the distribution of impacts upon the fluorescent screen *S* and other screens placed in the neighborhood. To be sure, the actual case of many nuclei distributed in a thin metallic foil is more complicated and its mathematical formulation is beyond the scope of this book, but the reasoning is based fundamentally on the model here presented.

Rutherford concluded that the charge on the nucleus was approximately equal to ½ the atomic mass times the charge on one proton. For gold, this would be approximately 98 protons. A number of heavy metals were tried, and the results were considered close enough to the atomic number to warrant the conclusion that the number of proton charges in the nucleus was actually equal to the atomic number. This conclusion was confirmed by much experimental work after 1911.

How large was this positively charged nucleus? To answer this question, Rutherford considered an alpha particle which had been deflected straight back after collision with the foil. Since the velocity of the alpha particle was known, its kinetic energy could be calculated. It was then reasonable to assume that the alpha particle should continue to move toward the positive nucleus until all this kinetic energy was used up in work against the Coulomb force of electrical

repulsion between the alpha particle and the known positive charge of the nucleus. Once this point of view was taken, the problem became one of elementary physics. The conclusion was that alpha particles approached to within 6×10^{-12} cm of the nuclear center and that therefore the radius of the nucleus could not be larger than this. Now the diameter of an atom is known to be of the order of 10^{-8} cm so that the extreme smallness of the nucleus is evident, and we come to the startling conclusion that a simple atom, tiny in actual magnitude, is nevertheless about 10,000 times as wide as its nuclear core.

These results are highly significant. Within limits of experimental error, the positive charges on the nuclei are equal to the atomic numbers of the elements or, in other words, the ordinal numbers of the elements in the periodic table. This discovery introduces a gratifying simplicity into the structural sequence of the atomic nuclei. If we accept this correspondence for all the elements, we may begin with hydrogen, whose nucleus contains one proton, and continue with helium, lithium, beryllium, etc., whose nuclei have respectively 2, 3, 4, etc., net proton charges. Each step forward in the periodic table adds one net proton charge to the nucleus and therefore also one more electron to the loosely held external structure.

However, there must be something besides protons in the nucleus of an atom. Helium, for example, has a mass number 4. Two protons in the nucleus account for only one-half of this mass. What other particles are in the nucleus?

Since radioactive atoms frequently emit beta particles (fast electrons) it is natural to assume that the nucleus also contains electrons. Prior to 1932 many physicists believed that the nucleus contained additional protons to make up the total mass but with an equal number of electrons to neutralize their charges. If the atomic number of an element was *Z* and the mass number was *M*, the nucleus was supposed to contain *M* protons and *M* − *Z* electrons. The helium nucleus, for example, was thought to contain four protons and two electrons. This belief is no longer held, but to properly judge such a model, we must consider a few more facts and experiments.

RADIOACTIVE DISINTEGRATION SERIES

Soon after the discovery of radioactivity by Becquerel in 1896 it was realized that each radioactive explosion was really a transmutation of one

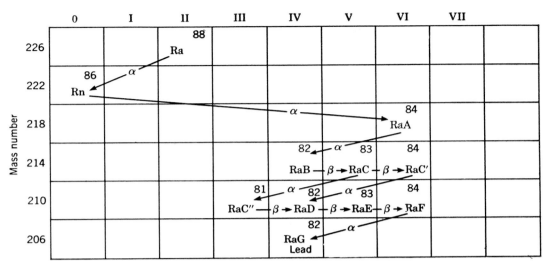

FIG. 170. Radioactive disintegration series.

element into another of totally different properties. This fact was established by study of the physical and chemical properties of the disintegration products. In 1898 Pierre and Marie Curie, in Paris, were able to identify a new radioactive atom which they called radium. Since this discovery by the Curies, a great deal of physical and chemical research has been done on radium and its disintegration products.

Radium was found to fit into the second column of the periodic table, since its valence was two and its chemical properties resembled those of calcium, strontium, and barium. However, when radium emitted an alpha particle, it not only lost four units of atomic mass but it became the totally different element, radon, an inert gas like helium, neon, argon, krypton, and xenon. This inert gas, radon, was also found to be radioactive, each atom of it that decomposed emitting another alpha particle and changing into a solid element called radium A with chemical properties which placed it in column VI of the periodic table. Radium A lost an alpha particle and shifted to column IV, becoming a new element, radium B, which, in turn, lost a beta particle, becoming radium C and behaving chemically like elements in column V. These disintegrations

continued until, at the end of the series, radium G was reached. Radium G was found to be stable and chemically like lead, that is, it was an isotope of lead.

Knowing that the number of proton charges on the nucleus is numerically equal to the atomic number, we are now in a position to organize the information revealed in such a series of elements. Figure 170 shows how the emissions of alpha and beta particles alter the chemical identities of the atoms. Each alpha emission decreases the mass number by 4 and decreases the atomic number by 2. This is represented as a backward shift of two columns in the table in Fig. 170. A beta emission, because of the small mass of the electron, causes no change in mass number but increases the atomic number by one. It is evident in the table that elements in the same column are isotopes, whereas those in the same horizontal row are isobars.

It is now known that radium itself is a disintegration product and that the series goes back to the element uranium. Hence this is called the uranium series to differentiate it from others which need not be considered in detail here. They all follow the essential pattern represented in Fig. 170.

PROBLEMS

1. These days, uranium ores are much sought after. From Fig. 165 and its description, how would you use a Geiger counter to detect such ores?

2. How can the Wilson cloud chamber be used to determine the mass of an unknown nucleus?

3. Frequently, in physical research, a cloud chamber is operated in a magnetic field. What additional information would such a procedure reveal from the cloud tracks?

4. Suppose an element X, with a valence of +3, is radioactive so that it emits an alpha particle, then a beta particle, and then another alpha particle. What chemical properties could you predict for the resulting element? How will its atomic mass compare with that of X?

. . . .

REFERENCE

1. *The Autobiography of Science,* Forest R. Moulton and Justus J. Schifferes, Doubleday & Co., 1950, pp. 506–509.

The Bohr Theory of the Atom

Following Rutherford's demonstration that an atom of matter contains an electropositive nucleus very much smaller than the whole atom, it remained to be discovered how the electronegative charge could be distributed in such a structure. As early as 1904 the Japanese physicist H. Nagaoka had proposed an atomic model in which electrons revolved about a central positive nucleus. Such a model would be useless, however, unless it were so designed as to account for the characteristic spectrum which each element produces when its atoms become excited.

The first atomic theory to furnish such an explanation was proposed in 1913 by the Danish physicist Niels Bohr (1885–   ), and its great merit was soon evident from Bohr's success in interpreting the spectral features of the element hydrogen by means of his atomic model.

It was already known that the hydrogen atom contained only one proton and one electron and that these could be rather easily separated from each other by collisions with other particles. The proton and the electron could not therefore be extremely close to each other in the neutral hydrogen atom. What kept the oppositely charged proton and electron from merging into an extremely compact structure held together by enormous electrical forces? The answer to this question was really the first assumption of the Bohr theory, and it was very much like the answer to the Newtonian question, "What keeps the planets in our solar system from falling into the sun under the action of the gravitational force?"

It was assumed that the relatively light electron revolved around the more massive proton and that the centripetal force tending to pull the electron in to the proton was the electrical force of attraction between them. More exactly,

$$\frac{mv^2}{r} = \frac{e \cdot e}{r^2} = \frac{e^2}{r^2}$$

where m and v are the mass and the speed of the electron, and e^2/r^2 is the attractive force, according to Coulomb's law, between a proton of charge $+e$ and an electron of charge $-e$ when they are separated by a distance r. Thus the two charges would remain in equilibrium so long as the electron whirled around the proton in an orbit of radius r at a speed v.

At first thought it would seem that the proposed model resembles a miniature solar system, excepting that the force holding the electron in its orbit is electrical instead of gravitational. The resemblance is superficial, however, for a planet could presumably move in any orbit consistent with its speed, whereas electrons, according to Bohr, are restricted and can revolve only in orbits which conform to a definite law.

The total energy of the atom consists partly of the kinetic energy of the moving electron and partly of the potential energy of the proton-electron system. With each orbit we must therefore associate a definite amount of energy. If we want to move an electron from one orbit to an orbit farther away from the nucleus we must do work equal to the increase in total energy of the atom. If the electron then falls back into the original orbit, this energy must be released by the atom and, according to the Bohr theory, the atom radiates this energy in the form of light.

If this radiation is emitted in quanta, as Planck supposed, the law of conservation of energy requires that

$$E_n - E_m = hf$$

where E_m and E_n are the energies of the atom for orbits m and n of the electron, h is Planck's constant, and f is the frequency of the radiated quantum of light. Since the total energy of the atom depends on which orbit the electron is occupying, each orbit is said to correspond to an energy level of the atom. Each spectral line is supposed to have a frequency consistent with the last formula, so that, if the energy levels of an atom were known, every line of its spectrum should be predictable. But the atom is observed to radiate only a sharply restricted assortment of frequencies, and so we must conclude that only certain electron orbits are possible. Which are the possible orbits?

The energy levels which are found to be possible are those for which the angular momentum (linear momentum, mv, multiplied by the radius, r) is given by the condition

$$mvr = \frac{nh}{2\pi}$$

where n may be any whole number, beginning with $n = 1$, and r is the radius of the orbit, as before. Such a condition seems extremely odd at first glance, and yet there is a logical connection between this assumption and the older classical theory. This is expressed in the famous *correspondence principle*, first stated by Bohr.

THE CORRESPONDENCE PRINCIPLE

When the electron is moving in sufficiently large orbits so that a shift from one orbit to the next smaller one produces long-wave radiation of low energy, then the old electromagnetic theory and the new quantum theory should correspond in giving the same predictions. This correspondence principle is plausible enough when we realize that the old theory gave a satisfactory interpretation of long-wave emission.

Here it must be explained that, according to the electromagnetic theory developed in 1864 by the great British physicist J. Clerk Maxwell (1831–1879), an electric charge which undergoes rapid periodic motion generates waves of radiant energy. Such waves have the same frequency as the oscillating charge. If this frequency is relatively small, the radiant energy is that which we now use in radio transmission. If the frequency is greater, the energy is called radiant heat or infrared radiation. Still greater frequencies produce visible light, ultraviolet light, X rays, and gamma radiation. Now Bohr adopted Maxwell's view for the hydrogen electron when it is moving in its largest orbits and therefore at relatively low frequencies.

Suppose then that the hydrogen electron jumps from one of these large orbits to the next smaller orbit. As the orbits get larger and larger, the difference between the radii of successive orbits is a smaller and smaller percentage of the total radius, so that the electrostatic attraction of the nucleus for the electron may be considered almost the same in the two orbits and we may express it in the familiar form of a centripetal force

$$F = mv^2/r$$

where v is assumed to have practically the same value in both orbits. The energy radiated during this small jump would be hf, as in all radiation, and this must equal the work it would take to move the electron out again over the small distance Δr. That is,

$$F(\Delta r) = hf$$

and since

$$F = mv^2/r$$

then

$$\frac{mv^2}{r} (\Delta r) = hf$$

Now the speed of the electron moving around its orbit may be written as

$$v = 2\pi rf$$

where f is the number of revolutions per second made by the electron around the nucleus. It is at this point that the connection between Bohr's model and the classical theory is most obvious, since the f in this expression is considered to be the same as the frequency of the emitted quantum whose energy is hf. Hence we can replace one of the v's in the foregoing equation by $2\pi rf$, getting

$$\frac{mv}{r}(2\pi rf)(\Delta r) = hf$$

or

$$mv(\Delta r) = h/2\pi$$

Since this equation tells us that the change in angular momentum from one orbit to the next amounts to $h/2\pi$, we now take $h/2\pi$ itself as the angular momentum of the electron when it is in the smallest orbit, twice as much when it is in the second, and so on. In general, for any permitted orbit, it is assumed to be true that

$$mvr = nh/2\pi$$

where n is any whole number.

To summarize, the essential assumptions of the Bohr theory for the hydrogen atom are:

1. The electron revolves around the nucleus so that the centripetal force is the electrostatic attraction. Stated mathematically,

$$mv^2/r = e^2/r^2$$

2. When an electron moves from an outer orbit, say n, to one nearer the nucleus, say m, the loss of energy of the atom is radiated in the form of a quantum.

$$E_n - E_m = hf$$

3. Only those orbits seem to be possible for which the angular momentum is a whole number multiplied by $h/2\pi$. That is,

$$mvr = nh/2\pi$$

From these three assumptions it was possible to derive the same formula which Balmer first obtained directly from the observed wave lengths of the hydrogen spectrum. Using the form later derived by Rydberg,

$$\frac{1}{\lambda} = R\left[\frac{1}{m^2} - \frac{1}{n^2}\right]$$

Not only was the form of the equation the same, but the constant R, now calculated from

Bohr's assumptions, was in excellent agreement with that previously obtained. It is very nearly 109,700 when λ is expressed in centimeters.

HYDROGEN SPECTRAL SERIES

If we draw a number of concentric circles, each representing an electron orbit, with radii inversely proportional to the various negative total energies possible for the hydrogen atom, then the energy of the quantum emitted as an electron falls from an outer orbit of radius r_2 to an

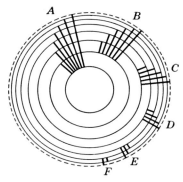

FIG. 171. The energy levels and spectral series of hydrogen, according to the Bohr theory. The radii are not drawn in true proportion here, since the circles actually get farther and farther apart as they get larger.

inner orbit of radius r_1 will be proportional to $(r_2 - r_1)/r_1 r_2$.

For example, all the possible transitions from outer orbits into the second orbit form the Balmer series represented by B in Fig. 171 (see Plate XXXVI). This was the first such series of spectral lines to be observed in the hydrogen spectrum. Using the Rydberg equation, the wave lengths of these spectral lines may be calculated by setting $m = 2$ and $n = 3, 4, 5, \cdots \infty$. The first five or six of these lines lie conveniently in the visible region, the first having a wave length of 6562×10^{-8} cm and the shortest (the limit of the series) represented by $m = 2$ and $n = \infty$, having a wave length of 3646×10^{-8} cm. Not all of these lines are equally intense; in general, the intensity decreases toward the violet end of the spectrum so rapidly that the higher members of a series cannot be observed at all. Nevertheless, more than thirty lines of the Balmer series have been photographed and measured, and the observed wave lengths are in gratifying agreement with the calculated values.

Now suppose $m = 1$ and $n = 2, 3, 4, \cdots \infty$. This also represents a series, first observed by Lyman in the ultraviolet and represented by transitions A in Fig. 171. The first of these lines has a wave length of 1216×10^{-8} cm. The limit of the series is 912×10^{-8} cm.

Other series observed by Paschen, Brackett, Pfund, and Humphreys are represented by C, D, E, and F in Fig. 171. The student should now be able to calculate the wave lengths of these lines as an exercise. All this is in agreement with the Balmer formula discussed in Chapter 26.

These are impressive successes for the Bohr theory, but there are many more. In this discussion we shall have time and space for only a few.

Normally, the electron in an unexcited hydrogen atom should be in the orbit nearest the nucleus. But, if the hydrogen atom is disturbed, as by collision with another particle, the electron may be displaced to some outer orbit or, if the impact is violent enough, may be completely detached from the atom. On the other hand, nothing at all will happen to the internal structure of the hydrogen atom if it collides with a particle whose energy is less than that necessary to move the electron from the lowest orbit to the second orbit. There is a type of experiment which proves this point in a most convincing way.

First let us calculate the work necessary to move an electron from the innermost to the second orbit in the hydrogen atom. This work must be equal to the energy of the quantum emitted as the first line in the Lyman series, whose wave length is 1216×10^{-8} cm. Since energy = hf and

$$f = \frac{\text{Velocity of light}}{\text{Wave length}} = \frac{3 \times 10^{10}}{1216 \times 10^{-8}}$$

$$hf = \text{Energy} = \frac{6.62 \times 10^{-27} \times 3 \times 10^{10}}{1216 \times 10^{-8}}$$

$$= 1.63 \times 10^{-11} \text{ ergs} \quad \text{or} \quad 10.2 \text{ ev}$$

This is the amount of energy acquired by an electron when it falls through a potential difference of 10.2 volts (see p. 211).

It is therefore the energy which an impacting particle must have in order to knock the electron from the first to the second orbit; unless it has at least that much energy, the particle can do no damage to the atom. This voltage is frequently referred to as a resonance potential.

IONIZATION POTENTIAL

In precisely the same way, we may calculate the energy which an electron must have so that, on impact with a normal hydrogen atom, the hydrogen electron will be completely separated from the atom. The potential difference through which the electron must move is given by

$$V = \frac{hf}{1.6 \times 10^{-12}} = \frac{6.62 \times 10^{-27} \times 3 \times 10^{10}}{1.6 \times 10^{-12} \times 912 \times 10^{-8}}$$

$$= 13.6 \text{ volts}$$

where 912×10^{-8} cm is the limiting wave length of the Lyman series, and where 1.6×10^{-12} is the electronic charge 1.6×10^{-19} multiplied by 10^7,

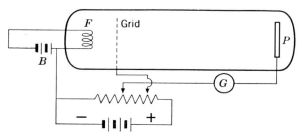

FIG. 172. Apparatus for measuring resonance and ionization potentials.

the number of ergs/joule. The voltage so calculated is called the ionization potential because the abandoned proton is really a hydrogen ion.

Let us consider next how this potential is measured. One form of the apparatus is shown in Fig. 172. It consists of a glass container in which the gas under examination is at a low pressure. A wire filament F at the left is kept hot by current from a battery B so that it emits electrons, like the central cathode in an ordinary radio tube. Near the filament is a metallic screen or grid which can be charged to convenient positive potentials. We shall call this potential V and express it in volts. The positive grid accelerates electrons from the hot filament so that, when they reach the grid, each has a kinetic energy that can be calculated from the product $Ve \times 10^7$ ergs. Some of these electrons hit the wire screen, but many of them pass through the openings with undiminished energy into the space to the right of the grid. Near the right end of the tube there is a metallic plate P which is kept slightly negative with respect to the grid so that electrons are repelled to a small extent in the region between the grid and the plate.

This experimental set-up has been used with many gases. Let us suppose that the gas is hydrogen and that it is atomic rather than molecular.

As the positive potential of the grid is gradually increased from very small values, more and more electrons will be able to reach the plate so that the reading of the galvanometer G rises steadily. Many of the electrons will collide with hydrogen atoms but at such low velocities they will rebound elastically and lose very little energy on that account. Suddenly, when the accelerating potential reaches 10.2 volts, the current registered by the galvanometer G begins to decrease. This is an indication that electrons have acquired sufficient energy to do damage to the hydrogen atoms. The damage consists in knocking an electron from the innermost orbit to the next higher orbit. In doing this amount of work, the impacting electron loses so much kinetic energy and velocity that it is unable to reach the plate P even against the small retarding potential. Such a collision is said to be inelastic. At this point the hydrogen should begin to radiate the first spectral line of the Lyman series, since the displaced electron is now free to fall back into the normal state, and, indeed, the single spectral line has been observed experimentally. Altogether, there is excellent agreement between the observed facts and the predictions of the Bohr theory, and the whole experiment becomes rich in meaning. For example, if the potential of the grid is increased beyond the first resonance potential, other resonance potentials are revealed corresponding to transitions of the electron to higher levels. Finally, at 13.6 volts the current is observed to increase strongly, indicating that both positive and negative ions are being formed in the space between the grid and the plate. Experimentally, this observation establishes 13.6 volts as the ionization potential, again in good agreement with the calculation from Bohr's theory.

Encouraged by the success of his hydrogen model, Bohr next tried to extend his ideas to the atoms of heavier elements. Take the case of helium, for example. Its atomic number is 2, meaning that the nucleus of the helium atom contains two net proton charges. Around the nucleus there must then be two electrons to make the normal atom neutral. These electrons can be removed by collision with other particles or by irradiation with light of sufficiently high frequency. The energy required, however, is much greater than the energy needed to ionize hydro-

gen. Expressed in electron volts, the energy needed to remove one electron from a helium atom is 24.5, almost twice as large as the 13.6 electron volts required for the ionization of hydrogen. In order to remove the second electron, thereby converting the helium atom into an alpha particle, He^{++}, 54.14 electron volts are necessary. This figure is not surprising considering that the helium nucleus has twice the positive charge of the hydrogen nucleus. Necessarily, the electrons of the helium atom are held more firmly to the nucleus than is the electron of a hydrogen atom. Indeed, if we derive an expression for the total energy of a helium nucleus with only one electron around it, we find this energy to be four times the energy of the hydrogen atom. Thus if one electron has already been stripped away from the helium atom, the removal of the second electron would cost four times as much energy as was needed for the hydrogen electron, and therefore the ionization potential should be four times as great. Four times 13.6 is equal to 54.4, a figure very close to the second ionization potential obtained from experiment.

The Bohr theory is equally successful when it is applied to the case of singly ionized helium, i.e., helium which has lost one of its electrons. The spectral series of ionized helium are completely predicted, as in the case of hydrogen. This is not surprising since the ionized helium structure is very much like the hydrogen structure—a positive nucleus with only one electron moving around it. But when the theory was applied to the case of ordinary helium, i.e., a nucleus with two electrons rotating around it, the Bohr model failed. Not only was the problem very difficult to attack, involving three bodies instead of two, but the special cases actually worked out gave wrong solutions. This again shows up the real nature of a theory or model. It may have brilliant success in a restricted range, but, sooner or later, its inadequacy becomes evident in its failure to explain another set of phenomena.

SIGNIFICANCE OF IONIZING POTENTIALS

Returning to the property called the ionizing potential of an atom, in Table 17 we now list the values of this characteristic for the first twenty elements. The ionizing potential can be obtained either by measuring the minimum energy needed by electrons for converting the neutral atoms of an element in the gaseous state into positive ions or by measuring the least energy which photons

TABLE 17

Atomic Number, Z	Element	Symbol	Ionizing Potential
1	Hydrogen	H	13.54 volts
2	Helium	He	24.46
3	Lithium	Li	5.36
4	Beryllium	Be	9.28
5	Boron	B	8.26
6	Carbon	C	11.22
7	Nitrogen	N	14.48
8	Oxygen	O	13.55
9	Fluorine	F	17.34
10	Neon	Ne	21.45
11	Sodium	Na	5.12
12	Magnesium	Mg	7.61
13	Aluminum	Al	5.96
14	Silicon	Si	8.12
15	Phosphorus	P	10.9
16	Sulfur	S	10.3
17	Chlorine	Cl	12.95
18	Argon	A	15.68
19	Potassium	K	4.32
20	Calcium	Ca	6.09

of radiation must have in order to produce the same result.

A careful study of the figures in Table 17 leads to some very important inferences. We have already remarked that the large ionizing potential of helium (helium has the largest value of any element) is attributable in part to the double positive charge on the helium nucleus. But the nucleus of a lithium atom ($Z = 3$) contains three positive charges and should therefore attract its three electrons with even greater force. Yet lithium has not a larger but a very much smaller ionizing potential than helium. Naturally we ask why it should need less than a quarter as much energy to remove one electron from a lithium atom as it does to remove one electron from a helium atom. An answer suggests itself. By Coulomb's law the electrostatic force of attraction falls off rapidly as the distance between charges increases. If, therefore, the third electron of a lithium atom is farther from the nucleus than the first two are, it must be much less firmly bound to the nucleus. This presumably weak binding is further confirmed through chemical reactions by the ease with which lithium atoms form univalent positive ions through the ready surrender of one electron apiece. The compound lithium chloride, for example, can be shown to consist not of Li and Cl atoms but of Li+ and Cl− ions.

It is quite possible to strip lithium atoms of two, or even of all three electrons, but only at a high cost in energy. The potential needed for removal of the second electron is more than 75 volts, which is three times the energy required for removing one helium electron.

Such facts lead us to infer that one electron of the lithium atom must be moving about the lithium nucleus in a much wider orbit than the paths pursued by the other two electrons. Likewise beryllium ($Z = 4$) with four electrons per atom, must have two of them in wide orbits and the other pair in much narrower orbits. Beryllium is ionized to Be+ at a cost in energy which is relatively small, although larger than the ionizing potential of lithium. Moreover, a second electron is removed from Be at a potential of about 18 volts, which is still fairly small when we consider that the beryllium nucleus contains four protons. On the other hand, the potential needed to strip a third electron from the beryllium atom is 153 volts.

Continuing down the list, we find a nearly consistent increase in the ionizing potentials of successive elements through neon ($Z = 10$). We conclude that each species of atom has the same core or kernel, consisting of a nucleus with two electrons revolving around it, but that outside this kernel a second layer of electrons is present, their number ranging from one for the element lithium to eight for the element neon.

The chemical properties of the elements also support this tentative view. Whereas lithium tends to form chemical compounds in which the lithium displays a valence of +1, beryllium in its compounds exhibits a valence of +2, and its customary ion is represented by Be+ + to show that the atom has lost two electrons. Again, boron has a usual valence number of 3 and carbon of 4, although in this latter case the compounds do not ordinarily show the presence of carbon ions. We conclude that the four electrons of carbon which are involved in chemical unions are not actually lost by the carbon atom.

Neon affords a negative sort of interest chemically, for neon, like helium, has no chemistry. That is to say, neither element participates in any chemical combinations. We recall that these inert gases do not even form diatomic molecules, as hydrogen, oxygen, nitrogen, and other elemental gases do. But, if we have reason to associate chemical activity with ease of losing electrons, then the high ionizing potentials of helium and neon are certainly consistent with the absence of any combining tendency in these elements. It appears as if the shell of two electrons around the helium nucleus, and the similar shells of two electrons in the kernels of subsequent atom types, is an arrangement of great stability. The same may be said about a second shell of eight electrons, which appears first in the configuration of the neon atom. If that is true, the atom of sodium ($Z = 11$) may be so constructed that, although ten of its electrons repeat the neon pattern, there is no place in these shells for the eleventh electron. Will it then begin a third shell? If so, the lone electron in the third shell should be even more easily removable than the outpost electron of the lithium atom is. Comparing the ionizing potential of 5.12 volts for sodium with that of 5.36 volts for lithium, we find adequate confirmation for this prediction. Moreover, the entire chemical behavior of sodium is much like that of lithium, a fact which was well known to chemists a century ago.

It is now apparent that we might arrive at a fair approximation of the periodic classification of the elements on the basis of ionizing potentials. Their occasional inconsistencies are traceable to more complex factors which we shall not discuss. Let us pursue, however, the suggestion that a shell of eight electrons, as exhibited by the neon atom model, represents extraordinary stability.

Throughout the realm of nature there operates a general rule which can be illustrated by countless examples. It is this:

All systems tend to achieve a state of maximum stability.

Or, alternatively:

All systems tend toward a state of minimum potential energy.

We see this rule carried out in such familiar processes as the spontaneous cooling of a hot body, the combustion of a fuel, and the fall of an elevated object. Granting the same disposition to atomic systems, is it not reasonable to suppose that atoms of nitrogen, oxygen, and fluorine, for example, should tend to attain, with a spontaneous loss of potential energy, the high stability possessed by the neon atom? In order to duplicate the electronic configuration of neon, the nitrogen atom would have to gain three electrons, the oxygen atom two electrons, and the fluorine atom one electron. That these elements readily unite with atom types which can supply such electronic needs is attested to by many simple chemical

combinations. Fluorine atoms unite avidly with lithium atoms, the former appropriating one electron apiece from the latter, so that in lithium fluoride, LiF, the lithium atom has achieved the stable configuration of helium, whereas the fluorine atom has taken to itself the eight-electron cloak that characterizes the stable neon.

The same hypothesis which offers an explanation for the marked reactivity between lithium and fluorine can be applied equally well to other elements which resemble lithium on the one hand and chlorine on the other in exterior electron arrangement. For example, the atoms of sodium, potassium, rubidium, and cesium are like those of lithium in having just one electron more distant from the atomic nucleus than the others are, and the atoms of chlorine, bromine and iodine resemble the atom of fluorine in having an outside shell of 7 electrons. We could predict that any of the former elements would react with any of the latter ones in the manner described. It is well known that they do. The resulting compounds are therefore representable by such formulas as the following:

LiF, lithium fluoride
NaI, sodium iodide
KCl, potassium chloride
CsBr, cesium bromide
RbCl, rubidium chloride

where the absence of subscripts means that in each compound a single atom of metal engages a single atom of non-metal. In chemical parlance each metallic element in this set has a valence number of $+1$, due to its having lost one electron and thereby becoming positively charged. Likewise, each non-metallic element has a valence number of -1 due to its having gained one electron.

Let us now proceed across the second horizontal row of the periodic table beginning with the element magnesium (atomic number 12). Assuming that the twelve electrons of a magnesium atom are disposed in a pattern similar to that of sodium (atomic number 11), we may represent them by the following scheme:

$$\left(12^+\right) \quad \big) \, 2e \quad \big) \, 8e \quad \big) \, 2e$$

Note: The successive groups of electrons surrounding the nucleus of any atom are designated as the K, L, M, N, etc., shells.

The argument for the reactivity of lithium or sodium can be repeated for magnesium, except that now two of the electrons would have to shift if the magnesium atom were to acquire a stable configuration of eight electrons like the atoms of inert gas elements. If the receiver of these electrons were again the element chlorine, it would take two chlorine atoms to utilize the electrons provided by one magnesium atom in a combination which can be represented schematically by:

It is to be expected, however, that an alternative possibility is even more likely in the cases of some of these elements. Let us skip silicon for the present and focus on the electronic structure of the phosphorus atom. We may represent the atom by:

$$\boxed{15^+}\quad 2e \quad 8e \quad 5e$$

since the atomic number of phosphorus is 15.

$$\text{Mg} \quad + \quad \text{Cl}_2 \quad \rightarrow \quad \text{MgCl}_2$$

One atom of magnesium plus two atoms of chlorine yields one molecule of magnesium chloride. Chemical evidence shows that magnesium does unite with chlorine in such a way as to involve twice as many chlorine atoms as magnesium atoms. The electronic structure of the magnesium atom is therefore in agreement with chemical evidence in stipulating for magnesium the valence number +2.

Application of the same line of thought to the electronic structures of aluminum (atomic number 13), silicon (atomic number 14), phos-

If we continue to assume that the most stable state of an atom is one in which its exterior cloak consists of eight electrons, that state would seem to be more readily attained for a phosphorus atom by the gaining of three electrons than it would be by the loss of five. In order to gain electrons, the phosphorus would have to be in contact with some substance disposed to donate or at least to share some of its electrons. Such a substance might be the element sodium. A plan of the proposed reaction between phosphorus and sodium would look something like this:

$$\text{P} \quad + \quad 3\text{Na} \quad \rightarrow \quad \text{Na}_3\text{P}$$

phorus (atomic number 15), and sulfur (atomic number 16) leads to the conclusion that atoms of these elements might surrender three, four, five, and six electrons respectively to suitable receiving atoms and thus enter into chemical combinations in which the valence numbers of these elements would be +3, +4, +5, and +6. These possibilities are borne out by the existence of such compounds as

Aluminum trichloride	$AlCl_3$
Silicon tetrachloride	$SiCl_4$
Phosphorus pentachloride	PCl_5
Sulfur hexachloride	SCl_6

One atom of phosphorus plus three atoms of sodium yields one molecule of sodium phosphide, where the numerals outside each nucleus stand for numbers of electrons as usual. There is a well-known compound called sodium phosphide whose composition as determined by chemical analysis agrees with the formula Na_3P, and this confirms our supposition that the valence number of phosphorus may be -3 as well as $+5$.

Lest we be tempted to expect too much of the atomic models, it should be noted that frequently the compounds represented in the above simple fashion cannot actually be prepared by direct union of the elements. Nevertheless, the plan does account correctly for atomic *proportions* in a molecule of the compound.

By identical reasoning sulfur (atomic number 16), which has six electrons in the outermost shell of its atom should have a tendency to acquire two more electrons from eligible atoms and thereby form compounds in which the valence number of the sulfur is −2. The two electrons might be donated by a single atom, like that of magnesium, or by a pair of atoms having the same exterior structure as potassium. Both possibilities are shown in the following diagram, and the compounds named have long been known.

atom. If the stablest atom is one with an outside shell of eight electrons (or two electrons in the case of helium), it is evident that the silicon and carbon atoms could attain maximum stability by either the loss or the gain of four electrons. Clearly it is a unique type of atom that offers these alternatives, and unique chemical behavior may be anticipated of elements so constituted. Their chemical behavior suggests that silicon and carbon do not literally appropriate electrons from elements with which they enter into chemical combination, nor do they surrender electrons to their reacting partners. Rather, it appears that electrons are *shared* between the carbon type

One atom of magnesium plus one atom of sulfur yields one molecule of magnesium sulfide.

of atom and the other atoms of the union. This sharing is depicted schematically in Fig. 173,

Two atoms of potassium plus one atom of sulfur yields one molecule of potassium sulfide.

The foregoing representations of probable electronic arrangements, consistent with the long-established valence numbers of various chemical elements, could be greatly extended. The atomic models are successful in accounting for the composition of innumerable compounds. Enough instances have been cited here to illustrate the principal rule by which preferred combining tendencies can be predicted.

We have purposely neglected the element silicon up to this point for a reason which may now be discussed. According to its atomic number (14), silicon, like carbon (atomic number 6), must have an electronic distribution such that four electrons make up the outermost shell of the

showing a carbon tetrachloride molecule. It is to be understood that each of the five atoms consists of an inner kernel surrounded by an envelope of eight electrons, some of which belong jointly to the outposts of carbon and chlorine atoms.

Atoms which share electrons with other atoms in a compound are said to be bound together by covalent linkage. This is in contrast to the electrostatic binding which results when electrons are transferred from one atom to another, in which case the atoms are said to be united by electrovalent linkage. Compounds like potassium chloride (KCl), in which the elements are joined together by electrovalent bonding, break up into oppositely charged ions (K^+ and Cl^-) when they are dissolved in water, and the solutions are good electrical conductors. Compounds in which all the bonding is covalent do not dissociate into ions, and their solutions are nonconductors.

Another practical distinction between the two kinds of linkage is the closer proximity between atoms which are united by shared electrons. It is possible by optical means to measure the actual distance separating the atoms of a solid compound, and these distances are found to be considerably less for covalent linkage than they are for electrovalent linkage. That such close packing of atoms should result in increased density is illustrated by the compound silicon carbide,

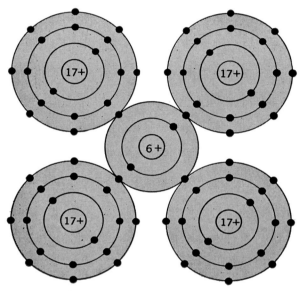

FIG. 173. The carbon atom shares electrons with the chlorine atom.

a substance which is widely used in industry for abrasive purposes under the technical name of *Carborundum.*

The elements making up silicon carbide are both of the type which we have been considering. It might well be expected, therefore, that in a chemical combination between silicon and carbon the exterior electrons of both kinds of atom would be fully shared between the two and that the quadruple covalent linkage resulting would give the compound a rather high density. Actually silicon carbide is almost twice as dense as either silicon or carbon.

With further reference to ionizing potentials, it should be noticed also that among chemically comparable elements the ionizing potential is less for the higher members than it is for the lower ones. The values for the three elemental families cited below show this trend clearly.

	Ionizing Potential
Alkali metals	
Li (No. 3)	5.36
Na (No. 11)	5.12
K (No. 19)	4.32
Rb (No. 37)	4.16
Cs (No. 55)	3.87
Alkaline earth metals	
Be (No. 4)	9.28
Mg (No. 12)	7.61
Ca (No. 20)	6.09
Sr (No. 38)	5.67
Ba (No. 56)	5.19
Halogens	
F (No. 9)	17.34
Cl (No. 17)	12.95
Br (No. 35)	11.80
I (No. 53)	10.6

It appears that, in a family of elements whose relationship is due to similarly constructed atoms, the larger the atomic number the smaller is the ionizing potential. This is certainly a reasonable relationship, since the higher members of any family are understood to have larger atoms than the lower members do, and since the more remote the external electrons are from the atomic nucleus, the weaker must be the binding force which the nucleus exerts on them.

ATOMIC VOLUMES

Merely by way of confirming the question of relative atomic size, we conclude this discussion with a graph of atomic volumes. Whenever a new electron shell is begun, as in the atoms of Li, Na, K, Rb, and Cs, we may expect a sudden increase in atomic size compared with the atomic sizes of the elements immediately preceding them. This increased bulk should make for a decrease in density, and, since density is a property that

FIG. 174

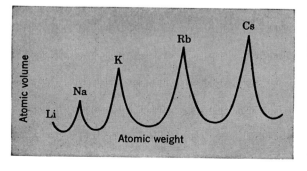

is easily measured, we can test the theory qualitatively by comparing elemental densities. The elements must, of course, be in the same physical state for the comparison to be valid. It will be recalled, by way of illustration, that the alkali metals just cited are all so light that they float in water while reacting with the water.

Atoms of the alkaline earth metals, Be, Mg, Ca, Sr, and Ba, are characterized by having two electrons in the outermost shell of their atoms. But each of these atoms has one more proton in its nucleus than its alkali metal predecessor has. The additional attraction due to an extra proton should pull all the electrons of such an atom a little closer to the nucleus with the consequence of making the alkaline earth atoms a little smaller and denser than the corresponding alkali atoms. It is not to be expected, however, that shrinkage in atomic size will continue consistently with increase in nuclear charge right up to the next alkali element, for, with the addition of more electrons to any shell, there must be increasing repulsion between them.

It is reasonable to expect that, at some element in a series which begins with an alkali metal and ends with an inert gas, the atomic size will again begin to increase. Figure 174 shows that this is indeed the case.

PROBLEMS

1. The atom is frequently described as a miniature solar system. To what extent is this true? False?

2. On the assumption that silicon is like carbon, draw a representation of the molecule which should result from its union with chlorine. How does this molecule differ from the NaCl molecule?

3. On the basis of Fig. 171, would you expect additional spectral series of hydrogen not yet discovered? In what part of the spectrum (infrared, visible, or ultraviolet) would you search for such spectra?

4. Summarize the experimental evidence which points to electron shells with two electrons in the first, eight in the second, etc.

5. What are the two fundamental kinds of valence? Illustrate each by an example.

6. An element X has a valence of $+2$ and is in the same row of the periodic table as element Y with a valence of $+3$. Which element would you expect to have the higher ionizing potential? Elements A and B both have a valence of $+2$, but A has a smaller atomic mass than B. Which element should have the higher ionizing potential?

7. Referring to Fig. 172, explain how it is possible to measure the energy necessary to remove an electron completely from an atom.

Artificial Transmutations

Up to 1896 the transmutation of elements was thought to be impossible. Then, suddenly, Becquerel's discovery revealed whole series of transmutations which had been going on undetected in nature. It then seemed impossible, however, to control these disintegrations; the radioactive atoms exploded at their own characteristic rates in spite of molecular combinations, changes in temperature or other factors of physical environment.

THE FIRST ARTIFICIAL TRANSMUTATION

In 1919, Rutherford succeeded in transmuting nitrogen into oxygen and hydrogen by bombarding nitrogen gas with alpha particles. This discovery by Rutherford marked the beginning of a series of controlled nuclear reactions which reached its dramatic climax when the first atomic bomb was successfully detonated at Alamogordo, New Mexico, on July 16, 1945.

Like many of Rutherford's experiments, this one was direct and simple. Alpha particles from radium C′ were projected into a chamber containing nitrogen known to be free from hydrogen. It was well known how far such alpha particles could travel in a gas like nitrogen, and it was therefore startling to observe the presence of some particles with much longer ranges than the alpha particles themselves. When deflected in a magnetic field, these long-range particles were found to have a value of e/m equal to that of the proton. The conclusion was that the fast alpha particle was actually able to penetrate the nucleus of the nitrogen atom and to knock out a proton with high velocity. This was brilliantly confirmed by Blackett in 1925 in an experiment which deserves our attention because it illustrates the extraordinary strength of the cloud chamber technique. Blackett performed Rutherford's experiment in a cloud chamber so that the paths of the various particles were rendered visible and could be photographed. Over 400,-000 tracks were examined on about 23,000 photographs! Among these there were many which showed the kind of forked path we have already described and which were known to be due to head-on collisions of alpha particles with nitrogen nuclei. With experience one learns to distinguish the paths of the various particles from the appearance of the fog tracks which they leave in the cloud chamber. For example, the recoil nitrogen nuclei in this experiment formed a thicker track than did the alpha particles; the nitrogen nuclei are more massive and produce more fog droplets per centimeter of path. Such a forked path is shown in Fig. 175a. Out of this vast number of photographs, eight showed forked paths of an unusual nature. In addition to the tracks due to the alpha particle and the heavy recoil nucleus, there appeared a third very thin track as shown in Fig. 175b. After collision, there was no track corresponding to the alpha particle; it had disappeared into the heavy nucleus of nitrogen, and a proton, detected by its long thin track, had emerged.

The accepted explanation for this transmutation is that the alpha particle is captured mo-

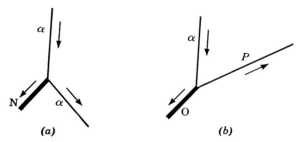

FIG. 175. Cloud chamber record of a transmutation.

mentarily by the nitrogen nucleus, forming fluorine with a mass number 18 and atomic number 9. It has become a custom to represent atomic nuclei by attaching these two numbers to the symbol for the atom. In this case the nucleus is described by the symbol $_9F^{18}$, the mass number being placed on the upper right-hand side and the atomic number on the lower left-hand side. This fluorine nucleus is unstable and breaks down into an isotope of oxygen, $_8O^{17}$, and a proton, $_1H^1$. The complete nuclear reaction is written as follows:

$$_7N^{14} + _2He^4 \rightarrow _9F^{18} \rightarrow _8O^{17} + _1H^1$$

Since this reaction was first observed, many of the light elements have been found to react like nitrogen when bombarded by alpha particles. In such cases the capture of an alpha particle forms an unstable nucleus which emits a proton.

DISCOVERY OF THE NEUTRON

The first controlled transmutation achieved by Rutherford set in motion a series of researches in which a wide variety of atoms was systematically bombarded by fast radioactive particles. We turn now to an especially interesting case.

In 1930 the German physicists Bothe and

Becker performed an experiment which was essentially as follows: An evacuated chamber (Fig. 176) contained a metallic plate P coated with the radioactive element polonium and a thin slab B of the light metal beryllium. The slab, thus exposed to a continual bombardment of alpha particles, proceeded to emit rays so penetrating that they could pass through considerable thicknesses of lead and still produce clicks in a Geiger counter G beyond.

At first it was supposed that these rays must be gamma radiation of very short wave length, that is, photons of high energy, because they failed to produce fog tracks in a cloud chamber and also because no material particles having such extraordinary penetration were then known. Moreover, the rays could not be deflected by a magnetic field.

Subsequently the French physicists Frédéric and Irène Joliot-Curie extended this experiment by placing blocks of various materials between the beryllium slab and the detecting instrument. When the intervening substance was paraffin, which is very rich in hydrogen atoms, they were able to identify the tracks of numerous protons which were ejected from the paraffin by the beryllium radiation.

From the range of these protons the energy imparted to them when they were dislodged from

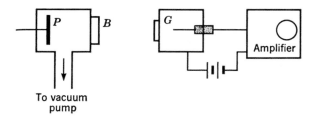

FIG. 176. Apparatus used to discover the neutron.

the paraffin could be calculated, and this in turn allowed calculation of the energy which gamma-ray photons must have had to produce such an effect. The latter energy was inordinately high for photons and entirely different from that determined by absorption measurements.

It was then (1932) that the British physicist James Chadwick made a brilliant assumption by which he succeeded in interpreting these baffling experiments. Chadwick's hypothesis was that an electrically neutral type of particle—a neutron—having approximately the same mass as the proton, was responsible for the effects observed. These neutrons, originally present in the beryllium atoms, were knocked out by the intense bombardment of the alpha particles, many of them striking hydrogen nuclei in the paraffin block and ejecting them with great force. In a series of convincing experiments Chadwick showed that such neutrons would have just about the right amount of energy to affect protons and other atomic nuclei in the way they did.

The existence of such a neutral particle had, in fact, been predicted by Rutherford more than ten years before but no experimental evidence to confirm it was known at that time.

Chadwick's hypothesis accounted for the remarkable ability of the neutrons to penetrate sheets of lead, which is a very effective barrier against charged particles like protons and helium ions. A positive ion moving through a lattice of lead atoms must soon lose most of its kinetic energy by encounters with electrons, besides suffering sharp deflections whenever it comes within the strong electric field of a lead nucleus. A neutral particle, on the other hand, will be unaffected by the electrons in or near its path and will be slowed down only by direct impact with the atomic nuclei. This slowing down, or loss of momentum, is greater when the neutron strikes nuclei having masses comparable to its own than it is when the nucleus is much more massive than the neutron. By analogy, consider a billiard ball rolling swiftly across a table. If it strikes a stationary billiard ball head on, it will transfer all its momentum to the other ball and immediately stop rolling. But if it were to hit a massive object like a croquet ball, it would rebound with almost as much momentum as it had before. We should therefore expect the flying neutron to be strongly retarded by collisions with the light nuclei of hydrogen or carbon in paraffin, whereas, when moving through an assemblage of lead atoms, the neutrons would suffer many deflections but little loss of motion.

The nuclear reaction which Chadwick first interpreted correctly is now written

$$_2\text{He}^4 + {}_4\text{Be}^9 \rightarrow {}_6\text{C}^{13} \rightarrow {}_6\text{C}^{12} + {}_0n^1$$

Many other light elements are now known to behave in the same way as beryllium.

Since neutrons have no electric charge, they leave no visible trail of ions in cloud chamber experiments, but their presence may be inferred by the visible tracks of nuclei which have been struck by neutrons. From such collisions the mass of the neutron may be calculated, since the

problem is like that of any two masses rebounding elastically after impact. The velocities of the two bodies must be known, and the mass of one of them must be known. From these, and other, experiments the mass of the neutron has been found to be equal to 1.00896 on the basis of O = 16. The neutron is therefore slightly more massive than the proton.

NUCLEAR STRUCTURE

Using this new particle, the neutron, as a building unit, we are now able to postulate the composition of atomic nuclei. Rutherford's experiment on the scattering of alpha particles showed clearly that the atomic number was equal to the number of net positive charges in the nucleus. If we assume no electrons in the nucleus, the atomic number is then numerically equal to the number of protons in the nucleus. However, the mass number is always larger than the atomic number, except in the case of ordinary hydrogen, and so it is necessary to add enough neutrons to make up the total mass of the nucleus.

Ordinary hydrogen contains only one proton in its nucleus. Heavy hydrogen (deuterium) contains one proton and one neutron; helium 4 contains two protons and two neutrons; lithium 6 contains three protons and three neutrons, and lithium 7, an isotope, contains three protons and four neutrons. To generalize, an atom of atomic number Z and mass number M must have Z protons and $M - Z$ neutrons in its nucleus. It is now believed that there are no free electrons in the nucleus. This seems strange when we recall that radioactive nuclei emit beta particles which are known to be high-speed electrons. The fact seems to be that beta particles are emitted as part of an energy transformation inside the nucleus, so that the electron does not exist, as such, until the moment of expulsion.

Atoms which are isotopes of each other have the same number of protons but different numbers of neutrons in their nuclei. The number of external electrons must be the same as the number of nuclear protons, and it is the configuration of these electrons which determines the chemical properties of that atom.

It is also possible for several atoms to have the same mass number, i.e., neutrons plus protons, but different numbers of protons, and hence to have different chemical properties. Such atoms are called isobars.

HIGH-VOLTAGE PARTICLE ACCELERATORS

The extraordinary success of the previous experiments with alpha particles suggested that similar effects might be produced by other particles like protons, electrons, and deuterons. In the experiments just discussed, however, the fast alpha particles were obtained from radioactive sources like polonium. The number of alpha

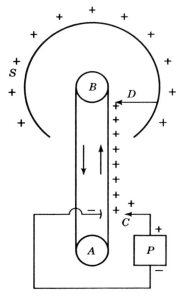

FIG. 177. The Van de Graaf generator.

particles available was therefore restricted by the amount of radioactive material used, and the maximum kinetic energy of such particles was limited by the nature of the radioactive source. Obviously there was need for devices which could produce more intense beams of particles at higher energies and controllable energies. The simplest method of accelerating charged particles is to allow them to move through intense electrical fields, and so the problem resolved itself into designing high-voltage generators.

One of the first of these high-voltage generators was designed by Van de Graaff in 1933, and the basic idea is still in common use in a variety of accelerators (Fig. 177). It consists of two pulleys A and B over which an insulating belt travels at high speed. At the lower end, electric charges are forced on to the belt by the action of a row of metallic points C which are charged positively from a moderately high-voltage source P. Around such points there is an electric glow or corona discharge, which simply means that the air is strongly ionized in that region. The negative ions in this corona discharge are attracted to the positive points, but the positive ions are pushed away toward the negative electrode behind the belt. However, the intervening belt, which is an insulator, prevents these positive ions from reaching the negative electrode; they stick on the belt which moves rapidly upward and carries the positive charges toward the pulley B. The transfer of this charge to the large sphere S is usually a little more elaborate, but it amounts to collecting the charges from the belt by metallic points D which are connected to the large metallic sphere S. The positive charges then distribute themselves over the outside surface of S and continue to raise its potential until a spark passes to the surroundings or until charge begins to leak off through the insulating supports. With such devices, potentials of about three million volts have been achieved.

By spraying negative ions on the belt, the sphere would have become negatively charged with respect to the ground. If two separate systems are set up and charged oppositely to each other, the total potential difference between the two will be twice that of either of them with respect to the ground.

THE LINEAR ACCELERATOR

Because high voltages were so difficult to generate, it was realized that it would be advantageous to accelerate the ions in steps, each step requiring only a modest voltage. Such a device, called a linear accelerator, was built by D. H. Sloan and E. O. Lawrence in 1931.

The linear accelerator (Fig. 178) consists of a series of coaxial cylindrical tubes A, B, C, D, E,

FIG. 178. A linear accelerator.

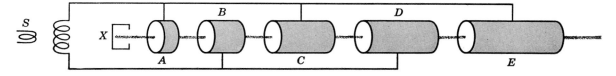

etc., which are charged alternately positively and negatively by high-frequency sources. Suppose a group of positive particles, say protons, are generated at X and begin to move toward A because A is momentarily negative with respect to X. This gives the protons a velocity which depends on the voltage between X and A. When the particles reach the middle of A, B is made negative with respect to A and the velocity of the protons is further increased. Before the protons can emerge from B, C has been made negative with respect to B, and so on, until the last cylinder has been traversed. The total energy in electron volts with which the protons emerge is then about equal to the number of cylinders multiplied by the potential drop between successive cylinders. It is evident that the cylinders must be progressively longer so that the protons will have to take the same time in moving from one cylinder to the next, making it possible to use a constant frequency of alternation of potentials on the cylinders. The whole system must, of course, be contained in a highly evacuated tube.

THE CYCLOTRON

The ion energies which are possible with the linear accelerator are limited because the paths of the ions are straight lines and only a few cylinders can conveniently be arranged, end to end, within the restricted dimensions of a laboratory. To overcome this limitation, Lawrence designed an accelerator, called the cyclotron, in which the ion paths were deflected into spirals by means of strong magnetic fields.

Figure 179 shows the essentials of such a cyclotron. The ions are produced at C and, assuming they are positive, are attracted into the hollow D-shaped electrode A which is momentarily charged negatively with respect to a similar electrode B. The accelerated ions do not proceed in a straight line into A because there is a strong magnetic field perpendicular to the plane of the page. This magnetic field turns the paths of the ions into semicircles. At the end of a half circle, B is made negative with respect to A and the ions cross the boundary into B with increased velocity. Again, the particles turn through a semicircle, but larger than before, and approach A just as it becomes negative with respect to B. The fortunate circumstance which makes the cyclotron possible is the experimental fact that the revolutions of the ions can be kept in step with constant high-frequency changes in potential on the electrodes. Thus the ions move faster and

faster and in larger and larger orbits until they reach the periphery where they can be made to pass out through a slit E into a region where they are used experimentally.

Each time the ions make a complete revolution they are accelerated twice by the electric field. If the potential difference between the electrodes were 10,000 volts and an ion made 50 revolutions before reaching E, the ion would acquire the same energy as if it had been accelerated by a total of 1,000,000 volts.

There are many designs of accelerators in laboratories throughout the world, but most of

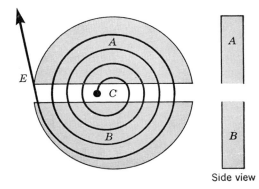

FIG. 179. The cyclotron.

them are variations or combinations of the three types we have described. The cosmotron, built at the Brookhaven National Laboratory, is an excellent example of such a combination, and it is able to produce protons with energies well over two billion electron volts.

CONVERSION OF MASS INTO ENERGY

Alpha and beta particles are emitted from radioactive atoms with extremely high velocities. Alpha particles have been observed with velocities as high as 12,000 mps, and beta-particle velocities may exceed 90% of the velocity of light. These facts alone should warn us that we would have a frightening amount of energy available from atomic nuclei if we could only control its release in large quantities of matter. Before 1932 this seemed impossible. In that year two British physicists, J. D. Cockcroft and E. T. S. Walton, observed a very interesting nuclear transmutation in lithium.

Cockcroft and Walton bombarded lithium 7 with protons which had been accelerated artificially by a high-voltage device. At about 250,000 volts, they observed that very fast alpha particles were emitted from the bombarded lithium, and the startling fact about this reaction was that the total kinetic energy of the emitted alpha particles was almost 70 times as great as the kinetic energy of the impacting protons! This was somewhat like shooting with small bullets at a stick of dynamite and occasionally making a direct hit, causing the dynamite to explode. As a practical source of energy, however, this method was a failure because, on the average, billions of protons had to be fired for one successful hit.

This nuclear reaction is written

$$_1H^1 + _3Li^7 \rightarrow _2He^4 + _2He^4 + Energy$$

Now a startling discovery was made. At first glance it looked as if the mass of the reactants was the same as the mass of the products. Two alpha particles, each of mass number four, added up to eight mass units. Hydrogen of mass 1 and lithium of mass 7 also gave a total of eight mass units. But a more careful addition of masses revealed a serious discrepancy.

$$\begin{aligned}
\text{Mass of hydrogen} &= 1.0081 \\
\text{Mass of lithium 7} &= 7.0180 \\
\hline
\text{Total mass} &= 8.0261 \\
\\
\text{Mass of helium} &= 4.0039 \\
&\times 2 \\
\hline
& 8.0078
\end{aligned}$$

Clearly, mass had been lost in the splitting of the lithium nucleus. This discrepancy recalled a theory proposed by Einstein many years before, which considered it possible to transform mass into energy, and, when energy was so released, the amount of energy was given by the simple equation

$$E = mc^2$$

where E was the energy in ergs, m the transformed mass in grams, and c was the velocity of light, 3×10^{10} cm/sec. It was also considered possible to transform energy into mass. The mass-energy formula could now be checked against experimental fact. The mass discrepancy in this case was 0.0183 mass units or 3.03×10^{-26} grams, since one mass unit is equivalent to 1.66×10^{-24} grams. Putting 3.03×10^{-26} grams into the Einstein equation, the calculated energy into which this much mass should be transformed equals 27.27×10^{-6} ergs or 13.63×10^{-6} ergs

per alpha particle. Since 1 ev is equivalent to 1.6×10^{-12} ergs, each alpha particle should be emitted from the exploding lithium nucleus with a kinetic energy of 8.5 million electron volts, if we neglect the small energy of the impacting proton. The energy obtained from experimental measurements was 8.6 million electron volts, a very gratifying agreement!

Since this discovery by Cockcroft and Walton, thousands of nuclear reactions have been studied in laboratories all over the world. Most of such reactions have been induced by particles which were accelerated artificially by devices like those we have described. Over and over again the Einstein equation $E = mc^2$ has been verified, so that it is now considered secure on experimental evidence. This means that the conservation laws for mass and energy must not be applied separately but together as one law. Mass and energy are truly equivalent. It must be pointed out, however, that this effect is observable experimentally only in nuclear reactions, and in other cases, like those studied in chemistry, the conservation laws for mass and energy are separately valid within the limits of experimental accuracy.

Most impressive is the enormous amount of energy which is released when mass is transformed. A single gram of matter, completely transformed into energy, would yield 9×10^{20} ergs or 25,000,000 kwhr of energy. If this were electrical energy, it would be sufficient to supply the average home with electricity for more than 5000 years. What usually happens, as in the case of lithium, is not complete annihilation of the atom, but only a fractional loss of mass. Even so, it is very impressive. One gram of lithium 7, split up into helium by proton bombardment, would yield more than 60,000 kwhr of energy, neglecting the energy of the protons required for the transmutation.

CHAIN REACTIONS

Consider what happens when a quantity of dynamite explodes. A single exploding molecule can detonate other molecules which in turn set off others, thereby causing complete chemical decomposition and sudden release of energy. This is called a chemical chain reaction. Suppose we try to do this with lithium 7. A proton having the right amount of energy causes a lithium 7 nucleus to explode into two fast alpha particles, but these alpha particles, striking other lithium atoms, do not cause them to explode. If the exploding lithium nuclei emitted several fast protons there would be some chance that such a chain reaction could be started, but no such reaction is known. In general, we need a reaction such that a particle X, striking a nucleus A, causes it to explode and emit several other fast X particles which, in turn, can explode more A nuclei. Such a nuclear chain reaction, because it involves a transformation of mass into energy, would be far more devastating than any molecular explosion known. Before 1939 no such reaction was known.

Then in 1939 O. Hahn and F. Strassmann in Germany discovered that uranium, when bombarded with neutrons, exploded into two nuclei much lighter than uranium, one of which was identified as barium. This process, which came to be called *fission*, was quite different from the usual nuclear reaction in which only light particles like electrons, neutrons, protons, and alpha particles were emitted. It was later discovered that it was the uranium isotope of mass number 235 which experienced fission when struck by slow neutrons. On this assumption, if barium (atomic number 56) were one of the fission products, the remaining atom must have a mass number 98 and an atomic number 36. The postulated reaction would be written

$$_{92}U^{235} + _0n^1 \rightarrow _{92}U^{236} \rightarrow$$
$$_{56}Ba^{138} + _{36}Kr^{98} + Energy$$

The atomic number 36 identified the other element as krypton, but no stable isotope of krypton was known with a mass number as high as 98. It seemed very likely, therefore, that this unstable krypton nucleus disintegrated and that a number of neutrons were emitted in the process. These neutrons might cause fission in other uranium 235 nuclei, thus setting off a chain reaction.

In 1941 the possibility of such a chain reaction was still uncertain, but the military importance of the problem was so great that substantial financial support of extended research was granted by the federal government. Thus began the largest and most dramatic scientific research project in history, involving thousands of scientists and engineers and costing millions of dollars. This extraordinary activity was not made public until 1945 when it was ably summarized by H. D. Smyth of Princeton (*Atomic Energy for Military Purposes*, Princeton University Press, 1945). Then it was revealed that success had been achieved first at Chicago on December 2, 1942,

when a self-sustaining chain-reacting pile was set into operation by Fermi and his collaborators.

It was found that the neutrons emitted from the fission of uranium 235 were too fast to produce additional fission in other uranium nuclei, but, when these fast neutrons were slowed down by passage through graphite, the chain reaction became possible. We shall describe the essential features of such a chain-reacting pile.

A large graphite block has carefully spaced holes in it to receive metallic rods which are rich in fissionable uranium 235. Since there are always a few free neutrons present under normal conditions, some uranium atoms will experience fission and emit a number of fast neutrons. These fast neutrons are slowed down by the graphite block so that when they strike uranium nuclei in neighboring rods they cause fission with the emission of more fast neutrons and the chain reaction begins. If the uranium nuclei always exploded within a millionth of a second after the slow neutron had been captured, the reaction could probably not be controlled, but, fortunately, there is a delay in fission which is long enough to make regulation possible. This may be done by use of control rods made of cadmium and boron steel which can be moved into or out of the graphite block in the spaces between the uranium rods. Cadmium and boron have been found to slow down neutrons so effectively that the neutrons do not produce further fission. It turned out that such rods could be easily controlled by automatic devices which pushed the rods deeper into the pile when the neutron density became too high.

Inside the graphite block or pile there is intense neutron activity and severe collisions which increase the kinetic agitation of the atoms of the structure. This is another way of saying that the temperature increases as the chain reaction builds up. A controlled pile operating at a high level of neutron activity could produce an enormous amount of energy available for useful work. The heat could be made to produce steam which would drive turbines which, in turn, would run generators of electric energy. This fortunate aspect of the chain reaction is already being developed in several ways. At Brookhaven National Laboratories, a small part of the heat energy from the pile is being used to drive electric generators. A submarine, now in successful operation, is driven by the heat energy released in a built-in pile.

Another fortunate result of neutron activity is

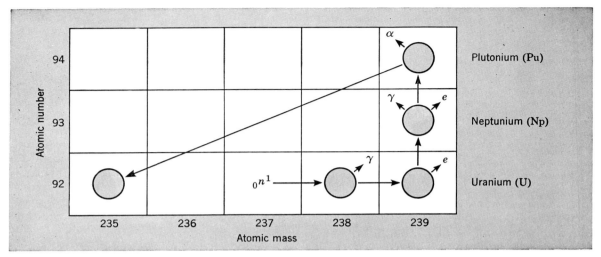

FIG. 180.   Formation of neptunium and plutonium from uranium 238.

the abundant transmutation which goes on inside such a pile. This has led to the discovery of several new elements beyond uranium in the periodic table. Figure 180 summarizes what happens when uranium 238 captures a neutron. The unstable uranium 239 isotope which is formed disintegrates into a new element, *neptunium,* which, in turn, is also unstable and disintegrates into another element *plutonium.* Plutonium is relatively stable, but over the years it emits alpha particles and turns into uranium 235.

Most interesting is the fact that plutonium also experiences fission and can therefore be used to make atomic bombs. For this reason a great deal of effort was expended during the war years in its production by means of large piles.

Inside a chain-reacting atomic pile, there are abundant transmutations of whatever elements are exposed to the neutron bombardment. Many of these transmutations result in isotopes which are themselves radioactive. Medical research in general, and particularly the treatment of cancers and tumors, has profited greatly from the abundant variety of these radioactive isotopes now easily available. It is no longer necessary to restrict research and treatment to the few radioactive elements found in nature.

Radioactive carbon is especially useful in physiological research since it can be incorporated in carbohydrate and protein molecules whose progress through the living organism is easily traced by means of Geiger counters.

PROBLEMS

1. Discuss the possibility that some alchemist may really have succeeded in transmuting one element into another but has not been given proper credit for it.

2. Summarize the immediate events leading up to the discovery of the neutron. Name the scientists who were directly connected with each step. In which countries did they work?

3. Using the equation for the discovery of the neutron on p. 307, calculate the number of mass units lost when one neutron is formed. How many ergs of energy are liberated? What becomes of this energy? Use Table 14 on p. 241.

4. Given that 1 kwhr of energy is equivalent to 36×10^{12} ergs, how many kilowatt-hours of energy are liberated when 1 gram of lithium 7 is changed to helium, as discussed on p. 310. Would this be a satisfactory reaction for generating atomic power? Explain.

5. In Rutherford's first controlled transmutation, could the law of conservation of energy be applied to the collision between the alpha particle and the nitrogen nucleus as it would be applied to two colliding billiard balls? Explain. Could the law of conservation of momentum be applied?

6. The neutron is a particle comparable in mass with the proton or hydrogen atom, and yet it was not discovered until 1932. Explain, in terms of experimental difficulties, why the neutron was so late in being discovered.

. . . .

REFERENCE

1. *Atomic Energy for Military Purposes,* H. D. Smyth, Princeton University Press, 1945.

Waves and Particles

The release of atomic energy, for peaceful or destructive use, is no doubt the most impressive scientific achievement in the history of mankind. We might dramatically conclude our discussion of science by leaving the student in awesome contemplation of this accomplishment if it were not for the fact that the scientist persistently seeks a deeper and deeper understanding of natural phenomena and is not satisfied with practical consequences alone.

The limitation of our understanding is easily tested by such questions as: Is light fundamentally of a wave or particle nature? What is the size of a quantum or of an electron? How accurately can we describe the motion of an electron? When we apply ourselves to the analysis of such questions, because we cannot answer them conclusively, it becomes evident that the mechanistic Newtonian point of view, which flourished for more than a century and a half, is no longer tenable.

Consider, for example, the conflict between the wave and particle theories of light. When we discussed the interference experiment with the two slits, first performed by Young, it seemed as if the wave theory must be a necessary conclusion. For, if light consisted of energy parcels, how could separate packets of energy (quanta) from each of the two slits possibly annihilate each other, as they must, in the dark spaces between the bright bands in the interference pattern?

But suppose the quantum of light has some complexity of structure so that it is in reality a wave chopped up into small sections, each of which remains intact as it travels through space, and therefore exhibits some of the properties of a particle. No one has been able to describe this complexity in structure in terms of any physical model, though it has sometimes been referred to as a "wavicle." If we are to explain the interference in Young's experiment we must assume that part of the "wavicle" goes through one slit and part through the other. This possibility depends on the size of the quantum; it has to be at least as large in diameter as the distance between the slits. If the slits are very close together, this does not seem unreasonable. However, to be on sure ground, we must investigate this point experimentally. How far apart can we place the slits and still produce interference? The answer to this question is found in an experiment performed in 1920 by the American physicist Michelson, who, at that time, was working at the Mount Wilson observatory on the problem of the diameter of stars. Designing his apparatus on the assumption that the light from the distant stars arrived at his telescope in the form of waves, he used two separate mirrors which played much the same role, fundamentally, as the slits in Young's experiment. The astonishing fact is that Michelson was able to obtain interference patterns when the mirrors were 20 ft apart. Hence, the quantum of light must, if we hope for this kind of solution, have a diameter of at least 20 ft!

On the other hand, if we turn to the experiment on photoelectric emission of electrons from illuminated metals, we seem driven to accept Einstein's conclusion that there is a particle to particle interaction between the incident quantum of light and the photoelectron which is emitted from the metallic surface. This conclusion can only mean that the quantum of light is extremely small—comparable in size to that of the electron with which it interacts. How can a quantum of light at least 20 ft long single out a tiny electron among billions of others and deliver its energy to that electron alone?

There is another experiment which we must not fail to mention here because it not only points to a particle nature for light but it enables us to calculate the effective momentum of the quantum of light. It is the experiment first performed by Arthur Compton (1892–) in 1922 and for which, primarily, he was granted the Nobel prize in 1927.

THE COMPTON EFFECT

Suppose very high frequency X rays are generated in a tube T (Fig. 181) and then narrowed down into a sharp beam by small holes H in lead sheets. This beam is then allowed to strike a material M which contains free electrons. The material could be any conductor like carbon, aluminum, copper, or silver. Such a material will scatter X rays in all directions, but, if one examines the radiation emerging at an angle Φ to the forward direction, he finds that some of the scattered radiation has the same wave length as the incident radiation, but that a substantial part of it has a longer wave length than the incident radiation. In the language of quantum theory, some of the scattered quanta are smaller than the incident quanta. This difference is found to depend only on the angle of scattering and is independent of the material M which does

the scattering. Compton's brilliant interpretation was that, in the scattering process, a quantum of X radiation having energy hf collided with a free electron in much the same way that two billiard balls collide with one another. The complication in this case was, however, that the quantum hf, after collision, assumed a new energy hf' instead of changing its velocity, since a quantum of light in a vacuum must always travel with the same speed. The energy and momentum of the struck electron were independently

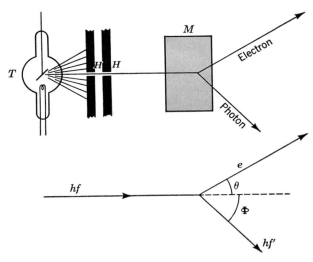

FIG. 181. The Compton effect.

measured. The main argument in Compton's analysis was that, if the momentum of the incident quantum was taken as hf/c and the momentum of the scattered quantum as hf'/c, where c is the velocity of light, then the angles θ, for the struck electron, and Φ, for the scattered quantum, were completely consistent with the laws of conservation of momentum and energy, just as they would be for two perfectly elastic steel balls. This experiment was so convincing that the name *photon* has now largely replaced the name quantum in common use, to emphasize its similarity to other fundamental particles like the electron and the proton.

Unfortunately, experiments of this kind seem to give no clues to any possible reconciliation of the two conflicting theories; each type of experiment reveals, sharply and unambiguously, either a particle or a wave nature for light.

Strangely enough, part of the difficulty came about because it was felt that particles and waves must of necessity be conflicting physical concepts.

Physicists were confident that the fundamental concept of a particle was quite clear, so that an electron, for example, could not possibly be mistaken for a wave. This confidence was forever shattered in 1927 as the result of an experiment performed cooperatively by two American physicists, C. J. Davisson and L. H. Germer, and shortly thereafter verified by G. P. Thomson in Britain.

DAVISSON AND GERMER EXPERIMENT

Davisson and Germer made their discovery while observing the scattering of electron beams from a nickel target. They were essentially in-

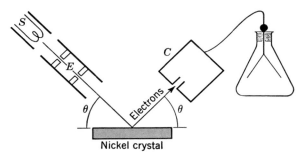

FIG. 182. Electron diffraction discovered by Davisson and Germer.

terested in the number of electrons scattered at various angles when the velocity of the incident electrons was varied. Electrons were emitted by a source S (Fig. 182), a hot filament, and accelerated toward an electrode E, which was positively charged with respect to the filament and at the same electrical potential as the target. Small holes in the electrode E formed an electron beam which could be directed at the nickel target. The velocity of these electrons was easily calculated from the relation

$$Pe = \tfrac{1}{2}mv^2$$

where P is the total potential difference between the filament and the target, e is the electronic charge, m is the mass of the electron, and v is the velocity of the electron when it hits the target. It is assumed that the velocity v is very small compared to the velocity of light. A small metal box or collector C could be moved so that scattered electrons at any angle θ would enter a small slit and be detected by the charge they contributed to the attached electroscope. It was therefore possible to compare the number of electrons which were scattered at various angles.

With non-crystalline nickel nothing very surprising was observed; the number of electrons was a steady, continuous function of the angle of scattering. But once, through accidental heating and cooling, the target became crystallized and then the result was startling. Certain preferred angles of scattering developed abruptly, in addition to the previous general scattering, and these preferred angles depended only on the velocity of the incident electrons. This was very much like the behavior of a beam of light striking a reflecting grating, i.e., a reflecting surface on which parallel grooves have been scratched. In other words, this was like the behavior of light in Young's experiment, except that the slits had now been replaced by parallel rows and layers of atoms in the crystal structure of the nickel. How was this behavior to be explained?

THE DE BROGLIE HYPOTHESIS

The explanation was evident when it was recalled that, a few years before (beginning in 1922) a French physicist, Louis de Broglie, had published some theoretical papers in which he suggested that material particles should have some of the properties of waves. He even calculated the wave length which a particle should exhibit. This wave length turned out to depend on the momentum of the particle concerned. If energy and mass are really equivalent, as Einstein supposed, then

$$E = mc^2 = hf$$

and

$$mc = \frac{hf}{c} = \frac{h}{\lambda}$$

since $c = f\lambda$, where λ means wave length. If m is now taken specifically to be the mass of the electron, and c, the velocity of light, is replaced by v, the much smaller velocity of the electron, then

$$mv = h/\lambda \qquad \text{or} \qquad \lambda = h/mv$$

In the Davisson and Germer experiment, λ could be calculated from the observed angle θ and the known distance between the parallel layers of atoms in the nickel crystal, just as one might, in Young's experiment, calculate the wave length of light from the angular displacement of the first bright band and the distance between the slits. From the de Broglie equation the wave length could also be calculated, since h (Planck's constant), m (mass of the electron), and v (velocity of the electron) were all known. The calculated value of wave length was in excellent agreement with the wave length obtained experimentally. Electrons did indeed behave like waves!

Instead of adding to the confusion, this result improves the situation. Both matter and radiation exhibit wave and particle properties. Which property they will exhibit depends on the physical situations which confront them. This is remotely like the problem of human behavior; an individual will exhibit vastly different facets of his personality under different circumstances.

THE ELECTRON MICROSCOPE

The wave nature of the electron is beautifully illustrated in a practical application called the electron microscope.

The ability of an optical microscope to resolve small detail in the object examined improves as the wave length of the illumination decreases. This fact has been known for a long time and is easily explained on the basis of the wave theory of light. Consequently, violet light is frequently used, instead of white light, to illuminate the object when the useful magnification is pushed to the limit. However, we are prevented from using light of shorter wave length than 0.000033 cm (3300 A) because the glass of the microscope lenses will not transmit such light. The lenses can, of course, be made of some material which is transparent to light in a restricted region of the ultraviolet, but this is extremely costly and, in any event, cannot be pushed very far. If, somehow, it were possible to overcome this limitation and to use light of very short wave length, the useful magnification of a microscope could be enormously increased. Since, by the de Broglie hypothesis, material particles are supposed to have wave properties, would it not be possible to design a microscope using streams of electrons instead of ordinary light?

To answer this question, let us first calculate the wave length of an electron having a speed which is easily achieved by modern techniques. Electrons which have been accelerated by a potential of 75,000 volts will have a speed approximately $\frac{1}{2}$ that of light (see equation on p. 238), i.e., about 1.5×10^{10} cm/sec. Using the de Broglie relation $\lambda = h/mv$

$$\lambda = \frac{6.6 \times 10^{-27}}{9 \times 10^{-28} \times 1.5 \times 10^{10}} = 0.05 \times 10^{-8} \text{ cm}$$

Since 10^{-8} cm is defined as one angstrom unit (A), the calculated λ is equal to 0.05 A. When we compare this wave length with 3300 A, the limit in the optical case, we are greatly encouraged, but there is a second problem. How are we going to form images with electrons? We need something comparable to the glass lenses in the case of visible light—some system by means of which divergent electron streams from a point source can be bent or refracted so as to bring them to a sharp focus. In general, one has the feeling that this should be possible since charged particles in motion are acted on by both electric and magnetic forces, and, in fact, the problem has been brilliantly solved by using electric and magnetic fields of such configurations that they bend the electron streams in the desired directions. Such systems are now referred to as electrostatic or magnetic lenses, and, like their optical analogs, they may be either convergent or divergent. The electron images are brought to a focus either on fluorescent screens, for visual examination, or on photographic plates, for permanent record. The developed images on the photographic plates are so sharp that they can be further enlarged to final magnifications of several hundred thousand! Plate XXXVII shows individual molecules on the surface of a crystal of catalase (a protein enzyme) magnified 150,000 times, and Plate XXXIX shows type II poliomyelitis virus magnified about 165,000 times.

THE WAVE VERSUS PARTICLE DILEMMA

We now feel quite certain that, if Young's experiment were repeated, using electrons of fixed velocity instead of light, we should get an interference pattern of bright and dark bands whose separation would depend on the wave length of the electrons as given by the de Broglie equation

$$\lambda = h/mv$$

Paradoxically, the light and dark bands could be observed on a fluorescent screen, where each electron impact would produce a tiny flash of light like that produced by any genuine particle. It appears as if, in a single experiment, the electron displays the incompatible properties of wave and particle, but, on closer examination, this is not true. There are really two experiments involved—the diffraction through the slits which reveals the wave characteristic, and the scintillation on the screen which reveals the particle characteristic. The two experiments are sharply separated, and they cannot be merged into a single experiment. For instance, if tiny fluorescent screens were placed immediately behind

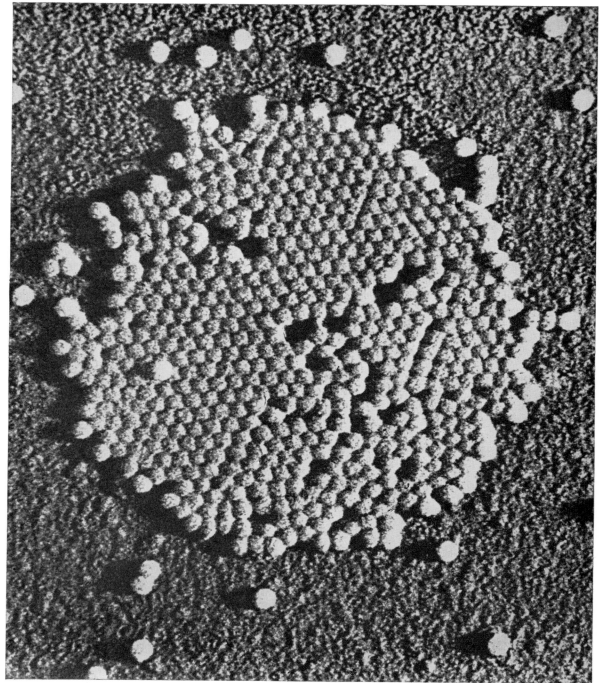

The National Foundation for Infantile Paralysis

PLATE XXXIX. The MEF-1 strain of type II poliomyelitis virus enlarged approximately 165,000 times under the electron microscope. The photograph was taken by Dr. Robley C. Williams, and the virus was purified by Drs. Carlton E. Schwerdt and Frederick L. Schaffer. All are from the virus lab of the University of California. The work was done under grants from The National Foundation for Infantile Paralysis.

each of the slits, in an effort to determine which of the slits the electron passes through and thus force the electron to reveal itself as a particle or wave, we would then have reduced the observation to a single experiment. A single flash of light would be observed on only one of the screens, and the experiment would be finished; the electron could not exhibit its wave characteristic because it had been stopped. This realization leads to a generalization. Our conceptions of wave and particle are indeed in conflict, but that is due to the fact that our conceptions of waves and particles are incomplete and not consistent with the physical reality. From our experiences with large objects we have preconceived notions of what waves and particles are, but these preconceptions are not truly applicable to objects as tiny as quanta or electrons.

One of the important applications of this kind of speculation concerns itself with the ultimate refinement which is possible in physical measurements.

Suppose that, on a fluorescent screen S (Fig. 183), we observe flashes of light which are known to be due to the impacts of electrons. We set ourselves the problem of determining, as precisely as we can, the path along which a single electron has traveled to reach the point P, where the flash of light is observed. To do this let us use a metal sheet with a hole H in it and place it so that we are sure the electron has gone through this hole. Our hope is that the hole H and the flash of light at P will serve as two points between which we can draw a straight line HP, but we will go further than that and extend the line HP in the direction of A. How precisely can we establish this path AHP? Obviously, if the hole H is very large, the path AHP is only approximately known. In an effort to refine our observation we begin to narrow down H until finally its diameter becomes comparable to that of the electron itself. Now we encounter serious trouble, owing to the fact that the electron behaves like a wave in going through such a small aperture, and the result is like that in the Davisson and Germer experiment—the electron is diffracted. This means that the extended part of the path we thought to be HA may in reality be HA', or HA'', or, in fact, any line from H drawn to the left of the metal sheet. Our efforts to refine the observation beyond a certain point have resulted in failure. This is a difficulty which we never can hope to overcome by clever experimental design or by increased skill in the

construction of apparatus; the difficulty is due to a fundamental property of matter itself. This does not necessarily mean that the true path of the electron through space is fundamentally uncertain or indefinite; it is only our observation of the path which is seen to be uncertain. In our attempt to establish the path exactly, we were forced to interfere with the natural progress of the electron and as a consequence we disturbed it seriously. This is like the problem of trying to find out what a living cell is like by probing into it; the cell is thereby killed, and we are no

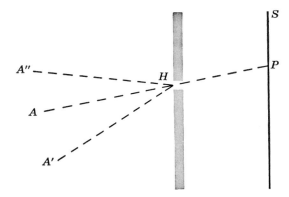

FIG. 183. Illustration of the principle of indeterminacy. The path of an electron cannot be determined beyond a certain accuracy.

longer able to study that which we set out to study.

This difficulty is so universal that it has been expressed as a general principle by Werner Heisenberg and Niels Bohr; it is called the *principle of indeterminacy*. This principle recognizes a final and natural limit to the exactness with which all measurements can be made. There appears to be a barrier in nature which we shall never be able to penetrate by measurements or observations, and which forever prevents us from obtaining the highly accurate data that were once hoped for.

It must be pointed out, however, that the uncertainties referred to in Heisenberg's principle are extremely small. For example, if one tries to measure the position X and the momentum p of an electron at the same time, then ΔX, the range of uncertainty in determining X, and Δp, the range of uncertainty in determining p, are related by the expression

$$\Delta X \cdot \Delta p \geq h \qquad \text{in which } h \text{ is Planck's constant}$$

(The symbol $\geqq$ means "equal to," or "greater than.") Recalling that h is numerically equal to 6.6×10^{-27} erg-sec, it is evident that ΔX and Δp are extraordinarily small. In the measurements of large objects these uncertainties are therefore completely masked by the usual, long-recognized, experimental errors which are enormously larger. Why, then, should anyone be concerned about them?

First of all, the principle is an important guide in physical speculations; it is intimately connected with such problems as causality in nature, for example. Second, the principle has attracted the attention of people outside the natural sciences, particularly in the field of philosophy. This is primarily due to the fact that it seems to bear on the problems of determinism and the possibility of free will.

After the Newtonian successes, the mechanistic philosophy quite naturally became very strong. The whole solar system had been set in logical order, and every detail of its motion had been shown to be the inevitable consequence of a universal gravitational force. One by one, impor-

tant physical and chemical problems yielded to the molecular point of view, until it was felt by many that it would only be a matter of time until such complicated mechanisms as nervous impulses and organic responses would be understood. That would be the end of free will; every human act would then be explained as the result of external environmental stimuli, and a human being would possess no more freedom than does a molecule, driven from place to place by irresistible physical forces. There could be no personal responsibility for human actions.

Suddenly it became evident that scientists would never achieve the refinement of measurement necessary to prove the mechanistic point of view, and this seemed to leave the way open for ultimate freedom of action. Here the reader must be strongly cautioned against using the principle of indeterminacy as a logical weapon against determinism and in defense of free will. The principle cannot be used in this way; it simply means that the determinist cannot look to the natural sciences for ultimate proof of his position.

PROBLEMS

1. Using the de Broglie formula on p. 316, calculate the wave length of a proton which has been accelerated by a potential of 75,000 volts. Comparing your result with that on p. 317, do you conclude that it would be better to use proton microscopes in place of electron microscopes?

Ans. $\lambda_{proton} = 0.001 \times 10^{-8}$ cm.

2. Accepting the principle of indeterminacy, do you feel that science loses: (*a*) Practical value? (*b*) Logical strength? (*c*) Beauty or dignity?

Appendices

APPENDIX A

Angle AOB is defined as one *radian* if the length of the arc AB is equal to the radius OA.

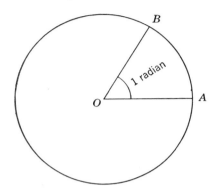

One complete circle $= 2\pi$ radians $= 360°$.
One radian $= 57.3° = 57°\ 17'\ 45''$.
$1° = 60'$ (minutes).
$1' = 60''$ (seconds).

In general, an angle (in radians) $= \dfrac{\text{Length of arc}}{\text{Radius}}$.

APPENDIX B

Given any right triangle ABC, the following relations are defined as shown in the table.

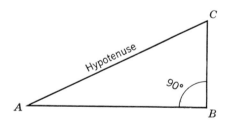

In General	Specifically	
Sine of an angle = $\dfrac{\text{Side opposite}}{\text{Hypotenuse}}$	$\sin \angle CAB = \dfrac{BC}{AC}$	$\sin \angle ACB = \dfrac{AB}{AC}$
Cosine of an angle = $\dfrac{\text{Side adjacent}}{\text{Hypotenuse}}$	$\cos \angle CAB = \dfrac{AB}{AC}$	$\cos \angle ACB = \dfrac{BC}{AC}$
Tangent of an angle = $\dfrac{\text{Side opposite}}{\text{Side adjacent}}$	$\tan \angle CAB = \dfrac{BC}{AB}$	$\tan \angle ACB = \dfrac{AB}{BC}$
Cotangent of an angle = $\dfrac{\text{Side adjacent}}{\text{Side opposite}}$	$\cot \angle CAB = \dfrac{AB}{BC}$	$\cot \angle ACB = \dfrac{BC}{AB}$

SINE LAW

Given any triangle ABC,

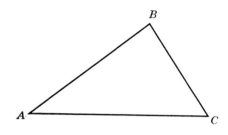

$$\frac{\sin \angle ABC}{AC} = \frac{\sin \angle BCA}{AB} = \frac{\sin \angle CAB}{BC}$$

APPENDIX C

The angle L is the latitude for all points on the circle $ABCD$ whose plane is parallel to the equatorial plane. L is measured either north or south of the equator.

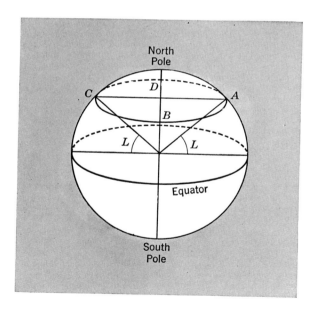

The longitude of a point X is the angle BOC measured between the plane $AXBD$ and a reference plane $AGCD$ which has been chosen so as to include G, the Greenwich observatory in England. Longitude is measured east or west of Greenwich.

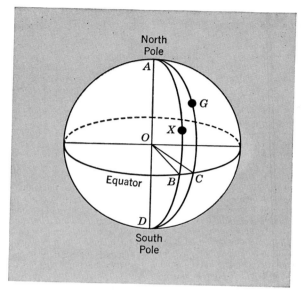

APPENDIX D

Circumference of a circle $= 2\pi R$
Area of a circle $= \pi R^2$
Surface of a sphere $= 4\pi R^2$
Volume of a sphere $= \frac{4}{3}\pi R^3$

APPENDIX E: CONVERSION FACTORS

1 meter $= 39.37$ inches
1 foot $= 30.48$ centimeter
1 kilogram $= 2.205$ pounds
1 inch $= 2.540$ centimeter
1 mile $= 5280$ feet
1 pound $= 453.6$ grams

APPENDIX F: IMPORTANT CONSTANTS

Electronic charge $= 4.80 \times 10^{-10}$ electrostatic units $= 1.60 \times 10^{-19}$ coulomb
Velocity of light $= 3.00 \times 10^{10}$ centimeters/second
Mass of proton $= 1.00758$ atomic mass units $= 1.672 \times 10^{-24}$ gram
Mass of neutron $= 1.00896$ atomic mass units $= 1.675 \times 10^{-24}$ gram
Mass of electron $= 9.108 \times 10^{-28}$ gram
1 atomic mass unit $= 1.660 \times 10^{-24}$ gram
1 electron volt $= 1.60 \times 10^{-12}$ erg
Planck's constant $= 6.61 \times 10^{-27}$ erg-second
Gravitation constant $= 6.67 \times 10^{-8}$ $\dfrac{\text{dyne-centimeter}^2}{\text{grams}^2}$
Avogadro's number $= 6.02 \times 10^{23}$ molecules per mole

Index